only the future toward which to look. Having left their parents, they rested their hope for stability on their children. Yet their offspring who were their only hope for a posterity always grew up in strangeness...members of a marginal group standing between two cultures—that of the parents, and that of the surrounding native milieu.

"To some degree, the second generation was alien to both. The culture of the parents was foreign in origin and not altogether comprehensible. On the other hand, residual ethnic traits prevented the native offspring of the immigrants from participating fully in the life about them. Sometimes they acquired a thin veneer of Americanization, changed their names, aped the local dress and manners and even intermarried. Still they stood apart in their consistent marginality."

The tensions of this marginality are strikingly revealed in the selections Professor Handlin has made from the writings of second-generation Americans over the past approximately one hundred years. The range and scope of their contribution, the part they played in "the significant epilogue to the drama of immigration," can be judged from the table of contents to be found on the back of this jacket.

OSCAR HANDLIN, author of the Pulitzer Prize book, *The Uprooted,* and numerous other works, is Charles Warren Professor of American History, Harvard University, and Director of the Charles Warren Center for Studies in American History.

CHILDREN
OF THE UPROOTED

CHILDREN OF THE UPROOTED

Selected and edited
with an introduction and notes by
OSCAR HANDLIN

GEORGE BRAZILLER *New York*

For information address the publisher,
George Braziller, Inc.
One Park Avenue, New York 16

First Printing

Library of Congress Catalog Card Number: 66-12906
Printed in the United States of America

Designed by Hilda Scott

ACKNOWLEDGMENTS

The editor and publisher have made every effort to determine and credit the holders of copyright of the selections in this book. Any errors or omissions may be rectified in future editions. The editor and publisher wish to thank the following for permission to reprint the material included in this anthology:

Augustana Historical Society Publications—for "The Third Generation," from "The Problem of the Third Generation Immigrant," by Marcus Lee Hansen. Rock Island, 1938. Reprinted by permission of the publisher.

The Dial Press, Inc.—for "The Fractional Man," from *Confessions of a Spent Youth*, by Vance Bourjaily. Copyright © 1952, 1959, 1960, by Vance Bourjaily and used with the permission of the publisher, The Dial Press, Inc. First published in *The New Yorker*.

Duell, Sloan & Pearce, Inc.—for "Democracy in Action," from *The American Cause*, by Archibald MacLeish, Copyright 1941 by Archibald MacLeish. Reprinted by permission of the publisher.

Harcourt, Brace & World, Inc.—for "Heroes among the Plain People," from *The People, Yes*, by Carl Sandburg. Copyright 1936 by Harcourt, Brace & World, Inc.; renewed, © 1964, by Carl Sandburg, and for "Believing in Every Religion," from *My Name is Aram*, by William Saroyan. Copyright 1937, 1938, 1939, 1940, by William Saroyan. Both selections reprinted by permission of the publisher.

Harper & Row, Publishers—for "The Trouble with Daylight," from *Never Come Morning*, by Nelson Algren. Copyright 1942 by Nelson Algren. Reprinted by permission of the publisher.

Hill & Wang, Inc.—for "Talking American," from *Mount Allegro*, by Jerre Mangione. Copyright 1942, 1952 by Jerre Mangione. Reprinted by permission of the publisher.

J.B. Lippincott Company—for "A Youth in Arizona," from *The Making of an Insurgent*, by Fiorello H. La Guardia. Copyright 1948 by J.B. Lippincott Company. Reprinted by permission of the publisher.

Little, Brown and Company—for "Without Those Consolations Called Religious," from *The Blood of the Lamb*, by Peter De Vries. Copyright © 1961 by Peter De Vries. Reprinted by permission of the publisher.

Pardee Lowe—for "The Ties of Clan," from *Father and Glorious Descendant*, by Pardee Lowe. Originally published by Little, Brown and Company, 1943. Reprinted by permission of the author.

The Macaulay Company—for "Tabloid Editor," from *Hot News*, by Emile Gauvreau. Reprinted by permission of the publisher.

The Macmillan Company—for "The Picnic," from *For the Grape Season*, by Henry Barba. Copyright © 1960 by Henry Barba; and for "Too Old to Work; Too Young to Die," from *Walter P. Reuther Selected Papers*, edited by Henry M. Christman. Copyright © 1961 by Henry M. Christman. Both selections reprinted by permission of the publisher.

The Massachusetts Review—for "What Remains of Life," from "The Lost Days," by Charles Bacas. Copyright © 1964 by The Massachusetts Review, Inc. Reprinted by permission of the publisher.

The National Education Association—for "The Teaching Profession," from "The Reorganization of the Teaching Profession," by Henry Suzzallo. Originally published in the *Journal of Proceedings and Addresses of the Fifty-First Annual Meeting*, Ann Arbor, 1913. Reprinted by permission of the publisher.

New Directions—for "America! America!" from *The World Is a Wedding*, by Delmore Schwartz. Copyright 1948 by Delmore Schwartz. Reprinted by permission of the publisher.

Random House, Inc.—for "No More Roses in the Lunch Pail," from *A Glass Rose*, by Richard J. Bankowsky. Copyright © 1958 by Richard J. Bankowsky. Reprinted by permission of the publisher.

Estate of Katharine Royce—for "The Community of Mankind," from *The Hope of the Great Community*, by Josiah Royce. Reprinted by permission of the Harvard Trust Company.

Arthur M. Schlesinger—for "The American—a New Man," from "What, Then, Is the American, This New Man?" by Arthur M. Schlesinger. Originally published by the *American Historical Review*, 1942. Reprinted by permission of the late author.

Charles Scribner's Sons—for "Religion in American Experience," from *Pious and Secular America*, by Reinhold Niebuhr. Copyright © 1957 by Reinhold Niebuhr. Reprinted by permission of the publisher.

David Shaber—for "Escape from Mother," from "A Nous la liberté," originally published in *The Transatlantic Review*, Spring, 1960. Reprinted by permission of the author.

The Viking Press, Inc.—for "Devout Observances," from *The Theory of the Leisure Class*, by Thorstein Veblen. All rights reserved. Reprinted by permission of the publisher.

The Wayne State University Press—for "A People Gone Astray," from *Democracy: a Man-Search*, by Louis H. Sullivan. Copyright © 1961 by The Wayne State University Press. Reprinted by permission of the publisher.

The World Publishing Company—for "Passage from Home," from *Passage from Home*, by Isaac Rosenfeld. Copyright 1946 by Vasiliki S. Rosenfeld. Originally published by The Dial Press, 1946. Reprinted by permission of the publisher.

CONTENTS

INTRODUCTION

by OSCAR HANDLIN

"These states are the amplest poem," sang Walt Whitman. "Here is not merely a nation, but a teeming nation of nations." He was celebrating the process which had turned an empty wilderness into a settled society dedicated to freedom.

Whitman understood, as most Americans have, that their country was a product of immigration. From the first planting of Jamestown to his days and to our own, the efforts of men and women who crossed the ocean from the Old World cleared the forests, cultivated the earth, laid the railroads, and manned the factories. Coming for the most part freely, by acts of their own individual choice, these people left behind settled communities and the life of habit and tradition to begin afresh with only the resources they carried with them.

Great achievements were the products of their labors; without their contributions the country could not have taken the form it did. But they paid a heavy price, not only in the painful process of crossing and resettlement but also in the continuing ache of uprootedness. The ocean separated them forever from the old home, from the church, the village, and above all, the kinfolk—the whole circle of people and places on which they depended for emotional security.

The newcomers could not look back; their departure was decisive. They had abandoned their past and consequently had only the future toward which to look. Having left their parents, they rested their hope for stability on their children. Yet their offspring, who were their only hope for a posterity, always grew up in strangeness. The native born were untouched by either the European background or the experience of migration. They grew up Americans, shaped by the society which was home to them. And to the extent that the process of settlement succeeded, a widening gulf developed between the uprooted immigrants and their children. The second generation thus played a part in a significant epilogue to the drama of immigration.

The second generation has hitherto been viewed within the limits of a very narrow perspective. It became a familiar subject of observation and discussion only when the immigrant population was distinctive enough to constitute a problem. Up until the middle of the nineteenth century, Americans clung to the easy assumption that all newcomers would shortly merge into a single indistinguishable mass; their children would be very much alike because the common influence of the free environment would shape the character and even the physical appearance of all of them.

That optimistic belief did not long survive the onset of the great migrations of the 1840's. The Catholicism of the Irish and the foreign language of the Germans were signs of cultural differences that did not at once disappear in the New World. Toward the end of the nineteenth century the great movements out of Southern and Eastern Europe and Asia raised still more troubling questions about the capacity of so many strange people to merge totally with the rest of the population. The concern persisted and became more intense when the sons and daughters of the immigrants did not lose their identity but remained recognizably different.

The most serious attention to this phenomenon came after 1890 as a phase of the general debate over immigration restriction. By then the second generation was numerous enough to provide subjects for study and the new social sciences supplied the tools for examining the nation's population critically. More important, an improved understanding of this problem promised to throw light on the long-range effects of immigration. There could be no better gauge of the desirability of receiving the uprooted millions who were then crossing the Atlantic than the experience of their children in the United States.

Attitudes toward restriction therefore deeply influenced the way in which other Americans understood the second generation. Those who favored continuation of the open-gate policy viewed the second generation with hope and equanimity; they expected it to contribute to the richness and diversity of life in the United States. By contrast, those who sought some limitation on the flow, in numbers or by nationality, were disturbed by the persistence in the population of alien elements; often even the native-born children were still marked by their foreign antecedents. For the critics of immigration, the failure of Old World traits to disappear justified a limitation of new arrivals until the old would be completely absorbed. But from either point of view, the second generation was transitional, expected slowly but surely to be assimilated.

The racist writers of the turn of the century went further. They were alarmed at the prospect of assimilation. Since they believed that cultural traits were genetically inherited, they could not view with equanimity the injection into the American bloodstream of other large and "inferior" racial strains. They anticipated endless difficulties in the future to pay for the errors of past tolerance.

Yet the racist attitude was always confined to a minority. Most serious students of American society continued to view the second generation as a cultural rather than a biological problem. Increasingly, they were disposed to regard the children of immigrants as members of a marginal group standing between two cultures—that of its parents and that of the surrounding native milieu. To some degree, the second generation was alien to both. The culture of the parents was foreign in origin and not altogether comprehensible. On the other hand, residual ethnic traits prevented the native offspring of the immigrants from participating fully in the life about them. Sometimes they acquired a thin veneer of Americanization, changed their names, aped the local dress and manners, and even intermarried. Still they stood apart in their consistent marginality.[1]

The tensions of marginality could never be resolved, for no man could wholly suppress the discordant influence of a foreign heritage that impeded adjustment to the environment. At its most optimistic, this view led to a belief that only the third generation could accept its origins dispassionately enough to avoid inner strain (see No. 18). Among the more pessimistic, the assumption of the marginality of the second generation created serious doubts about the future capacity of these people or their children to blend into American society.

Yet this definition of the problem involved a narrow view of acculturation and rested upon the experience of a limited segment of the second generation, that which was most visible at the end of the nineteenth century. The prototype of this analysis was the alienated youth, situated in a slum environment and cut off from society by his foreign antecedents.

This volume proposes to draw together the materials upon the basis of which the adequacy of the interpretation of marginality may be judged. The characteristic writings of members of the second generation in the period of high immigration will reveal the themes that attracted their attention and will set their marginality in a more comprehensible context.

The second generation proves to encompass a wider variety of types than is generally supposed. Among the children of immigrants are people of English as well as of European and Asian descent. Some bear mixed heritages; Louis Sullivan and Joel Chandler Harris had Irish fathers, but the mother of one was Swiss, of the other, native American. Some were conscious of their ethnic situation, others never gave it a thought. By using an inclusive definition of the second generation as that native to the United States but with foreign parentage, it is possible to arrive at a more rounded and more comprehensive

[1] See E. V. Stonequist, *The Marginal Man* (New York, 1937); William C. Smith, *Americans in the Making* (New York, 1939), pp. 341ff.

view of the problem. The broadened perspective will make possible meaningful judgments about the aftereffects of migration and about the role of ethnicity in the American experience.

Before Independence, the second generation existed but was scarcely noticed. American life was colonial not only in the sense of political dependence upon Britain but also in the preoccupation with the tasks of settlement and with the creation of cultural and social institutions. There was little awareness of the ethnic factor in the differences among generations. Comparisons between the first European settlers and their descendants born in the New World expressed concern about whether life in the wilderness was conducive to deterioration—"declension" the Puritans called it. But these discussions focused on the effects of environment rather than of heritage. That was to be expected because the sense of national consciousness was still unclear through most of the colonial period.

The chief problems of this society were those of survival. It took continuous effort and great stores of energy to clear the forests and establish productive farming, to operate the trading and fishing fleets, to build cities and to sustain churches, newspapers, and schools. These precarious enterprises were always short of hands and any labor that could contribute to the work to be done was welcome, whatever its source.

The preponderant majority of the arrivals of these years were English not only because the colonies belonged to Britain but also because in that country social, economic and religious disorders most frequently generated the surplus population that spilled over into migration. However, there were also substantial contingents from other parts of Western Europe and, in addition, a somewhat different type of newcomer—the involuntary cargoes of the ships engaged in the African trade.

The subjects then of most concern to the second generation were not related to marginality but to the social environment. Down through the outbreak of the Revolution, the wilderness remained the most challenging element in the experience of the colonists. The total strangeness of the forest and of its savage denizens frightened men whose heritage was European. There was danger from the Indians and from their Papist French and Spanish allies even in the interludes of peace that interrupted the succession of colonial wars; only the faith that these attacks were evidence of God's judgment made them comprehensible.[2] Furthermore the primitive setting had a profound effect upon the people subjected to it. William Byrd noted with interest the extent to which the frontier weakened religion, modified manners and molded the character of the colonists. He did not yet draw the conclusion that a new type of man was emerging from the encounter he observed; but his account touched upon the beginnings of that process.[3]

After 1750 evidence of the gradual discovery of a national identity was clearer. Benjamin Franklin speculated about the distinctive destiny and future greatness of his country long before he thought of political independence.[4] The Revolution brought national sentiments out into the open, clarified them and endowed them with patriotic emotions. David Ramsay, the son of a Scotch-Irish Presbyterian, envisioned great social changes as the outcome; and William Wirt, of German-Swiss parentage, decades later was still apologetic for the limited cultural achievements of the new nation.[5]

Little was distinctive in the writings of such second-generation authors. Their ideas conformed in general to those of other contemporary Americans. Significantly, when William Dunlap, whose father was Irish, touched upon a theme that later would acquire special meaning for the second generation —the search for a lost son's father—he did so within the comic

[2] See, e.g. Stephen W. Williams, ed., *The Redeemed Captive Returning to Zion: or, A Faithful History of Remarkable Occurrences in the Captivity and Deliverance of Mr. John Williams* (Northampton, 1853), pp. 9–17, 34–7, 54–60.

[3] William Byrd, *Writings*, J. S. Bassett, ed. (New York, 1901), pp. 47, 57–8, 60–1, 75–7, 79–81, 94–102.

[4] Benjamin Franklin, "Observations Concerning the Increase of Mankind," *Papers*, L. W. Labaree, ed. (New Haven, 1961), IV, pp. 227–33.

[5] David Ramsay, *History of the American Revolution* (Philadelphia, 1798), II, pp. 315–24; William Wirt, *The Old Bachelor* (Richmond, 1814), pp. 9–13.

conventions common to his times.[6] The children of the immigrants were not yet so set off as a group in their society as to have acquired a peculiar perspective of their own.

Those offspring of immigrants born between 1776 and 1845 faced an altogether different world. In the post-Revolutionary years the United States gained and consolidated its independence, and attempted to establish its own identity in politics, in economics, and in culture. Enormous expansive energies increased its population, spread the line of settlement to the Mississippi, and planted a vigorous outpost in California, and at the same time sustained a high rate of economic growth. A reckless optimism and a speculative temperament persuaded the people of the Republic that all their problems were susceptible of immediate solution and that there were no limits to their potential expansion.

The Revolutionary War interrupted the movement of population across the Atlantic and for a long time thereafter international conflicts reduced the flow to a trickle. Not until after 1820, with peace definitely restored, did migration begin to climb toward its former level. It brought, at first, the artisans and peasants displaced by economic changes in Europe and then it swept along other groups discontent with political and social conditions.

The migration still originated mostly in Western and Northern Europe, the largest contingents being from England, Ireland, and Germany. Many newcomers were now forced to struggle for their livelihood as laborers; and their children were not likely soon to take to the pen.

Those who did observed a nation in process of rapid change. Many of them indeed lived on beyond the Civil War to the end of the century and were able to react to the problems the war created. As time passed, they became aware—although still in a preliminary form—of the special quality of their own status.

These writers absorbed and gave particularly intense expres-

[6] William Dunlap, *The Father or American Shandyism*, T. J. McKee, ed. (New York, 1887).

sion to the prevailing nationalism of their times. When it came to cultural achievements, they maintained the apologetic stance of their predecessors. But those born after the United States was already a republic were eager also to ground their national loyalty upon distinctive social and cultural traits, to establish the fact that the Americans were a unique kind of people. Robert Walsh and Henry M. Brackenridge, both sons of Irish immigrants, emphasized the fluidity of class lines and the importance of a frontier quite different from that of the seventeenth century.[7] In the well-known novel by John P. Kennedy, of Scotch-Irish descent, hostility toward the former mother country helped to establish the identity of the American.[8] Francis Wayland, whose parents were English, also assumed that differences in institutions set the Old World apart from the New.[9]

Such judgments affected the attitudes of the second generation toward the current political and social problems it faced. Its members by no means stood apart from other Americans to whom sectional or class ties linked them. But foreign parentage heightened the sensitivity to such issues as minority rights. The Irish antecedents of Ignatius Donnelly added to the passion with which he spoke on behalf of the freedmen of color; and toward the end of the century when the movement to restrict immigration began to gain force, Joaquin Miller, of German parentage, eloquently restated the national ideal of America as the land of refuge for the victims of persecution everywhere.[10] There was nothing marginal about these positions. The consciousness of their own background, no doubt, gave the reaction of the children of the immigrants peculiar

[7] Robert Walsh, *Didactics: Social, Literary, and Political* (Philadelphia, 1863), II, pp. 27–40; H. M. Brackenridge, *Recollections of Persons and Places in the West*, 2nd ed. (Philadelphia, 1868), pp. 10–27, 42–53.

[8] John P. Kennedy, *Horse-Shoe Robinson. A Tale of the Tory Ascendency* (New York, 1907), pp. 66–80.

[9] Quoted in Francis and H. L. Wayland, *A Memoir of the Life and Labors of Francis Wayland* (New York, 1867), II, pp. 10–28, 41–2.

[10] Ignatius Donnelly, *Speech Delivered in the House of Representatives, February 1, 1866* (Washington, 1866), pp. 3–14; Joaquin Miller, *Complete Poetical Works* (San Francisco, 1897), pp. 197–8, 249–50.

intensity. But their response drew upon central elements in their country's tradition and had the support of many of their fellow citizens.

Although the second generation was more readily distinguishable than earlier, it still displayed no consciousness of its distinctiveness as a group. His French background did not affect the way in which Augustus J. Requier treated the relationships of fathers to sons.[11] Nor did the Irish heritage of Henry James affect his protest against a formal religion that obscured the living spirit of faith.[12] There seemed as yet no special significance to the fact that the Atlantic crossing had created a complicating gap between the immigrants and their children.

Awareness of the second generation was a concomitant of the great migrations that began in the 1840's and extended on into the 1920's. In those eighty years, a great flow of peoples carried almost thirty-five million immigrants into the United States. They entered a country that was itself rapidly changing. Between 1845 and 1890, the nation expanded to its continental limits and at the same time began the process of industrial growth with its attendant problems of urbanization, poverty, and disorder. In the next thirty years, the United States adjusted painfully to the consequences of industrialization. And since 1920, it has discovered, with great difficulty, the implications of its novel role in the world affairs.

The shifting conditions of these three periods set the terms within which the children of the immigrants sought the meaning of their Americanization. The documents which follow illustrate the course of that quest. They demonstrate the extent to which consciousness of a distinctive situation influenced the way in which the second generation regarded the world about it.

[11] A. J. Requier, *The Old Sanctuary. A Romance of the Ashley* (Boston, 1846), pp. 11–23.

[12] Henry James, *Society the Redeemed Form of Man* (Boston, 1879), pp. 42–51, 53–4, 68–80.

The most significant variations among the children of the uprooted were those created by changes in the society in which they lived. Their writings have therefore been arranged chronologically by the date of their birth, on the assumption that the significant attitudes were shaped in childhood and youth.

PART I

Expansive America and Its Problems

1845-1890

The men and women born in the forty years between 1850 and 1890 could not escape the consciousness of their parents' foreign antecedents. Swift changes in the world which the second generation then entered made them aware that they occupied an intermediate position between the immigrants and the native born.

These were decades of rapid national growth. Expansion had always been an important part of American experience; now it became the dominant factor. The flow of settlers subdued the immense distances between the Mississippi and the Pacific coast. But the expansion of these years was more than territorial. The population rose, an elaborate railroad network crisscrossed the country, the pace of economic activity quickened, and the productive system took its modern form. Large-scale farming transformed agriculture and the modern factory mechanized manufacturing. The rising importance of steel was characteristic of the new industrial order in which a growing proportion of the population lived in large metropolitan cities.

The children born in this period confronted a highly complex, increasingly urban society in which the laborer on the verge of destitution was more characteristic than the yeoman farmer. Political and communal institutions were slow to adjust to the needs of the new situation; and substantial parts of the population had no recognized means for seeking redress of their grievances. Furthermore, new ideas shook the traditional faith both of the immigrants and the native born. Darwinism was the eye of a scientific tornado that tore apart accepted intellectual landmarks and left unsettled all but the most firmly anchored.

The second generation born between 1850 and 1890 was particularly vulnerable to the effects of change because it was itself the product of a far more complex pattern of migration than formerly. The collapse of the traditional peasant agriculture and handicrafts of Europe under the pressure of large-scale farming and manufacturing set adrift millions of placeless men whose misery deepened as famine swept across the continent after 1845. Some of these people fled to the growing cities; others escaped across the ocean. The great flow of refugees mounted to a peak in 1854 and continued, although at a declining rate, for almost another decade thereafter. The Civil War was only a temporary interruption. The movement resumed shortly after the peace and reached another peak in 1882. Migration was now sweeping along a great variety of men and women although the majority still originated in Western and Northern Europe.

The national backgrounds of the second-generation writers born in these years, therefore, were more diverse than earlier. The majority were still English, Irish, and German. But there were also significant representatives whose parents had left Scandinavia, Yugoslavia, and Italy; and among them were a number of Jews.

The themes that attracted these writers reflected the altered conditions under which they lived. The frontier was still large in their consciousness. But the wilderness had all but disappeared and recollections of the harshness of actuality faded with the passage of time. The frontier was no longer the place of danger it had been for the pioneers. It became instead a setting for nostalgia. Whether in the reminiscences of La Guardia (No. 13) or in the sentimental daydreams of Belasco (No. 2), its characteristics of innocence, openness, and virtue reflected the urban perspective from which it was regarded.

As significant were the efforts to understand the old and the new problems of the times. Joel Chandler Harris (No. 1), although a Southerner, understood the isolation of the Negro who suffered only slightly less under freedom than under slavery. The second-generation writers were even more aware of the consequences of the novel forms of labor in their society. These men witnessed, and often themselves experienced, the pressures of industrialization and urbanization. Many of them felt a sense of direct involvement in, and concern about, the harsh conditions under which the mass of immigrant workers existed. The novelist Dreiser (No. 10), using the tool of literary naturalism, aimed at a realistic portrayal of an environment destructive of humane values. It was hard to reconcile the degradation of the slums with the promises of American life or to square the hopeless poverty of millions with the premises of democracy. The tragic frustrations of his own life gave a somber cast to Louis Sullivan's reflections (No. 4) on the development of civilization in the United States.

More optimistic observers, however, hoped that progressive adjustments to the new conditions would produce gains for the whole society. Familiarity with both the law and business thus persuaded Brandeis (No. 5) that significant improvements in the workingman's lot could come within the existing system; and Ryan (No. 9) found hope in the application to the immediate situation of traditional spiritual values.

The urgent tones in which these men wrote reflected their perception of the seriousness of the crisis rather than any loss of faith in democracy or in the capacity of the common man to solve his problems. In the very depths of depression, Sandburg (No. 12) delivered a ringing affirmation—*The People, Yes.* Most clung to the belief in education, basic to the expectation of men like Suzzallo (No. 11), that a professionally organized teaching profession could lead the way to reform.

The situation developed within the second generation an ambiguous attitude toward its ethnic antecedents. Thoughts about the homeland of its parents inevitably bore a gloomy cast that reflected the circumstances of migration. Louise Imogen Guiney's sentimental story (No. 7) thus revealed her horror at the poverty of Ireland. Yet such people still found values in their heritage. Ryan (No. 9), for instance, looked to his ancestral church for concepts that would help solve current social problems. On the other hand, Veblen's destructive analysis (No. 6) treated the devout observances of religion as the products of an irrational human trait. So, too, Broun (No. 15) re-examined his relationships to his father for their positive influence upon his own character. But other writers like Eugene O'Neill saw in the parental heritage primarily the forces that destroyed the sons.[1]

With regard to the ethnic group itself, the attitude was mostly sentimental. These people were Americans and saw no particular need for an explicit rejection of the identification as the children of Germans or Irishmen. They regarded the survivals of the culture of their parents with affectionate warmth, as Edna Ferber did[2] or with the familiar good humor that spoke through the phrases of Dunne's Mr. Dooley (No. 8). Its members were likely to feel strongly about such issues close to them as the Irish question or immigration restriction; but the second generation found no conflict between its ethnic attachments and its own American nationalism. With Schlesinger (No. 14), they understood that the American was a new man, in whose national character diversity of origins was an important element. Indeed, some of them were, like Royce (No. 3), reaching out toward a larger definition of loyalty, one which would provide the basis for a sense of community in a world in which distances were shrinking and the alternative to cooperation was the cataclysm of war. Those who lived long enough were all too well aware of how close that alternative was.

[1] See, e.g. Eugene O'Neill, *Long Day's Journey Into the Night* (New Haven, 1956), pp. 125–149; J. H. Raleigh, "O'Neill's Long Day's Journey," *Partisan Review*, XXVI (1959), pp. 575ff.

[2] See, e.g., Edna Ferber, *Dawn O'Hara* (New York, 1911).

1. JOEL CHANDLER HARRIS

*Free Joe and the Rest of the World**

Joel Chandler Harris' father, an Irish laborer, eloped with Mary Harris of Putnam County, Georgia, and deserted his wife soon after the birth of their son in 1848. Joel was raised by his mother who supported herself by dressmaking, and he received only the fragments of an education before he went to work as a printer's devil. The young man drifted through a succession of newspaper jobs until he established a connection with the Atlanta Constitution *in 1876 from which his Uncle Remus stories made him famous. His background of childhood hardships left him an outsider in Southern society; his wife was French-Canadian and he himself became a Roman Catholic before his death in 1908. Perhaps that was why he chose to speak through a Negro's voice and covered with humor his oblique observations on his society. See also Alvin F. Harlow,* Joel Chandler Harris *(New York, 1946).*

The name of Free Joe strikes humorously upon the ear of memory. It is impossible to say why, for he was the humblest, the simplest, and the most serious of all God's living creatures, sadly lacking in all those elements that suggest the humorous. It is certain, moreover, that in 1850 the sober-minded citizens of the little Georgian village of Hillsborough were not inclined to take a humorous view of Free Joe, and neither his name nor his presence provoked a smile. He was a black atom, drifting hither and thither without an owner, blown about by all the winds of circumstance, and given over to shiftlessness.

* Joel Chandler Harris, *Free Joe and Other Georgian Sketches* (New York, 1887), pp. 1–20.

The problems of one generation are the paradoxes of a succeeding one, particularly if war, or some such incident, intervenes to clarify the atmosphere and strengthen the understanding. Thus, in 1850, Free Joe represented not only a problem of large concern, but, in the watchful eyes of Hillsborough, he was the embodiment of that vague and mysterious danger that seemed to be forever lurking on the outskirts of slavery, ready to sound a shrill and ghostly signal in the impenetrable swamps, and steal forth under the midnight stars to murder, rapine, and pillage,—a danger always threatening, and yet never assuming shape; intangible, and yet real; impossible, and yet not improbable. Across the serene and smiling front of safety, the pale outlines of the awful shadow of insurrection sometimes fell. With this invisible panorama as a background, it was natural that the figure of Free Joe, simple and humble as it was, should assume undue proportions. Go where he would, do what he might, he could not escape the finger of observation and the kindling eye of suspicion. His lightest words were noted, his slightest actions marked.

Under all the circumstances it was natural that his peculiar condition should reflect itself in his habits and manners. The slaves laughed loudly day by day, but Free Joe rarely laughed. The slaves sang at their work and danced at their frolics, but no one ever heard Free Joe sing or saw him dance. There was something painfully plaintive and appealing in his attitude, something touching in his anxiety to please. He was of the friendliest nature, and seemed to be delighted when he could amuse the little children who had made a playground of the public square. At times he would please them by making his little dog Dan perform all sorts of curious tricks, or he would tell them quaint stories of the beasts of the field and birds of the air; and frequently he was coaxed into relating the story of his own freedom. That story was brief, but tragical.

In the year of our Lord 1840, when a negro-speculator of a sportive turn of mind reached the little village of Hillsborough on his way to the Mississippi region, with a caravan of likely negroes of both sexes, he found much to interest him. In that day and at that time there were a number of young men in the village who had not bound themselves over to repentance for the various misdeeds of the flesh. To these young men the negro-speculator (Major Frampton was his name) proceeded to address himself. He was a Virginian, he declared; and, to prove the statement, he referred all the festively inclined young men of Hillsborough to a barrel of peach-brandy in one of his covered wagons. In the minds of these young men there was less doubt in regard to the age and quality of the brandy than there was in regard to the negro-trader's birthplace. Major Frampton might or might not have been born in the Old Dominion,—that was a matter for consideration and inquiry,—but there could be no question as to the mellow pungency of the peach-brandy.

In his own estimation, Major Frampton was one of the most accomplished of men. He had summered at the Virginia Springs; he had been to Philadelphia, to Washington, to Richmond, to Lynchburg, and to Charleston, and had accumulated a great deal of experience which he found useful. Hillsborough was hid in the woods of Middle Georgia, and its general aspect of innocence impressed him. He looked on the young men who had shown their readiness to test his peach-brandy, as overgrown country boys who needed to be introduced to some of the arts and sciences he had at his command. Thereupon the major pitched his tents, figuratively speaking, and became, for the time being, a part and parcel of the innocence that characterized Hillsborough. A wiser man would doubtless have made the same mistake.

The little village possessed advantages that seemed to be providentially arranged to fit the various enterprises that Major Frampton had in view. There was the auction-block in front of the stuccoed court-house, if he desired to dispose of a few of his negroes; there was a quarter-track, laid out to his hand and in excellent order, if he chose to enjoy the pleasures of horse-racing; there were secluded pine thickets within easy reach, if he desired to indulge in the exciting pastime of cock-fighting; and various lonely and unoccupied rooms in the second story of the tavern, if he cared to challenge the chances of dice or cards.

Major Frampton tried them all with varying luck, until he began his famous game of poker with Judge Alfred Wellington, a stately gentleman with a flowing white beard and mild blue eyes that gave him the appearance of a benevolent patriarch. The history of the game in which Major Frampton and Judge Alfred Wellington took part is something more than a tradition in Hillsborough, for there are still living three or four men who sat around the table and watched its progress. It is said that at various stages of the game Major Frampton would destroy the cards with which they were playing, and send for a new pack, but the result was always the same. The mild blue eyes of Judge Wellington, with few exceptions, continued to overlook "hands" that were invincible—a habit they had acquired during a long and arduous course of training from Saratoga to New Orleans. Major Frampton lost his money, his horses, his wagons, and all his negroes but one, his body-servant. When his misfortune had reached this limit, the major adjourned the game. The sun was shining brightly, and all nature was cheerful. It is said that the major also seemed to be cheerful. However this may be, he visited the court-house, and executed the papers that gave his body-servant his freedom. This being done, Major Frampton sauntered into a convenient pine thicket, and blew out his brains.

The negro thus freed came to be known as Free Joe. Compelled, under the law, to choose a guardian, he chose Judge Wellington, chiefly because his wife Lucinda was among the negroes won from Major Frampton. For several years Free Joe had what may be called a jovial time. His wife Lucinda was well provided for, and he found it a comparatively easy matter to provide for himself; so that, taking all the circumstances into consideration, it is not matter for astonishment that he became somewhat shiftless.

When Judge Wellington died, Free Joe's troubles began. The judge's negroes, including Lucinda, went to his half-brother, a man named Calderwood, who was a hard master and a rough customer generally,—a man of many eccentricities of mind and character. His neighbors had a habit of alluding to him as "Old Spite;" and the name seemed to fit him so completely, that he was known far and near as "Spite" Calderwood. He probably enjoyed the distinction the name gave him, at any rate, he never resented it, and it was not often that he missed an opportunity to show that he deserved it. Calderwood's place was two or three miles from the village of Hillsborough, and Free Joe visited his wife twice a week, Wednesday and Saturday nights.

One Sunday he was sitting in front of Lucinda's cabin, when Calderwood happened to pass that way.

"Howdy, marster?" said Free Joe, taking off his hat.

"Who are you?" exclaimed Calderwood abruptly, halting and staring at the negro.

"I'm name' Joe, marster. I'm Lucindy's ole man."

"Who do you belong to?"

"Marse John Evans is my gyardeen, marster."

"Big name—gyardeen. Show your pass."

Free Joe produced that document, and Calderwood read it aloud slowly, as if he found it difficult to get at the meaning:—

"To whom it may concern: This is to certify that the boy Joe Frampton has my permission to visit his wife Lucinda."

This was dated at Hillsborough, and signed "*John W. Evans.*"

Calderwood read it twice, and then looked at Free Joe, elevating his eyebrows, and showing his discolored teeth.

"Some mighty big words in that there. Evans owns this place, I reckon. When's he comin' down to take hold?"

Free Joe fumbled with his hat. He was badly frightened.

"Lucindy say she speck you wouldn't min' my comin', long ez I behave, marster."

Calderwood tore the pass in pieces and flung it away.

"Don't want no free niggers 'round here," he exclaimed. "There's the big road. It'll carry you to town. Don't let me catch you here no more. Now, mind what I tell you."

Free Joe presented a shabby spectacle as he moved off with

his little dog Dan slinking at his heels. It should be said in behalf of Dan, however, that his bristles were up, and that he looked back and growled. It may be that the dog had the advantage of insignificance, but it is difficult to conceive how a dog bold enough to raise his bristles under Calderwood's very eyes could be as insignificant as Free Joe. But both the negro and his little dog seemed to give a new and more dismal aspect to forlornness as they turned into the road and went toward Hillsborough.

After this incident Free Joe appeared to have clearer ideas concerning his peculiar condition. He realized the fact that though he was free he was more helpless than any slave. Having no owner, every man was his master. He knew that he was the object of suspicion, and therefore all his slender resources (ah! how pitifully slender they were!) were devoted to winning, not kindness and appreciation, but toleration; all his efforts were in the direction of mitigating the circumstances that tended to make his condition so much worse than that of the negroes around him,—negroes who had friends because they had masters.

So far as his own race was concerned, Free Joe was an exile. If the slaves secretly envied him his freedom (which is to be doubted, considering his miserable condition), they openly despised him, and lost no opportunity to treat him with contumely. Perhaps this was in some measure the result of the attitude which Free Joe chose to maintain toward them. No doubt his instinct taught him that to hold himself aloof from the slaves would be to invite from the whites the toleration which he coveted, and without which even his miserable condition would be rendered more miserable still.

His greatest trouble was the fact that he was not allowed to visit his wife; but he soon found a way out of this difficulty. After he had been ordered away from the Calderwood place, he was in the habit of wandering as far in that direction as prudence would permit. Near the Calderwood place, but not on Calderwood's land, lived an old man named Micajah Staley and his sister Becky Staley. These people were old and very poor. Old Micajah had a palsied arm and hand; but, in spite of this, he managed to earn a precarious living with his turning-lathe.

When he was a slave Free Joe would have scorned these representatives of a class known as poor white trash, but now he found them sympathetic and helpful in various ways. From the back door of their cabin he could hear the Calderwood negroes singing at night, and he sometimes fancied he could distinguish Lucinda's shrill treble rising above the other voices. A large poplar grew in the woods some distance from the Staley cabin, and at the foot of this tree Free Joe would sit for hours with his face turned toward Calderwood's. His little dog Dan would curl up in the leaves near by, and the two seemed to be as comfortable as possible.

One Saturday afternoon Free Joe, sitting at the foot of this friendly poplar, fell asleep. How long he slept, he could not tell; but when he awoke little Dan was licking his face, the moon was shining brightly, and Lucinda his wife stood before him laughing. The dog, seeing that Free Joe was asleep, had grown somewhat impatient, and he concluded to make an excursion to the Calderwood place on his own account. Lucinda was inclined to give the incident a twist in the direction of superstition.

"I 'uz settin' down front er de fireplace," she said, "cookin' me some meat, w'en all of a sudden I year sumpin at de do'—scratch, scratch. I tuck'n tu'n de meat over, en make out I aint year it. Bimeby it come dar 'gin—scratch, scratch. I up en open de do', I did, en, bless de Lord! dar wuz little Dan, en it look like ter me dat his ribs done grow tergeer. I gin 'im some bread, en den, w'en he start out, I tuck'n foller 'im, kaze, I say ter myse'f, maybe my nigger man mought be some'rs 'roun'. Dat ar little dog got sense, mon."

Free Joe laughed and dropped his hand lightly on Dan's head. For a long time after that he had no difficulty in seeing his wife. He had only to sit by the poplar-tree until little Dan could run and fetch her. But after a while the other negroes discovered that Lucinda was meeting Free Joe in the woods, and information of the fact soon reached Calderwood's ears. Calderwood was what is called a man of action. He said nothing; but one day he put Lucinda in his buggy, and carried her to Macon, sixty miles away. He carried her to Macon, and came back without her; and nobody in or around Hillsborough, or in that section, ever saw her again.

For many a night after that Free Joe sat in the woods and waited. Little Dan would run merrily off and be gone a long time, but he always came back without Lucinda. This happened over and over again. The "willis-whistlers" would call and call, like phantom huntsmen wandering on a far-off shore; the screech-owl would shake and shiver in the depths of the woods; the night-hawks, sweeping by on noiseless wings, would snap their beaks as though they enjoyed the huge joke of which Free Joe and little Dan were the victims; and the whip-poor-wills would cry to each other through the gloom. Each night seemed to be lonelier than the preceding, but Free Joe's patience was proof against loneliness. There came a time, however, when little Dan refused to go after Lucinda. When Free Joe motioned him in the direction of the Calderwood place, he would simply move about uneasily and whine; then he would curl up in the leaves and make himself comfortable.

One night, instead of going to the poplar-tree to wait for Lucinda, Free Joe went to the Staley cabin, and, in order to make his welcome good, as he expressed it, he carried with him an armful of fat-pine splinters. Miss Becky Staley had a great reputation in those parts as a fortune-teller, and the schoolgirls, as well as older people, often tested her powers in this direction, some in jest and some in earnest. Free Joe placed his humble offering of light-wood in the chimney-corner, and then seated himself on the steps, dropping his hat on the ground outside.

"Miss Becky," he said presently, "whar in de name er gracious you reckon Lucindy is?"

"Well, the Lord he'p the nigger!" exclaimed Miss Becky, in a tone that seemed to reproduce, by some curious agreement of sight with sound, her general aspect of peakedness. "Well, the Lord he'p the nigger! haint you been a-seein' her all this blessed time? She's over at old Spite Calderwood's, if she's anywheres, I reckon."

"No'm, dat I aint, Miss Becky. I aint seen Lucindy in now gwine on mighty nigh a mont'."

"Well, it haint a-gwine to hurt you," said Miss Becky, somewhat sharply. "In my day an' time it wuz allers took to be a bad sign when niggers got to honeyin' 'roun' an' gwine on."

"Yessum," said Free Joe, cheerfully assenting to the proposition—"yessum, dat's so, but me an' my ole 'oman, we 'uz raise tergeer, en dey aint been many days w'en we 'uz 'way fum one 'n'er like we is now."

"Maybe she's up an' took up wi' some un else," said Micajah Staley from the corner. "You know what the sayin' is, 'New master, new nigger.' "

"Dat's so, dat's de sayin', but tain't wid my ole 'oman like 'tis wid yuther niggers. Me en her wuz des natally raise up tergeer. Dey's lots likelier niggers dan w'at I is," said Free Joe, viewing his shabbiness with a critical eye, "but I knows Lucindy mo' good en I does little Dan dar—dat I does."

There was no reply to this, and Free Joe continued,—

"Miss Becky, I wish you please, ma'am, take en run yo' kyards en see sump'n n'er 'bout Lucindy; kaze ef she sick, I'm gwine dar. Dey ken take en take me up en gimme a stroppin', but I'm gwine dar."

Miss Becky got her cards, but first she picked up a cup, in the bottom of which were some coffee-grounds. These she whirled slowly round and round, ending finally by turning the cup upside down on the hearth and allowing it to remain in that position.

"I'll turn the cup first," said Miss Becky, "and then I'll run the cards and see what they say."

As she shuffled the cards the fire on the hearth burned low, and in its fitful light the gray-haired, thin-featured woman seemed to deserve the weird reputation which rumor and gossip had given her. She shuffled the cards for some moments, gazing intently in the dying fire; then, throwing a piece of pine on the coals, she made three divisions of the pack, disposing them about in her lap. Then she took the first pile, ran the cards slowly through her fingers, and studied them carefully. To the first she added the second pile. The study of these was evidently not satisfactory. She said nothing, but frowned heavily; and the frown deepened as she added the rest of the cards until the entire fifty-two had passed in review before her. Though she frowned, she seemed to be deeply interested. Without changing the relative position of the cards, she ran them all over again. Then she threw a larger piece of pine on the fire, shuffled the cards afresh, divided them into three piles, and subjected them to the same careful and critical examination.

"I can't tell the day when I've seed the cards run this a-way," she said after a while. "What is an' what aint, I'll never tell you; but I know what the cards sez."

"W'at does dey say, Miss Becky?" the negro inquired, in a tone the solemnity of which was heightened by its eagerness.

"They er runnin' quare. These here that I'm a-lookin' at," said Miss Becky, "they stan' for the past. Them there, they er the present; and the t'others, they er the future. Here's a bundle,"—tapping the ace of clubs with her thumb,—"an' here's a journey as plain as the nose on a man's face. Here's Lucinda"—

"Whar she, Miss Becky?"

"Here she is—the queen of spades."

Free Joe grinned. The idea seemed to please him immensely.

"Well, well, well!" he exclaimed. "Ef dat don't beat my time! De queen er spades! W'en Lucindy year dat hit'll tickle 'er, sho'!"

Miss Becky continued to run the cards back and forth through her fingers.

"Here's a bundle an' a journey, and here's Lucinda. An' here's ole Spite Calderwood."

She held the cards toward the negro and touched the king of clubs.

"De Lord he'p my soul!" exclaimed Free Joe with a chuckle.

"De faver's dar. Yesser, dat's him! W'at de matter 'long wid all un um, Miss Becky?"

The old woman added the second pile of cards to the first, and then the third, still running them through her fingers slowly and critically. By this time the piece of pine in the fire-place had wrapped itself in a mantle of flame, illuminating the cabin and throwing into strange relief the figure of Miss Becky as she sat studying the cards. She frowned ominously at the cards and mumbled a few words to herself. Then she dropped her hands in her lap and gazed once more into the fire. Her shadow danced and capered on the wall and floor behind her, as if, looking over her shoulder into the future, it could behold a rare spectacle. After a while she picked up the cup that had been turned on the hearth. The coffee-grounds, shaken around, presented what seemed to be a most intricate map.

"Here's the journey," said Miss Becky, presently; "here's the big road, here's rivers to cross, here's the bundle to tote." She paused and sighed. "They haint no names writ here, an' what it all means I'll never tell you. Cajy, I wish you'd be so good as to han' me my pipe."

"I haint no hand wi' the kyards," said Cajy, as he handed the pipe, "but I reckon I can patch out your misinformation, Becky, bekaze the other day, whiles I was a-finishin' up Mizzers Perdue's rollin'-pin, I hearn a rattlin' in the road. I looked out, an' Spite Calderwood was a-drivin' by in his buggy, an' thar sot Lucinda by him. It'd in-about drapt out er my min'."

Free Joe sat on the door-sill and fumbled at his hat, flinging it from one hand to the other.

"You aint see um gwine back, is you, Mars Cajy?" he asked after a while.

"Ef they went back by this road," said Mr. Staley, with the air of one who is accustomed to weigh well his words, "it must 'a' bin endurin' of the time whiles I was asleep, bekaze I haint bin no furder from my shop than to yon bed."

"Well, sir!" exclaimed Free Joe in an awed tone, which Mr. Staley seemed to regard as a tribute to his extraordinary powers of statement.

"Ef it's my beliefs you want," continued the old man, "I'll

pitch 'em at you fair and free. My beliefs is that Spite Calderwood is gone an' took Lucindy outen the county. Bless your heart and soul! when Spite Calderwood meets the Old Boy in the road they'll be a turrible scuffle. You mark what I tell you."

Free Joe, still fumbling with his hat, rose and leaned against the door-facing. He seemed to be embarrassed. Presently he said,—

"I speck I better be gittin' 'long. Nex' time I see Lucindy, I'm gwine tell 'er w'at Miss Becky say 'bout de queen er spades—dat I is. Ef dat don't tickle 'er, dey ain't no nigger 'oman never bin tickle'."

He paused a moment, as though waiting for some remark or comment, some confirmation of misfortune, or, at the very least, some indorsement of his suggestion that Lucinda would be greatly pleased to know that she had figured as the queen of spades; but neither Miss Becky nor her brother said any thing.

"One minnit ridin' in the buggy 'longside er Mars Spite, en de nex' highfalutin' 'roun' playin' de queen er spades. Mon, deze yer nigger gals gittin' up in de pictur's; dey sholy is."

With a brief "Good-night, Miss Becky, Mars Cajy," Free Joe went out into the darkness, followed by little Dan. He made his way to the poplar, where Lucinda had been in the habit of meeting him, and sat down. He sat there a long time; he sat there until little Dan, growing restless, trotted off in the direction of the Calderwood place. Dozing against the poplar, in the gray dawn of the morning, Free Joe heard Spite Calderwood's fox-hounds in full cry a mile away.

"Shoo!" he exclaimed, scratching his head, and laughing to himself, "dem ar dogs is des a-warmin' dat old fox up."

But it was Dan the hounds were after, and the little dog came back no more. Free Joe waited and waited, until he grew tired of waiting. He went back the next night and waited, and for many nights thereafter. His waiting was in vain, and yet he never regarded it as in vain. Careless and shabby as he was, Free Joe was thoughtful enough to have his theory. He was convinced that little Dan had found Lucinda, and that some night when the moon was shining brightly through the trees, the dog would rouse him from his dreams as he sat sleeping at the foot of the poplar-tree, and he would open his eyes and behold Lucinda standing over him, laughing merrily as of old; and then he thought what fun they would have about the queen of spades.

How many long nights Free Joe waited at the foot of the poplar-tree for Lucinda and little Dan, no one can ever know. He kept no account of them, and they were not recorded by Micajah Staley nor by Miss Becky. The season ran into summer and then into fall. One night he went to the Staley cabin, cut the two old people an armful of wood, and seated himself on the door-steps, where he rested. He was always thankful—and proud, as it seemed—when Miss Becky gave him a cup of coffee, which she was sometimes thoughtful enough to do. He was especially thankful on this particular night.

"You er still layin' off for to strike up wi' Lucindy out thar in the woods, I reckon," said Micajah Staley, smiling grimly. The situation was not without its humorous aspects.

"Oh, dey er comin', Mars Cajy, dey er comin', sho," Free Joe replied. "I boun' you dey'll come; en w'en dey does come, I'll des take en fetch um yer, whar you kin see um wid you own eyes, you en Miss Becky."

"No," said Mr. Staley, with a quick and emphatic gesture of disapproval. "Don't! don't fetch 'em anywheres. Stay right wi'em as long as may be."

Free Joe chuckled, and slipped away into the night, while the two old people sat gazing in the fire. Finally Micajah spoke.

"Look at that nigger; look at 'im. He's pine-blank as happy now as a killdee by a mill-race. You can't 'faze 'em. I'd in-about give up my t'other hand ef I could stan' flat-footed, an' grin at trouble like that there nigger."

"Niggers is niggers," said Miss Becky, smiling grimly, "an' you can't rub it out; yit I lay I've seed a heap of white people lots meaner'n Free Joe. He grins,—an' that's nigger,—but I've ketched his under jaw a-trimblin' when Lucindy's name uz brung up. An' I tell you," she went on, bridling up a little, and speaking with almost fierce emphasis, "the Old Boy's done sharpened his claws for Spite Calderwood. You'll see it."

"Me, Rebecca?" said Mr. Staley, hugging his palsied arm; "me? I hope not."

"Well, you'll know it then," said Miss Becky, laughing heartily at her brother's look of alarm.

The next morning Micajah Staley had occasion to go into the woods after a piece of timber. He saw Free Joe sitting at the foot of the poplar, and the sight vexed him somewhat.

"Git up from there," he cried, "an' go an' arn your livin'. A mighty purty pass it's come to, when great big buck niggers can lie a-snorin' in the woods all day, when t'other folks is got to be up an' a-gwine. Git up from there!"

Receiving no response, Mr. Staley went to Free Joe, and shook him by the shoulder; but the negro made no response. He was dead. His hat was off, his head was bent, and a smile was on his face. It was as if he had bowed and smiled when death stood before him, humble to the last. His clothes were ragged; his hands were rough and callous; his shoes were literally tied together with strings; he was shabby in the extreme. A passer-by, glancing at him, could have no idea that such a humble creature had been summoned as a witness before the Lord God of Hosts.

2. DAVID BELASCO

*The Golden West**

David Belasco was born in San Francisco in 1853 soon after his parents had arrived from England. Frequent family moves interrupted his schooling and he early became involved in the theater. He was not much of a success as an actor, but he learned a good deal from Dion Boucicault whom he served briefly as secretary. After 1874 he was primarily a manager, operating in San Francisco until 1882 when he moved to New York. There he attained widespread popularity as a manager, director, and writer. In the extract that follows, from one of his most popular plays, the opportunities of the West offer the Girl and Johnson (a bandit in his other identity as Ramerrez) the means of fulfilling their true love. See also Craig Timberlake, The Bishop of Broadway *(New York, 1954).*

GIRL *(Entering from the dance-hall).* Nick, you can put the lights out. *(Nick puts out the candle over the table.)* Put the lights out here, too. Oh, you ain't goin'?

JOHNSON. Not yet, no, but . . .

GIRL. I'm glad of that. Don't it feel funny here? It's kind of creepy. I suppose that's because I never remember seeing the bar so empty before. *(Putting a chair in place.)*

NICK *(Putting out the candle on the mantelpiece).* I'm goin' to close the shutters. *(He closes the shutters.)*

GIRL *(Crossing to the table).* What for — so early?

NICK *(In a half whisper).* Well, you see, the boys is out huntin' Ramerrez — and they's too much money here.

* David Belasco, *The Girl of the Golden West* (1905; copyright 1915) in *Six Plays* (Boston, 1928), pp. 342–9, 402–3.

GIRL. Oh, all right. Cash in. Don't put the head on the keg. I ain't cashed in m'self yet.

NICK *(Rolling out the keg).* Say, Min . . .

GIRL. Huh?

NICK *(Looking uneasily at the keg, and then darting a glance towards Johnson).* Know anything about – him?

GIRL. Oh, sure.

NICK. All right, eh?

GIRL. Yes. *(Nick blows out the lights at the door, and goes into the empty dance-hall.)* Well, Mr. Johnson: it seems to be us a-keepin' house here to-night, don't it?

JOHNSON. Strange how things come about. . . . Strange to be looking everywhere for you, and to find you at last at the Polka. *(Sitting on the table.)*

GIRL. Anything wrong with the Polka?

JOHNSON. Well, it's hardly the place for a young woman like you.

GIRL. How so?

JOHNSON. It's rather unprotected, and –

GIRL. Oh, pshaw! I said to Ashby only to-night: "I bet if a road-agent come in here, I could offer him a drink an' he'd treat me like a perfect lady." Say, won't you take something? *(Going back of the bar for a bottle.)*

JOHNSON. No, thank you. I'd like to ask you a question.

GIRL. I know what it is – every stranger asks it, but I didn't think *you* would. It's this: am I decent? Yep, I am – you bet!

JOHNSON. Oh, Girl: I'm not blind – that was not the question.

GIRL *(Leaning over the bar, looking at him).* Dear me suz!

JOHNSON. What I meant to say was this: I am sorry to find you here almost at the mercy of the passer-by . . . where a man may come, may drink, may rob you if he will; and where I daresay more than one has even laid claim to a kiss.

GIRL. They's a good many people claimin' things they never git. *(She is putting her money in a cigar-box.)* I've got my first kiss to give.

JOHNSON *(Studying her)*. You're clever. Been here long?

GIRL. Yep.

JOHNSON. Live in the Polka?

GIRL. Nop.

JOHNSON. Where do you live?

GIRL. Cabin up the mountain a little ways.

JOHNSON. You're worth something better than this.

GIRL. What's better'n this? I ain't boastin', but if keepin' this saloon don't give me a sort of position round here, I dunno what does. Ha! Look here: say, you ain't one of them exhorters, are you, from the missionaries' camp?

JOHNSON. My profession has its faults, but I am not an ex horter.

GIRL. You know I can't figger out jest exactly what you are.

JOHNSON. Try.

GIRL *(Getting a chair from behind the poker table)*. Well – you ain't one of us.

JOHNSON. No?

GIRL. Oh, I can tell – I can spot my man every time. I tell you, keepin' saloon is a great educator. *(Sitting.)* I dunno but what it's a good way to bring up girls. They git to know things. Now, I'd trust you.

JOHNSON. You would trust me?

GIRL. Notice I danced with you to-night?

JOHNSON. Yes.

GIRL. I seen from the first you was the real article.

JOHNSON. I beg pardon.

GIRL. Why, that was a compliment I handed to you.

JOHNSON. Oh . . .

GIRL *(Confidentially)*. Your kind don't prevail much here . . . I can tell – I got what you call a quick eye.

JOHNSON. I'm afraid that men like me – prevail, as you say, almost everywhere.

GIRL. Go on! What are you giving me? Of course they don't. Ha! Before I went on that trip to Monterey, I thought Rance here was the genu*ine* thing in a gent – but the minute I kind o' glanced over you on the road – I – I seen he wasn't. Say — take your whiskey — and water. *(She rises.)*

JOHNSON. No.

GIRL *(Calling)*. Nick? *(Changing her mind.)* No, I'll help you to a drink myself.

JOHNSON. No, thank you.

GIRL *(Leaning against the bar, studying him)*. Say, I've got you figgered out: you're awful good, or awful bad. . . .

JOHNSON *(Half amused.)* Now what do you mean by that?

GIRL. Well, so good that you're a teetotaler — or so bad that you're tired of life an' whiskey.

JOHNSON *(Rising and going up to her)*. On the contrary, although I'm not good — I've lived, and I've liked life pretty well, and I am not tired of it: it's been bully! *(Leaning on the bar.)* So have you liked it, Girl, only you haven't lived — you haven't lived. *(He attempts to take The Girl's hand, but she retreats.)* Not with *your* nature. You see, I've got a quick eye, too.

(Nick enters slowly and prepares to seat himself in a chair back of the poker table.)

GIRL. Nick, git! *(Nick casts an inquisitive glance at the pair and hastens out.)* Say, what do you mean by — I haven't lived?

JOHNSON *(Insinuatingly, half under his breath)*. Oh, you know.

GIRL. No, I don't.

JOHNSON. Yes, you do.

GIRL. Well, say it's an even chance I do and an even chance I don't.

JOHNSON *(In a low voice)*. I mean life for all it's worth . . . to the utmost . . . to the last drop in the cup . . . so that it atones for what's gone before, or may come after.

GIRL. No, I don't believe I do know what you mean by them words. Is it a — *(She crosses to the poker table and sits down on her revolver which is in her pocket. She rises hastily.)* Oh, Lord! Excuse me — I set on my gun. *(Impulsively.)* I can't pass you on the road. I take your dust. Look here: I'm goin' to make you an offer.

JOHNSON. An offer?

GIRL. It's this: if ever you need to be staked –

JOHNSON. Eh?

GIRL. Which of course you don't, – name your price – jest for the style I'll git from you an' the deportment.

JOHNSON. Deportment? Me?

NICK *(Re-entering).* Oh, er – I'd like to say –

GIRL *(Annoyed).* Oh!

(Nick goes off hurriedly.)

JOHNSON. Well, I never heard before that my society was so desirable. Apart from the financial aspect of the matter – I –

GIRL *(Admiringly, half to herself).* Ain't that great? Ain't that great? Oh, you got to let me stand treat. *(Calls.)* Nick? *(She slips down from the table where she has been seated.)*

JOHNSON. No, really. Say, Girl: you're like finding some new kind of flower.

GIRL. You know the reason I made you that offer is – we're kind of rough up here, but we're reaching out. Now, I take it that what we're all put on this earth for – every one of us – is to rise ourselves up in the world – to reach out.

JOHNSON *(With a change of manner).* That's true – that's true. I venture to say there isn't a man who hasn't thought seriously about that. I have. If only a man knew how to reach out for something he hardly dare even hope for. It's like trying to catch the star shining just ahead.

GIRL. That's the cheese. You've struck it.

(Nick enters.)

NICK. I *have* been a-tryin' to say –

GIRL. What *is* it, Nick?

NICK. I jest seen an ugly lookin' greaser outside a winder.

GIRL *(Going up to the door).* A greaser? Let me look.

JOHNSON *(Who knows that it is his man, awaiting the signal – speaking with an air of authority).* I wouldn't.

GIRL. Why not?

NICK. I'll bolt all the winders. *(He goes off.)*

(A whistle is heard outside. Johnson recognizes the signal.)

GIRL. Don't that sound horrid? *(Getting behind the counter.)*

I'm awful glad you're here. Nick's so nervous. He knows what a lot of money I've got. Why, there's a little fortune right in that keg.

JOHNSON *(Crossing over to the keg and looking at it).* In that keg?

GIRL. The boys sleep round it nights.

JOHNSON. But when they're gone – isn't that a careless place to leave it?

GIRL *(Coming down to the keg).* Oh, they'd have to kill me before they got it.

JOHNSON. I see – it's *your* money.

GIRL. No, it belongs to the boys.

JOHNSON. Oh, that's different. Now, I wouldn't risk my life for that.

GIRL *(Putting the bags of gold-dust in the keg, and closing the keg and standing with her foot on it).* Oh, yes, you would – yes, you would – if you seen how hard they got it. When I think of it – I – I nearly cry. You know there's something awful pretty in the way the boys hold out before they strike it – awful pretty – in the face of rocks and clay and alkali. Oh, Lord, what a life it is, anyway! Why, they eat dirt – an' they sleep dirt, an' they breathe dirt till their backs are bent, their hands twisted, their souls warped; they're all wind-swept an' blear-eyed – an' some of 'em just lie down in their own sweat beside the sluices, an' they don't never rise again. I've seen 'em there. I got some money of old Brownie's. *(Pointing to the keg.)* He was lyin' out in the sun on a pile of clay two weeks ago an' I guess the only clean thing about him was his soul – an' he was quittin' – quittin' right there on the clay – an' quittin' hard. . . . *(Remembering the scene with horror.)* Oh, he died – jest like a dog . . . you wanted to shoot him to help him along quicker. Before he went, he sez: "Girl, give it to my old woman," and he – left. She'll git it. *(Slight pause.)* An' that's what aches you. They ain't one of these men working for themselves alone. The Almighty never put it in no man's heart to make a beast or pack-horse of himself – except for some woman, or some child. Ain't it wonderful? Ain't it wonderful, that instinct, ain't it? – What a man'll do when it comes to a woman. Ain't it wonderful? Yep, the boys use me as a – ha – sort of lady bank. *(She wipes her eyes.)* You bet I'll drop down dead before any one'll get a dollar of theirs outer the Polka!

JOHNSON *(After a short pause).* That's right. *(Taking The Girl's hand.)* I'm with you. I'd like to see any one get *that.* *(They shake hands over the keg – not heroically, but very simply.)* Girl, you make me wish I could talk more with you, but I can't. By daybreak I must be a long way off. I'm sorry. I should have liked to call at your cabin.

GIRL *(Wistfully).* Must you be movin' – so – soon?

JOHNSON. I'm only waiting till the posse gets back and you're safe. *(Listening.)* There. . . . They're coming now. . . .

GIRL. I'm awful sorry you got to go. I was goin' to say: *(rolling the keg up stage, she takes a lantern off the bar and sets it on the keg)* if you didn't have to go so soon, I'd like to have you come up to the cabin to-night, and we would talk of reaching out up there. You see, the boys will come back here. . . . We close the Polka at one – any time after that.

JOHNSON. I – I should ride on now – but – I'll come.

GIRL. Oh, good! *(Giving the lantern to Johnson.)* You can use this lantern. It's the straight trail up – you can't miss it. Say, don't expect too much of me – I've only had thirty-two dollars' worth of education. *(Her voice breaks, her eyes fill with tears.)* P'raps if I'd had more – why, you can't tell what I might have been. Say, that's a turrible thought, ain't it? What we – might have been? And I know it when I look at you.

JOHNSON *(Touched).* God knows it is! What we might have been – and *I* know it when I look at *you,* Girl – I know it – when I look at you.

GIRL *(Wipes away a tear).* You bet! *(Suddenly collapses, burying her face on her arm on the bar, sobbing, speaking through her tears.)* Oh, 'tain't no use – I'm ignorant – I don't know nothin' and I never knowed it till to-night. The boys always told me I knowed so much — but they're such damned liars.

JOHNSON *(Comes up and leans on the bar. Earnestly, with a suggestion of tears in his voice).* Don't you care — you're all right, Girl — you're all right. Your heart's all right — that's the main thing. As for your looks, — to me you've got the face of an angel. I — I'll just take a glance at my horse. *(He takes up his saddle, crosses to the door, then turns back. To himself.)* Johnson, what the devil's the matter with you? *(He goes out hastily, carrying the lantern and slamming the door behind him.)*

(The Girl stands immovable for a moment, then calls suddenly.)

GIRL. Nick! Nick! *(Nick enters quickly. She turns her face away, wiping off a tear.)* You run over to the Palmetter rest'rant an' tell 'em to send me up two charlotte rusks an' a lemming turnover — jest as quick as they can — right up to the cabin for supper. *(Nick goes off.)* Ha! *(She crosses to the poker table and sits on the edge, the light above shining down on her face. Strumming on a guitar and mandolin is heard as though the musicians were tuning up for the boys.)* He says . . . He says . . . *(sentimentally)* I have the face of an angel. *(A little pause, then turning her face away.)* Oh, hell!

CURTAIN

. . . .

ACT IV

The boundless prairies of the West.
On the way East, at the dawn of a day about a week later.

"Oh, my beautiful West!
Oh, my California!"

The scene is a great stretch of prairie. In the far background are foothills with here and there a suggestion of a winding trail leading to the West. The foliage is the pale green of sage brush, — the hills the deeper green of pine and hemlock. In the foreground is a little tepee made of two blankets on crossed sticks. The tepee is built against a grass mound and is apparently only a rude shelter for the night. Back of the tent is an old tree stump which stands out distinctly against the horizon. Here and there are little clumps of grass, bushes and small mounds of earth and rocks. A log fire is burning to the left of the tepee, a Mexican saddle lies beside the fire.

As the curtain rises, the stage is in darkness. Johnson is lying on the grass, leaning against his saddle, smoking a cigarette. The Girl is inside the tepee. Gradually the dawn begins to break. As the scene becomes visible, The Girl pushes aside the blanket and appears in the opening.

GIRL. Dick, are you awake?

JOHNSON *(Turning to her).* Another day . . . the dawn is breaking.

GIRL *(Looking towards the unseen hills in the distance).* Another day . . . Look back . . . the foothills are growing fainter — every dawn — farther away. Some night when I am going to sleep, I'll turn — and they won't be there — red and shining. That was the promised land.

JOHNSON *(Rising).* We must look ahead, Girl, not backwards. The promised land is always ahead.

(A glimmer of the rising sun is seen on the foliage of the foothills.)

GIRL. Always ahead . . . Yes, it must be. *(She comes out of the tepee and goes up the path.)* Dick: all the people there in Cloudy — how far off they seem now — like shadows in a dream. Only a few days ago, I clasped their hands; I saw their faces — their dear faces! And now they are fading. In this little, little while, I've lost them . . . I've lost them. *(There are tears in her voice.)*

JOHNSON. Through you, all my old life has faded away. I have lost that.

GIRL. Look! *(Pointing to the left as she notices the sunrise.)*

The dawn is breaking in the East – far away – fair and clear.

JOHNSON. A new day . . . Trust me. *(Stretching out his hands to her.)* Trust me . . . A new life!

GIRL. A new life. *(Putting her hands in his.)* Oh, my mountains – I'm leaving you – Oh, my California, I'm leaving you – Oh, my lovely West – my Sierras! – I'm leaving you! – Oh, my – *(turning to Johnson, going to him and resting in his arms)* – my home.

CURTAIN

3. JOSIAH ROYCE

*The Community of Mankind**

Josiah Royce was born in 1855, the fourth child of an English family that had come to Grass Valley, California, by way of New York and Iowa. They had crossed the continent in a hard journey which his mother described in a memorable diary. The family finally settled in San Francisco and Josiah was educated in the public schools and at the new University of California. After a year of study in Germany he went to Johns Hopkins where he obtained a Ph.D. degree in 1878. He taught briefly at Berkeley and then, attracted by William James, went in 1882 to Harvard where he remained until his death in 1916. The frontier experience and recollections of his family's mobility remained vivid in his mind and perhaps entered into his conceptions of community and loyalty. The outbreak of the First World War, during which he took a vigorous pro-English stand, seemed to him a test of those conceptions. See also Vincent Buranelli, Josiah Royce *(New York, 1964).*

I

In order rightly to estimate the ideal issues which are at stake in the present crisis of humanity, it is first necessary to make clear a matter concerning which there is a good deal of confusion in recent discussion. Some of this confusion is benevolent and well-meaning; some of it is due to wilful disregard of certain ethical issues which ought to be as obvious as they are deep. The matter to which I refer can best be brought nearer to clearness by contrasting two views of the world's

* Josiah Royce, *The Hope of the Great Community* (New York, 1916), pp. 30–59.

present moral situation which frequently appear in recent expressions concerning the morals of the war. According to one of these views, the present war is essentially a conflict between nations and between national ideals. The essence of this doctrine is, that just as the conflicting powers are nations, so the main moral concern ought to be expressed in hopes that this or that nation will obtain a deserved success.

Opposed to this view is a second and very different view of the moral situation of the world and of the meaning of the war. According to this view, the present war is a conflict more conscious, more explicit, and for that very reason more dangerous than any we have ever had before, a conflict between the community of mankind and the particular interests of individual nations. Consequently, no nation engaged in this war is, or can be, right in its cause, except in so far as it is explicitly aiming towards the triumph of the community of mankind. As a fact, the various warring nations are at present acting with a decidedly various degree of clearness about their relation to the unified interests of humanity; that is, to what I call the cause of the community of mankind. Hence the various nations differ in the degree to which, at any stage of the conflict, their cause is just. In certain respects and with regard to certain of their enterprises, they may be, and are, explicitly aware that they intend to serve the community of mankind; while in other respects, or in regard to other matters, they may act with a more or less explicitly deliberate hostility to the cause of the community of mankind. Their moral position may, therefore, vary accordingly. But owing to the vastness and to the definiteness of many of the special international passions and issues concerned in the present conflict, the outcome of the war promises to be either a victory or a defeat, not for any one of the warring nations nearly so much as for humanity in its wholeness, and hence for what I shall venture also to call the church universal. It is important, therefore, to indicate as clearly as possible what in this discussion I mean by the community of mankind, and what by the church universal.

Ancient Israel somewhat early reached a religious ideal

which it expressed in the doctrine of some of its Prophets, that the redeemed and transformed Jerusalem of the future was to be the centre of a redeemed humanity, the spiritual ruler of a kingdom which should have no end. In reaching this ideal, the religion of the Prophets did not look forward merely to a political conquest of the rest of the world by the future people of Israel. The ideal of the transformed humanity of the future had, indeed, in case of the religion of the Prophets, its political metaphors and inevitably its political coloring. The subsequent results when the ideal religion of the Prophets degenerated into the formalities of later Judaism, were in many ways disastrous both for the morals and for the religion of Judaism. But the ideal city of Zion, the centre of a new heaven and earth, passed over as an ideal into the possession of the early Christian church. The Apostle Paul gave to its inner life the character which he called "charity," and which he expounded to the Corinthians in one of the greatest documents of Christian literature.

The often misunderstood heart and essence of the Pauline vision of charity is that it is a virtue belonging to a community, a community which Paul conceives as finding its future home in a heaven where the Divine Spirit both informs it and fulfils its life and its desire. Charity does not mean mere love of individuals for individuals; since if, according to Paul, I gave all my goods to feed the poor, and my body to be burned, I might still be without charity, and then be as a sounding brass or as a tinkling cymbal. Charity, for Paul, is not a merely mystical power to prophesy, nor does it consist in any other form of merely individual efficiency or proficiency. It is a virtue which Paul recommends to his Corinthians as to an united community who, in the bonds of the spirit, are one body despite the multitude of the members. Charity never faileth, and outlasts all earthly vicissitudes in its own heavenly world, because there we know even as we are known, and our mutual relations are those of a perfected spiritual community.

Paul viewed the salvation of humanity as consisting in the triumph of the Christian church. This triumph was for him something miraculous, catastrophic, and future; and his expectations regarding the triumph and end of humanity were obviously quite mythical. But this triumph of humanity, this hope of all the faithful, this salvation of a community through an universally significant human transformation, without which no salvation of an individual man would be possible, this idea, in terms of which the Apostle Paul universalized the ideal Jerusalem of the early Prophets, this became the most essential and characteristic idea of the Christian church.

The historical church has never been true to it and has seldom understood it. Most Christians suppose that the salvation of men is an affair involving the distinct, and in many ways the isolated, spiritual fortunes of individual men. Such Christians, however, have not understood what the vision of the New Jerusalem was in which the seer of the Apocalypse gloried. What the tree of life bears for the healing of the nations, such Christians have never rightly comprehended. What the farewell address of the Logos of the Fourth Gospel meant, when the departing Lord prayed to the Father, "That those whom Thou hast given me may be One as We are One," such individualistic Christianity (which has been only too popular in the various Protestant sects) has neglected, if not forgotten. But however ill-comprehended, the "sign" in which and by which Christianity conquered the world was the sign of an ideal community of all the faithful, which was to become the community of all mankind, and which was to become some day the possessor of all the earth, the exponent of true charity, at once the spirit and the ruler of the humanity of the future.

Such is a bare suggestion of that ideal of the community of mankind which it was the historical mission of Christianity to introduce into the world, to keep alive through centuries of human crimes, oppressions, rebellions, and hatreds, and to hold before the world for the healing of the nations. The present situation of humanity depends upon the fact that for good reasons, which have to do not merely with the sentimental and romantic aspirations of humanity, but also with the most serious business in which men are engaged, the idea of the community of mankind has become more concrete, more closely related to the affairs of daily life, has become more practicable than ever before. At this very moment the material aspect of civilization favors, as never before, the natural conditions upon which the community of mankind, if it were reasonably successful, would depend for its prosperity. The growth of the natural sciences as well as of the technical industries of mankind also makes possible and comprehensive forms and grades of coöperation which men have never before known. Some motives which tend to render the genuine Pauline charity, the genuine love of the unity of the great community to which all civilized men may, when enlightened, consciously belong,—such motives, I say, have been furthered by the arts, the industries, the sciences, and the social developments of the nineteenth and twentieth centuries, as thousands of years of previous human activity have never furthered them. The brilliant coloring, the luxuriant images with which the fancy of the seer of the Apocalypse adorned his New Jerusalem, readily suggest themselves to the imagination of the lover of human kind, who dwells on some of the more benign aspects of our recent civilization, and who considers how far-reaching the abundant powers of human life are tending to become under the influence of those humane arts and sciences which of late have so successfully combated disease, and have brought together nations and races of men who once could not in the least feel their brotherhood, or mutually understand the tongues which they spoke.

These benevolent and benign influences do not, indeed, of themselves constitute the true Pauline charity; but within the last two centuries we have for the first time seen glimpses of how, under perfectly human conditions, they could become a basis for a charity which might transform our society in many of its most significant features into a social order worthy both of a new heaven and of a new earth. In brief, the last two centuries have given us a right to hope for the unity of mankind, a right of which we had only mythical glimpses and mystical visions before. This right we gained through the recent development both of our natural sciences and of our modern humanities. The idea of the human community has tended of late to win a certain clearness which it never could possess until now.

Paul could believe in his vision of the redeemed humanity of the future, because he had his own perfectly concrete and human, if to him unsatisfactory, experiences of the apparently miraculous life which was present in his enthusiastic little churches. When he talked of the redeemed humanity in heaven, and had his vision of the charity that never faileth, he could say to his brethren: "Thus the Spirit manifests itself amongst you." When, in an unquestionably more fantastic manner and language, the author of the Fourth Gospel made the speaker of the farewell addresses characterize the present life and the future life of his little company of disciples, whom "having loved them, he loved them to the end," the writer of this Gospel could use his concrete, although historically idealized, portrait of the last meeting between the Lord and his disciples as the basis and background of this vision of the salvation of mankind.

In our day this vision of the salvation of mankind, while indeed far enough away from us to cause constant and grave concern, and to demand endless labor, has been for a long time becoming clearer than ever, while both science and industry have tended to bring men together in new fashions of coöperation, in new opportunities and exercises that involve an expressed charity in its true form, as a devotion not merely to individuals but to the united life of the community. The belief that mankind can be and in the end shall be one, has thus for a long time had an increased concreteness, definiteness, practical applicability, and despite all the vast evils of our modern social order, a genuine hopefulness. What has to be borne in mind is, that in former centuries, and above all in ancient times, the community of mankind was hindered from becoming an object either of experience or of reasonable hope by the confusions of men's tongues, by the mutual hostilities of nations, of religions, and of sects, and by the absence of means whereby men might learn to work together. Since the beginning of the modern world, not only have the sciences and the arts helped us to work together in a material way and to understand one another regarding our various ideas, but very many of our modern intellectual and practical modes of progress have possessed a significance not only material, but deeply spiritual and, what is more to the point in our present discussion, wisely international. The modern world has become in many ways more and more an international world. And this, I insist, has been true not merely as to its technical and material ties, but as to its spiritual union.

It has been this vision upon which a recent international crime has so violently intruded. The hope of the community lies in trying to keep before us a vision of what the community of mankind may yet become despite this tragic calamity.

II

In speaking at such a moment of the community of mankind viewed simply as an ideal of the future, there are two matters which, as I believe, we ought to bear in mind. First, its members will not be merely individual human beings, not yet mere collections or masses of human beings, however vast, but communities of some sort, communities such as, at any stage of civilization in which the great community is to be raised to some higher level of organization, already exist. Ethical individualism has been, in the past, one great foe of the great community. Ethical individualism, whether it takes the form of democracy or of the irresponsible search on the part of individuals for private happiness or for any other merely individual good, will never save mankind. Equally useless, however, for the attainment of humanity's great end would be any form of mere ethical collectivism, that is, any view which regarded the good of mankind as something which masses or crowds or disorganized collections of men should win.

For this reason Bentham's utilitarianism, in the form which he gave to it, and which the English political Liberals of the middle of the nineteenth century emphasized, does not express what the community of mankind needs for its existence and for its general welfare. That is why mere philanthropy, merely seeking for the greatest happiness for the greatest number, merely endeavoring to alleviate the pains of individual men or of collections of men, will never bring about the end for which mankind has always been seeking, and for the sake of which our individual life is worth living. That, too, is the reason why at the present time many humane people, despite their former horror of war, in view of its sorrows and of the misery which it causes, find to their surprise that, as Mr. Robert Herrick has said in a recent number of "The New Republic," war seems to them now no longer as great an evil as it used to seem; for in each of the warring peoples the war has brought about a new consciousness of unity, a new willingness to surrender private good to the welfare of the community, a new sense of the sacredness of duty, a new readiness to sacrifice.

Such converts to the doctrine that war is good ascribe their sudden conversion to the wonder and reverence which have been aroused in them by the sight of France regenerated through the very dangers which the invader has brought with him, awakened to a new sense that the value of life lies not in what individuals get out of it, but in what the exertions and the perils of war call out and illustrate, namely, the supreme and super-individual value of loyalty. Loyalty, the devotion of the self to the interests of the community, is indeed the form which the highest life of humanity must take, whether in a political unity, such as in a nation, or in the church universal, such as Paul foresaw. Without loyalty, there is no salvation. Therefore loyalty can never completely express itself in the search for individual happiness, whether the happiness that is in question be that of the individual who teaches, or that of the mere collections of masses of individuals for whom some philanthropist seeks happiness.

Therefore it is indeed true that, if the only alternative for mankind were either to continue the arts of war or to lose its vision of high attainment in the form of a mere search for happiness, then it would be better that war should rage, with all its horrors, so long as humanity lasts, rather than that what Emerson called "hearts in sloth and ease" should live in an endlessly dissatisfied search for pleasures which deceive and which fade in the enjoyment, and for a happiness which no human individual can possibly attain, unless indeed he is viewed as a member of the community.

The detached individual is an essentially lost being. That ethical truth lies at the basis of the Pauline doctrine of original sin. It lies also at the basis of the pessimism with which the ancient southern Buddhism of the original founder of that faith, Gotama Buddha, viewed the life of man. The essence of the life of the detached individual is, as Gotama Buddha said, an unquenchable desire for bliss, a desire which "hastens to enjoyment, and in enjoyment pines to feel desire." Train such a detached individual by some form of highly civilized cultivation, and you merely show him what Paul called "the law." The law thus shown he hereupon finds to be in opposition to his self-will. Sin, as the Pauline phrase has it, "revives."

The individual, brought by his very cultivation to a clearer consciousness of the conflict between his self-will and the social laws which tradition inflicts upon him, finds a war going on in his own members. His life hereupon becomes only a sort of destruction of what is dearest to him. For as a social being, he has to recognize both the might of his social order and the dignity of its demands. But as a detached individual, he naturally hates restraint; that is, as Paul says, he hates the law. However correct his outward conduct may be, he inwardly says: "Oh, wretched man that I am, who shall deliver me from the body of this death?"

Such is the picture of the essentially disastrous life of the detached individual which you find in the much misunderstood, and in our day comparatively unpopular seventh chapter of the Epistle to the Romans. In the following chapter, Paul characterizes the only mode of salvation which can be offered with any hope to such a detached individual. Gotama Buddha sought the salvation of the detached individual through an act of resignation whereby all desires are finally abandoned. Paul describes what is essentially salvation through loyalty, salvation through the willing service of a community, the salvation of those whom he characterizes by the words: "They are in Christ Jesus, and walk not after the flesh, but after the spirit." But for Paul the being whom he called Christ Jesus was in essence the spirit of the universal community.

The lesson with regard to which both Buddhism and Christianity agree, is the lesson that for the detached individual there is no salvation. Since, therefore, you can never make the detached individual securely and steadily happy, it is useless to try to save him, or any mere crowd or collection of detached individuals, by mere philanthropy. Since the detached individual is essentially a lost being, you cannot save masses of lost individuals through the triumph of mere democracy. Masses of lost individuals do not become genuine freemen merely because they all have votes. The suffrage can show the way of salvation only to those who are already loyal, who already, according to their lights, live in the spirit, and are directed not by a mere disposition to give good things to everybody, or to give all their goods to feed the poor, or to give their body to be burned, but by a genuinely Pauline charity.

Since, then, it is only the consciously united community—that which is in essence a Pauline church—which can offer salvation to distracted humanity and can calm the otherwise insatiable greed and longing of the natural individual man, the salvation of the world will be found, if at all, through uniting the already existing communities of mankind into higher communities, and not through merely freeing the peoples from their oppressors, or through giving them a more popular government, unless popular government always takes the form of government by the united community, through the united community, and for the united community.

Therefore, while the great community of the future will unquestionably be international by virtue of the ties which will bind its various nationalities together, it will find no place for that sort of internationalism which despises the individual variety of nations, and which tries to substitute for the vices of those who at present seek merely to conquer mankind, the equally worthless desire of those who hope to see us in future as "men without a country." Whatever that form of loyalty which is now patriotism expresses, must be in spirit preserved by the great community of the future. That unity within the national growth which the observers of the war watch with such fascination, when they see how each people is better knit and more serious, more conscious of the sacredness of its national life than it was before the great peril, that unity will not, and must not, be lost when the new international life comes into existence. There can be no true international life unless the nations remain to possess it. There can never be a spiritual body unless that body, like the ideal Pauline church, has its many members. The citizens of the world of the future will not lose their distinct countries. What will pass away will be that insistent mutual hostility which gives to the nations of to-day, even in times of peace, so many of the hateful and distracting characters of a detached individual man. In case of human individuals, the sort of individualism which is opposed to the spirit of loyalty, is what I have already called the individualism of the detached individual, the individualism of the man who belongs to no community which he loves and to which he can devote himself with all his heart, and his soul, and his mind, and his strength. In so far as liberty and democracy, and independence of soul, mean that sort of individualism, they never have saved men and never can save men. For mere detachment, mere self-will, can never be satisfied with itself, can never win its goal. What saves us on any level of human social life is union. And when Webster said, in his familiar reply to Hayne, that what alone could save this country must be described as "Liberty and Union, now and forever, one and inseparable!"—Webster expressed in fine phrase, and with special reference to this country, the true doctrine of the church universal.

Liberty alone never saves us. Democracy alone never saves us. Our political freedom is but vanity unless it is a means through which we come to realize and practise charity, in the Pauline sense of that word. Hence the community of mankind will be international in the sense that it will ignore no rational and genuinely self-conscious nation. It will find the way to respect the liberty of the individual nations without destroying their genuine spiritual freedom. Its liberty and union, when attained, will be "now and forever, one and inseparable."

III

I have now mentioned one character which, as I believe, must belong to the international community of the future. Hereupon I must turn to a second character, which seems to me of equal importance with the first, although reformers and the creators of Utopias have almost uniformly neglected, or misunderstood this second character.

The distinct national unities must remain intact, each with its own internal motives for loyalty and with its modes of expression whereby the loyalty of its individual citizens will be won and sustained in the community of mankind, which the ideal future must contain if humanity is to be really saved. In the far-off future, as in the past, humanity will include amongst its number nations whose citizens belong not merely to various national types but to distinct races. No dream of universal conquest, if it were carried out, could ever lead to anything but to a more or less universal community of hate, to a social world essentially distracted, much as the world of the Gentiles, depicted by Paul at the outset of the Epistle to the Romans, was distracted. In and for such a community, no man, still less a nation, could deeply feel or long retain any genuine loyalty. Neither the pan-Germanists nor the pan-Slavists, neither the partisans of the white race nor those who hope for the supremacy of the yellow race, have any true conception of what the community of mankind is intended to be or of what the spirit of loyalty demands that it shall be. Both the nations and the races are needed for the future of mankind. The problem of humanity is to see that their liberty and their union shall remain "forever one and inseparable."

But what the lovers of national rivalries, who look forward to an endless strife of peoples, as well as the makers of the Utopias of universal peace, have equally failed to see is that amongst the many social functions of a nation or, for that matter, of any human community, the political functions of such a community, at any rate, as they have been conceived and carried out up to the present time, are ethically amongst the least important.

Greece never attained political unity. Today it rules the world, as Germany will never rule it, though its inventions and its efficiency should continue and grow for a thousand years. Greece rules a spiritual world, and rules it spiritually. No modern nation that has won political power has ever expressed its best contribution to humanity through this political power, or has ever made a contribution to the community of mankind which is nearly equal to the contribution made by Greece, and made by a nation which proved wholly incapable of political unity. The greatest rival which Greece has ever possessed as a contributor to the cause of the community of mankind is the nation Israel—by which I mean, not the Israel whose history was rewritten from the point of view of later Judaism and was so misrepresented in what we call the Old Testament. The Israel of which I speak is the Irsael of the great formative period of the prophetic religion, the Israel whose religious beginnings are sketched for us in that brief and impressive fragment of poetry called the Song of Deborah—the Israel whose maturer consciousness found its voice in Amos and Isaiah, and in the records of the prophetic literature. Even after its formative period was past, and after Judaism had nearly quenched the spiritual fire which had burned in the religion of the Prophets, Israel still gave us the Psalms, still expressed, in the great speeches which an unknown master put into the mouth of Job, ideas and problems which are with us to-day, and which will record some of the great problems of human destiny for all coming ages of mankind, just as the great Greek tragedians of the formative period of the Hellenic mind have spoken for all time. But Israel, like Greece, never won, and from the nature of the case could not win, a lasting political unity.

When we remember how all the highest products of the German mind have so far been the products of times when the national unity in a political sense was not yet attained, while the mightiest accomplishment of Prussian domination has thus far been that, like the base Indian of Othello's last words, this Prussian domination, in dealing with the magnificent ideal legacy of the Germanic mind, has simply "thrown a pearl away, richer than all his tribe"; and when we remember how an analogous rule holds in case of several other European nations, we are reminded that, on the whole, there seems to be some opposition between the political power of a nation and its power to contribute to the ideal goods of the community of mankind.

The political contributions of nations either to the unity or to the life of the great community are by no means their only or, on the whole, their principal contributions. For that very reason it is not wise to hope that when the Holy City of the community of mankind descends from heaven to earth, it will come in political form. According to a well-known tradition, the Master said: "My kingdom is not of this world, else would my servants fight." I do not think that this reported word of the Master represents what the ideal course of human progress ought to be. The ideal community of mankind, whenever it really descends from heaven to earth, will indeed appear in a definitely worldly fashion. If the ideal is approximately realized, the kingdom will be in this world, yet its servants will not fight, simply because they will be loyally engrossed in much better business than fighting. That upon which I here insist is, that in learning such business they will not principally be guided by political arts and motives.

IV

But if the great community is not to win its loyal consciousness through inventing new political forms and through depending upon political institutions for its principal advances, must it then be confined to "the empire of the air"? Must it always be dependent upon its poets and its prophets? or upon their brethren, the great scientific discoverers, the genuinely inventive leaders of thought? Must its kingdom be a wholly ideal kingdom? Must its fortunes be those which, in a somewhat disheartening sequence of faiths and of practices, have so far constituted the history of religion?

I do not believe this. I believe that the future will invent, and will in due time begin very actively and productively to practise, forms of international activity which will be at once ideal in their significance and business-like in their methods, so that we shall no longer be dependent upon the extremely rare and precious beings called prophets or poets, to show us the way towards the united life of the great community.

4. LOUIS SULLIVAN

*A People Gone Astray**

Louis Henri Sullivan, who was born in Boston in 1856, considered himself of "mongrel origin." His father was a wandering Irish musician who arrived in Boston in 1847 and opened a dancing school there. His mother was Swiss, although her own parents were French and German. Louis attended the local public schools and then studied for a year in the course of architecture at the Massachusetts Institute of Technology. He worked for a while, then attended the Beaux Arts in Paris, and finally settled in Chicago. He had twenty productive years as an architect in partnership with Dankmar Adler. But the World's Fair of 1892 seemed to him evidence of corruption not only in taste but in society. His practice declined and he devoted increasing energy to social criticism. He died, relatively neglected, in 1924. See also Hugh Morrison, Louis Sullivan, Prophet of Modern Architecture *(New York, 1935); Sherman Paul,* Louis Sullivan *(New York, 1962).*

I have returned at last, my friends, wanderer that I am, from a long sojourn in a strange, far-off country, where, singular though it may seem, men think and act in a closed circle of inversions, and falsify in unanimity.

The country—a vast expanse—is fair to look upon, well watered, fertile, rich in every form of nature's bounty. All aspects of this land are on a scale simple, broad, impressive: —great plains, prairies, mountains, rivers and lakes—and a long, double-frontage on the seas.

* Louis H. Sullivan, *Democracy: a Man-Search,* Introduction by Elaine Hedges (Detroit, 1961), pp. 82–109.

It is a land of four seasons, which successively spread their flowing influences in a simple and impressive rhythm; and the land responds to the seasons in as simple and gracious a way—forming thus an ever-moving picture of impressive, satisfying beauty.

Famine is unknown. The broad-flowing land is crossed and recrossed by railways, telegraph and telephone lines, and many and varied other means of communication, and interchange. Nearly all the people read and write; and daily papers, magazines, and books are sown broadcast, like winged seeds upon the winds.

Moreover, the land is dotted o'er with free public schools, especially founded and maintained for the education of the children; and seminaries, colleges, technical schools and universities for the training of young manhood and womanhood are numerous.

It is, indeed, a far-flung, sumptuous, inspiriting land; and so situate, in its large serene isolation, that it may be at peace, if it will, in tranquil strength.

The activities of its people are varied and commensurate. Huge sections of its population are engaged in the art of agriculture, in the pursuit of commerce, and in the development of industries—all on a basis of diversified immensity. The energy of this people is intense, quick-witted, practical and material. And there are, in all, some eighty millions of souls. The form of government is called by them democratic; specifically, as they say, a government of the people, by the people, for the people. There are not acknowledged social castes; speech is asserted to be free; and religious tolerance is universal. The representatives of the people, that is, those to whom the exercise of political powers is delegated, are elected by a universal male suffrage; every citizen of twenty-one years or over, having an unqualified vote. A single language is in use throughout the length and breadth of the noble land. Local divergences in usage are so slight as to be quite negligible. Never was a great multitude placed in so free, so expansive, so adequate, so bountiful, gracious and simple a setting. Never, to receive and nurture a vast people, were Nature's preparations so benign, so inclusive, so unspeakably gracious.

This land is known to you, no doubt, under its politico-geographical name: The United States of America. But the nature of its people—their thoughts and their acts—is a singular enigma, of compelling power to engage the thoughtful and searching mind. For you might—and rightly—infer that a land so noble, a people so situate, so completely equipped with all the instrumentalities of advanced civilization, would surely bring forth out of themselves, life-results of simple noble, strong and fruitful harmony. Yet the precise opposite is the case; and it is this singular, nay, startling paradox that I wish to illuminate, because it is so impressive an object lesson of a people gone astray through neglect and disdain of a lucid guiding principle; or, if I may say so, through its failure to evolve a sound philosophy of simple things, and a sane ideal.

When I went abroad in the land, I early noted its fair face, but as quickly observed that its cities, of which there are many, were blemishes thereon. This strange contrast impressed me at once and deeply, and awakened a mingled feeling of curiosity and doubt. This perplexity was further increased and at the same time made more elusive, as I began to discern, in the throngs upon the streets of these cities, an almost universal type of face; a face with features singularly decomposed, disorganized and sordid, and that the bodies carrying these faces walked and moved with a rhythmless irregularity—devoid of elasticity and cohesion.

The fair, youthful land, and the decadent faces and movements seemed to me in sharpest contrast; a juxtaposition and divergence that caused me not only to wish an explanation, but as well to resolve to search it out. For land and face, each in its opposite way, spoke eloquently and persistently to me. Further, there was in the faces of these people an aspect of absence. They seemed devoid of radiance; the eyes neither lustrous nor clear; the complexions sodden. These observations filled me with a haunting sense of sadness; an intimation, as it were, that something within the desires, the thoughts, the ideals of this people must be deeply awry—thus to afflict them. This impression quickly grew into a firm sense of certainty. But how to search, I knew not.

However, I determined to mingle freely with them in hope of finding a clue, a thread, as it were, that might lead somewhere.

I met many of them, in almost every walk of life. They were affable enough, in a way, although somewhat brusque. But in the very affability and good nature, in the very brusqueness—sounded a note that arrested my attentive ear. Why? I inquired, should they be thus both superficially brusque and superficially affable? There was a false note in it all; as though, in each case, the real man were not speaking; as though the real man was in hiding; and that these seemingly frank, open people were in reality secretive. This latter impression seemed strange enough; for what need was there to be secretive? And then it occurred to me, as by an inspiration of the moment, that their real life must be quite below the surface; that the dominant impulse, the first, and really controlling thought, must be insidious, and might, perhaps, be found behind what I had come to believe a screen of institutions, appearances and manners.

I listened much to the talk around and about me, and caught in it strains of manifest falsehood and specific truth. I observed, after a time, that nearly every man I met had two systems of speech; the one rather flat, formal and colorless, the other surprisingly forceful, compact, vivid and direct; and that he passed with a significant, almost unconscious freedom from one to the other. The former repelled me as much by its imitative sophistication and inadequacy, as the latter attracted by an ardent, almost youthful reach and force of its locutions. Somewhere between the two, I thought, might lie the center of gravity of their minds—around which all the verbiage would be found to resolve, like a stream or cloud of fragments.

The more I mingled and talked with them, (keeping always an eye on the great fair land and the magnificence of its equipment), the more I seemed to sense their lives. And the more I sensed, the more the sensing suggested a something furtive, fugitive and yet abiding; hidden, open, attractive, and repellent. I soon began to surmise that these people were, in fact, leading double lives—one, as a concession to appearances, and one for the sake of a something else. That *else* was what I resolved, then and there, to search out. For I had become convinced that on a "show-down," as they would say in their terse fashion—an untranslatable expression signifying a revelation of the actual facts—there would come into view an element of sinister and somber reality.

I had noted, early in my search, that these people, individually and in mass, were significantly wanting in a sense—properly so called—of the spiritual life; and equally devoid of a sensibility concerning the true meaning of Nature, and of man's place therein. Concerning these two great, simple aspects of life, their minds seemed indeed empty, and the vacant places usurped by a frivolous cynicism, and a most repellent form of cant.

When I had begun really to appreciate the bearing of these aspects, I sought again—this time with a deeper-seeing eye—the faces in the streets;—for all classes of people are on the streets, and move by one in shoals.

These faces ceaselessly haunted me; and I became ever more perturbed; for they seemed really less living than dead:—and this—in a fair, noble, prolific land. And I said to myself: These faces, these movements are telling the truth!—Whatever that truth may be. And, what seemed stranger still, everyone appeared to take these faces for granted—no one remarked them; no one sought to interpret them; no one deemed them paradoxical and uncanny. And thus came into my mind a suggestion that these people generally, and in reality, tell the actual truth concerning themselves; but do so unconsciously, in ways, only, that they cannot control, because unaware of them.

Then I noted the buildings which lined the streets—and found them just like the faces. And concerning the buildings, likewise, no one made any comment; no one sought to interpret them, no one suggested or sought an underlying explanation common to buildings and faces. And so it was with many many things I noted. These things, these aspects told me truths —truths which the people themselves did not utter in words; truths the very opposite of what the people, particularly the better educated, set forth as their assurances and avowed beliefs.

Then, with these accumulating impressions in mind, I began to look into the personal habits of the people. I soon became aware that they ate too much, drank too much, over-stimulated recklessly, and consumed quantities of drugs of all kinds for all manner of purposes, in what seemed to me a universal suicidal dementia. And this held true of all classes; the variation being merely in externals—in the mere place or fashion of the doing. An excessive tax upon the digestive, the nervous system, and hence upon the brain and the senses was of course inevitable; and I began to see from a new angle, one reason why these people could not perceive the beauty and clarity of simple things, nor think in a straightforward way concerning them. Nor was it a surprise, upon further probing, to learn that these people suffer from anxiety, and from every variety of self-induced disease—functional and organic. A curious index of the prevailing physical decay and shortness of life compared with that of normal health and length of days, I found in the enormous business of their life insurance companies; even while that business pointed to a more far-reaching social illness —some other, deep-seated cause, that made men's lives unstable and brief. . . .

The discovery that their foods and drinks were widely adulterated, and inoculated with quick and slow poisons, that even the milk given to infants was all too frequently a deadly poison, came as another shock—a shock so startling that it immediately gave point and definite aim to my inquiry.

Hence I immediately searched out their mental food, as well. I looked first for the philosophies and the theories of economics, as being most significant. Of these I found that they had created not one that met with general acceptance. That, in stale fact, their philosophies and economic doctrines had been taken by them from the European civilization and culture, and were and are therefore, in their very nature, a monarchial and feudal dead weight upon a naturally free people. For the virus of feudal culture cannot be otherwise than an insidious and deadly poison to the minds, bodies, hearts and souls of a people really wishing and seeking freedom.

Now then, I said, here, at last, am I upon the track. Here at last are two, strong, pivotal facts: First, this people, alleging itself to be free and democratic, has failed to utter out of its life and its beautiful land a valid statement of Democracy. Second, this people, asserting its freedom and democracy, has inoculated itself with a feudal taint which runs in its very blood and thought—and hence inevitably in its acts and their logical consequences.

Further, the feudal taint had existed from the beginning of this people, first as a scattered population and then as a nation; and among its historical sequences had brought forth a terrible curse in the form of millions of imported black slaves, an ensuing gigantic internecine war, pathetic in its waste of human lives, and its aftermath of progressive corruption. Never has the ancient doctrine of feudalism wrought such unspeakable havoc among a people—never have the effects of its disastrous, devastating virus been shown on so great and so obvious a scale. These people boast that they have no plague no famine in their land, unaware, the while, that their very feudalism constitutes both a plague and a famine, as widespread as the land, and which, like a malignant and unspeakable disease, attacks at its very root, its very beginnings, the health, the thought, and the social usefulness of every man, woman and child of the eighty millions. . . .

It thus became clear enough what the secretiveness meant; what the superficial cheerfulness and brusqueness meant; what the typical face on the street meant; what the buildings meant; what all the talk meant; and whence arose the inability to see, think, and talk straightforwardly.

With the veil of feudalism drawn aside, and the quivering

facts laid bare it was all plain enough; and the hideous face of the reality looked into mine with awful nearness, and with the veritable aspect of a fiend.

Now it was all clear. Any man with this clue could instantly interpret, one by one, and all at a glance, the vast congeries of facts which at first so puzzled and bewildered me. Now it was plain, now it was but too plain—that seeming paradox—how a fair land, a most lovable land, the very acme of Nature's goodness, bounty and beneficence, had harbored a people in sweetest hospitality, as it were, only to see that people make a very hell on earth—a maelstrom of corruption—a wilderness of stealthy murder—a dark jungle of betrayal of every normal heart's desire, of every pure and wholesome aspiration.

Now it was clear how the sacred name of Democracy had become with them a mere empty word to cajole and conjure with.

This is what those faces mean that I saw drifting by me in the streets. . . . Now it was clear what the city meant for them —clear why it was so unspeakable a blemish on the fair land. Now it was clear why human life, with them, was held cheaper than the dirt in their thoroughfares. Now it was clear why they could not withhold the poisoned cup even from the child. Now it was clear why and how the powerful and eminently unscrupulous few were growing richer, while the weaker but likewise unscrupulous many were passing into acquiescent slavery—for, historically, their black slavery was but the prophet of the present white serfdom.

And then I inquired in amazement, What do all these schools colleges and universities mean?—what do they teach? And I found in accordance with the prevailing feudal law, that they taught a little of everything official and conventional, and nothing whatsoever concerning the realities of life—not one word concerning those simple, easily understood truths, the wide diffusion of which is essential to the health of the social body and mind, essential to all,—to every individual—if he and they would live.

It was the same in their countless churches—what was

preached, carefully abstained from mention of the integrity of man, his normal and upright place in the integrity of Nature, his normal spiritual relation to his neighbor and to the vast, silent integrity of the Spirit of us all. The preachers were mere social parasites, kept by the well to do and the rich, like so many kept women. Now and then, if one of them, by chance suffered an access of manhood and spoke aloud, he was ejected bodily, and branded as heretic to the church and to the feudal God of the church—because he had dared be loyal to man and the God of man. Hence, in that fair land man is honest at his peril—he speaks truth at his peril—and every man's hand is against every man. What wonder that a civilization whose basic motive is betrayal, should now be swiftly moving toward that reckoning day which Nature had ever exacted from those who betray her? . . .

The key-note of the active, aggressive American life is commercialism. And this means, that, underneath the huge and tangled mass of their nominal laws, is to be found the real, the guiding and controlling basic law, namely the law of dog eat dog. And those who, in their dealings, follow this law unswervingly towards its logical limit—become their great, their eminent. And these are thus exalted from the mass because they typify the ideal, the very heart's desire of practically every American in active life. Thousands upon thousands are yearly broken by this law, and go down and down; while the few of greater daring, the few who stop at nothing, as gradually, but with ever increasing swiftness go up and up. And thus is approaching ever nearer, daily nearer, that most dreaded of human antithesis—the two contrasting and mutually explanatory phases of the single and unitary feudal law—the enormously rich and the pitifully poor:—That age-long historical picture of splendor and squalor, which but makes visible and palpable, the ideal of selfishness which all have held in common.

Does it not seem as though Fate had made a most cunning trap, that it might end, in one huge enclosure, the vast and frantic urge of western civilization—lured thereto by the compelling odor of gold—the little bait with which their mighty trap is baited! Their hour is seemingly at hand. How this people will meet its crisis, fills me with profoundest apprehension and concern. For I discerned things in them, little aspects of their lives, other than those I have mentioned; things that call up, now, vividly before my mind's eye a strange legend of the European middle ages. It had to do with a romantic and pessimistic view of life, as held by the common people—of a sense of despair and a helpless fear of both life and death, coupled with a superstitious horror of the night. Briefly; it set forth the fate of a luckless wayfarer who, in the heavy dusk of nightfall unwittingly wandered among graves in the consecrated ground of a church yard, and there, lay down and slept. The people believed, in those days, that their God lived in a great mansion in the sky, much as their feudal lords and overlords lived on earth. So they provided a house for him, to which he might come when he wandered on earth; and adjoining this house or church they buried their dead; and the keeper of the house was called a priest, and this man was on familiar terms with both the God and the people, and acted as a go-between; all of which seems curious enough now. According to the popular myth, the sleeping wayfarer, suddenly awakening with a start, exactly at midnight—which was with these lowly people, a mystic hour, fraught with dire potencies—found himself surrounded by thirteen hideous skeletons, which had arisen from out of the ground, and had begun a wild and mocking dance about him. Terrified—because he had long heard of such things—he quickly died of shock; and it was told at many an humble fireside, that the things—thirteen because of their Savior Christ—the son of their God—and his twelve disciples—one of whom, it would appear, betrayed Him,—danced on and on, ever more madly, until they caught fire from the friction of their rattling bones. And there was much more ado of the same sort—as becomes so seemingly trivial a tale.

So far, so good. It was called the Dance of Death. But that is not the thought—nor the hope that hovers within my spirit, like an azure butterfly; that same fairy wayfarer of the scented air which the imaginative Greeks called Psyche, and thus delicately symbolized the spirit. It is the second part of the legend which specially interests me, because of its present suggestiveness and fitness concerning the American people. For it seems that, when the dance was at its maddest, just at the first faint approach of oncoming dawn–suddenly a cock crowed! the dread phantoms vanished; and a new day came on apace!

It seems to me, now, as though the crowing of that cock at dawn, the ringing, jubilant, awakening voice of chanticleer, must have stood, within the darkened minds of those past and gone people as a symbol of hope, as a neighborly but mystic herald of a brighter day; of the reassuring dawn of a coming day that might be theirs, and, perhaps, would come to pass, if not for them, then for their children, or their children's children—a clear way out of their agony, their darkness, their helplessness.

It is evident enough that the American people are in the maddest pitch of their Dance of Death; that they have killed their man, and will soon be aflame with friction. But!—and this is a momentous, a wistful but—will a cock crow for them a shrill new day? And will the hideous orgy be gone? I do not know. Nevertheless, before I left their land—ah, such a land! —a land made for freemen!—I had begun to ponder, vaguely, something of the sort. For when I had done with my studies of their feudal corruption, believed myself at the end, and looked forward only and surely to disaster, my thought, one day, in its musings, left the people and the cities, and reverted to the far-flung, joyous land—in the midst and amplitude of which I was, in the open air. And I then and there felt a strange, dimly awakening consciousness arising, within me, like a whisper, from without, that disturbed the solidity of my conclusions. And I said:—It cannot be! There is more beyond! I have not looked deeply enough, nor affectionately enough. So fair a land cannot forever be burdened and betrayed by such monstrous, inhuman thinking. It is not the end! It cannot be! It is against Nature—even though it test to the breaking point my faith in Nature's kindliness: a faith which I have deemed so serene, so secure. Even though it test my faith in the serene and mobile ever-present God of Life—a faith in which, so long, you and I and all our people have lived and loved—a faith so integral with our lives and our deeds:—That abiding and consecrating faith which made us useful one to all and all to each. Even though it shake my faith in man—that faith which is the inspiration whereby we create, and whereby alone, we may continue to create in the fullness and the joy of living.

Perhaps I undervalued the goodness of their hearts? Perhaps, in my own ignorance, in my own insensibility, I laid to malice that which may be justly traceable to ignorance alone—an ignorance of grown children, untrained and untried in the real vigor, the real purpose of living; undisciplined in the affirmative and aggressive utterance of their truer powers of thought; of that unitary, cohesive thought and action which must exist purposely and solely to create, sanction and sustain a beneficent integrity of all the people, to the end that they may live in the fullness of their days and proclaim the open, lucid utterance of their individual and collective life. Alas! they do not seem to know, even to suspect—that this is happiness!

And yet they have the mental powers. They have a sufficient physical equipment; they possess a land exhaustless in its supporting power. If, in their mad dance they have turned the use of all these agencies into abuse, may they not—if the cock cries—suddenly transform abuse into use? Who knows?—in fairness I must ask, who knows? . . .

But this I do know. A psychological hour is now approaching the entire world of mankind. It has been eons in preparing. It is immanently near. Its coming is world-significant. It can delicately be felt in the air—in the world-atmosphere of the spirit of man.

This hour will come—and it will pass. If it is not seized and held, America will sink into the morass of its corruption—and man will perforce begin anew the long, long wretched struggle, and perhaps may be doomed to wait unnumbered ages for such a pregnant hour again to come.

But, if it be seized, as it moves, the American people will change, and rise at once, regenerate! to become the greatest, noblest people the earth has known. A people that the vast race of man, from the beginning onward, has prophesied and looked and waited for. A people that long-yearning time has waited for. A people that a long-yearning, long-loving, long-creating and preparing God has waited for. A truly Messianic people—a veritable incarnation of the Great Life—the Great Spirit—an inspiration, a joy, a hope, a promise and a pledge to all the illusioned, suffering and aspiring peoples of the fair round earth.

What will they do? With their great earth-grip, will they also at that psychic hour take a great grip on the Creative spirit? And thus cease, once and for all, to be victims of Destiny, and, so, *create* their Destiny out of the heart, out of justice; and, so, hold it, safe and secure?—Or—will they miserably fail? . . .

If, when it comes to the psychic hour, that floating spiritual hour, the American man, by an inspiration as ineffable as it shall be divine, and clear and near, looks into his own heart, he will see all and know all; and will be born anew. If he denies that gentle and approaching hour, hovering in the flow of life, and come to fertilize his soul, it will not plead again, it will not wait; but will pass on, silently as the light; and then farewell to hope, for centuries to come, perhaps forever; for, then, European civilization, now trembling will come to its sure swift downfall. And this will be the end. For the savagery, unloosened, will become brute real, instead of artificial; and, in their mad and sanguinary orgy, they will vanish exhausted, from the earth, to join the fading caravans of the past, moving into the abysmal dusk. . . .

Enough of fairy tales: Let us again go forth into the world of men. To see them there as they are. To come upon the lurking thought. To see men pictured forth before our eyes; to see men in living dramas. . . .

Behold: This is the Great City! Murk fills the air. Would you know what the people think here? *That!* is what they think;

therefore it is here! So stands the picture forth before our gaze: In it the brutal fact, murk, stands face to face with the brutal thought, murk; here in the open; not now in hidden sanctuary of any one, behind the veil of each, although it is there also; but now before the veil, in the open; where you and I may see, where all may see a thought at work! Where each man in the great city may see the picture of his secret thought and his open deed, painted dark against the sky and gloomy upon all things under the sky.

Had you thought all pictures garnered into galleries? Come forth out of yourself! Be disillusioned! Awake! The *telling* pictures are in the open. They cannot be hidden. Who can hide them? They cannot be obscured, explained away or denied. There they are. Anyone can see what they mean.

This is the Great City! Behold, filth in the streets! Would you know what the filth means? It is the people's thought. It is their *desire!*—else it would not be here. The filth is of a piece with the murk. The two thoughts, the two things merge into one thing, one thought, one picture:—one pessimism.

You say there are practical difficulties? Come down from your high horse. This is an expedition on foot. Stay here by me, with your feet on the ground, and look *straight* at things, so that things and thoughts may look *straight* at *you!* and connect up with you, and you with them. This is the first step toward the open eye; and the open eye is the first step to the seeing eye. You shall not evade nor shall you quibble. For men have evaded and quibbled these thousands of years, just as you are proposing to do. They refused to see straight. You propose to refuse to see straight. But it won't go. The time is past for that.

There are difficulties. There is one difficulty; and that *one* is practical indeed. That one difficulty *concentrates in you.* You are the obstructionist. It is *you* who create the difficulties that you now evoke and invoke. To conjure difficulties is your carefully trained talent; but that *one* difficulty you avoid and evade. For you dread the truth. You dread to find it in the open, pointblank and plain, where all may see. Above all you dread lest others perceive that identical truth in you.—*Just where it is!* Hence you parley; and palaver and pull wool.

That one practical difficulty which concerns you directly, individually, is precisely the one difficulty around which all others revolve, as on an axle. Have you ever seen a wheel *at work* without an axle? No? Yet you see all these practical difficulties *at work,* and do not see, or rather do not wish to see the axle; at least you say you do not see; and meanwhile you bewail the state of affairs and the iniquity of the neighbor, or else you prate of prosperity, which is merely stating the same thing in a different set of words. In each case you avoid the issue, which is neither prosperity nor iniquity but *yourself! and your secret thought.*

But I know the axle. And where do you suppose I found it? Do not waste time in guessing—I found it in *myself! Therefore* I know it is in you, and in us all. For you and I are alike. All other men are like us. Therefore you and I shall find it in them all.

You have heard it said that clothes do not make the man. Neither do clothes hide the man. And whether the clothing be of cotton, wool or silk, or whether it be woven of words or thoughts or deeds shall make not a whit of difference with us, for we shall see the nakedness of the thought and the act. They must and shall stand bare before us.

This is the Great City. It is the crux of things.

Men are crowded here, hence they must be put to test.

We see them better, here, than scattered sparsely over the land. We see them in their bulk. We shall see better what they create! We shall see the direct consequences of their thinking. We shall see the axle-thought at work! turning the other thoughts about itself and making them work! And we shall see men clinging to the rim of the fly-wheel, men on the spokes, men hidden in the axle—as the wheel ponderously turns, day in day out, night in night out. And we shall see the iron truth of it. And this truth shall suddenly become alive and jump into a horrid, kaleidoscope smear, before our eyes. So will I make the iron feudal truth without you, within me, within us all—

jump out alive!—stare at us, whine at our hearts, and look formidably into our souls—face to face in the open. The darkened soul of the Great City shall confront our own—like unto like.

For had I not found this truth in myself, I could not have found it in you. And had I not glimpsed it in the Great City, I could not have found it in myself. For what I saw in the Great City was the soul of its people confronting my own, like unto like! And I could not escape! There was nowhere to go but that soul would follow mine and inhabit it.

Hence I know that in the Great City men now see dimly in the daylight. See things human with untaught glassy eyes. They see not their fellow men because of the Great pestilential City they have created. They see not the City they have created because of the crowding and surging pestilence of their fellowmen.

But, just so sure as the men living in the Great City and continuously creating and sustaining it as it is, *once see it as it is!* and their fellow men *as they are,* within it; all the men, women and children within it; as they are—two millions of them in all (What Power!!)—they will, that hour, begin to destroy it, and to remake it.

As it stands today, they see men of all kinds, everywhere, and do not know what they are. They see the city, everywhere, and do not know what it is!—For they are, one and all, insensible, in the world-old trance of Feudalism! Hence they wander, phantom-like, and create, phantom-like, unheeding a crowded world of realities within they move as wantons, even as they jostle realities, look squarely at them—and see nothing.

Behold! This is the Great City! How many hearts break daily here? Who knows? Who cares? What other useful end can there be for hearts, in the Great City?

What sorrow is here in the Great City? Who knows? Who cares? Do you care? Do I care?—provided it be not our sorrow? And if it be our sorrow do we not think the Great City heartless indeed? Does it not weigh upon us like iron; does it not seem monstrous, and stone cold? And who cares about our sorrow? Why should anyone care? Are we so different in thought and act that our sorrow particularly signifies? Why complain, if we would receive and have not given? Why curse? —when we have helped create the gloom? Let us then accept our logic. Let us not whine—if we cannot see and think and feel and act to better purpose than to create sorrow.

How many poor are here? Who knows! Who cares! Do the poor themselves care? Do the rich care? Do we care? Obviously, graphically not. For the poor are here; the poor, the demented, the crippled, the criminal and the outcast, are all here in the Great City. They are our thought, our deed—as well as their own. And are the poor therefore white-winged and as angels? Or are they the sinners, and the rich they favor, —white-winged and pure? No! Poor and rich, the broken, the demented, outcast, criminal are, all, just like you and me! There is something interchangeable in us that fits exactly with them all. That something is a *thought!* It is the *Feudal Thought;* the axle-thought of all civilizations of the past and of today. That thought which has been hugged secretly and blazoned openly by the Man of the Past—and which we hug and blazon this day. Only we mask it. We call it, good-times, or hard-times, as the case may be; we call it by every name but its own. We even call it Charity; we even call it Religion! We even call it Philosophy! When you get down to our last thought—it is the same in all. *Therefore!* things are exactly as they are! The conventionality whereby one man is called a priest, another a pauper, this one is called an economist, another an imbecile, one a scholar, another a thief, one a senator, another a blacksmith, does not make an iota of difference when we come to deal with the simple, the obvious and the fundamental in man,—stripped of all subterfuge, casuistry, sophistry, fine language, fine art and fine nonsense, and scientific self-deception.

Thus do we see ourselves pictured forth in the Great City. Anything and everything we see there, is ourselves.

All the people think in terms of murk and filth, wealth and

poverty, crime and misfortune, and the rest of the long list? And there is the thought, pictured for you, point blank, in the open, where all may see. The smoke, the filth, the rich, the poor, are merely parts of a great picture—the picture of the Great City. The picture itself but the open showing of our one thought *at work!* continually painting fleeting and permanent pictures for us all to see and heed. . . .

Now you, in your list of practical difficulties, complain of corrupt politicians, in the Great City—shoals of them. Now who has corrupted them! Did not you? Did not I? Did not they themselves? Have not we all? Have they not accepted corruption because we asked them to, because we set them alluring examples, because we sanctioned them, because we drove them, willing, unwilling, or hesitating, or wishing, though they might be? Were they not, in fact, as chaff before the silent whirlwind of our stormy heart's desire, our secret predatory thought, within our multitudinous sanctuaries of one? That sanctuary of the poor man as well as the rich man, that sanctuary of the ditch, the coal mine, the railroad yard and the mill, as well as of the pulpit, the altar, the university, the editorial chamber and the private office? Are they not therefore a picture of our thought? The thought of all the people? Look at them near and square, look at them as brothers; not on terms of superiority or inferiority as you would like, but on terms of likeness, as you must! Look near and searchingly; get up close! Are they not your very image? Can you not see clearly the thought you hold in common with them? Does not that thought join your hands with theirs in fellowship?—those whom you affect to despise? Are they not your secret thought *at work* in the open? whoever you may be, rich or poor, or in between—or in any walk of life!

Do you suppose that because you have held up your hands in pious horror and have bellowed or squeaked in protest, that you are immune to responsibility? Do you assert that "righteous indignation" is other than a farcical phrase? Search your memory from the cradle up! Test your life-thought with acid reality. You know! I know!

Do you suppose that because you have remained sadly silent, that you are immune? Do you suppose that because you have pitied the depravity *of others* that you are immune? Do you suppose that because you have led an "upright life," as you call it, that you are immune? Do you believe yourself immune because you place your trust in Jesus and the feudal God, and the Sunday school, and heaven, and all the rest, and are of the elect? Do you really believe that you can thus escape the shrill call to personal responsibility and accountability here! The cock-crow of dawning Democracy! That cry which shall awaken men to realities! That cry which shall awaken men to you! and to themselves!

If you have so thought, then you have another thought coming. A thought that I shall lead to the threshold of your door and cause to enter your soul. And there it may grow and amplify until it brings you to a genuine and willing utterance. . . .

But do not fear. For if I shall show you many pictures, and explain them all clearly, it is to be solely that you may see at last how it must have come about that all the little pictures and the great picture are your true portrait the likeness of each and all of us. . . .

As together we walk the streets of the Great City, roaming here and there, passing a mansion on a boulevard, and then, elsewhere, passing sweat-shops lining streets not called boulevards because not respectable enough, not well enough paved, not tree-planted and grass-platted, vacant of fair equipages going and coming, and children prettily dressed; but crowded with other things, unseemly; do you believe there is no connection between the two pictures, the two realities? Do you think there is really not a modern ghost, making a modern trinity of your one, ancient, persistent thought? Uniting parent and offspring in one? Is not the sweat-shop the parent? Is not the mansion the child? Does not the man in the mansion know it? Is he not content? Is not the mother on whom he sponges seemingly resigned? Is it not fate! Have we not been told that an all-wise providence has thus arranged for the good of all? That it is through the benevolence of the rich that the poor are given work? That were it not for the Charity of the rich the poor might sometimes starve? Have not the poor long drawn inspiration from this comforting thought? Did not the poor create this thought out of their sweet, sad dream?—as they have created all things? Is it not also our thought? Are we not, all, agreed? Is it not therefore our portrait, one and all?—this little picture in the Great City!

And thus, ever unfolding, as we cross and recross many paths, appear picture upon picture, revealing in vibrant form and varied coloring the multitudinous aspects of a single thought the people hold and stand for:—some in overwhelming contrasts, others blending into a gray insipid monotone. Pictures painted not by artists, so-called, but by ourselves—by all the people. Pictures, without frames, conjoining, interblending to form a huge, graphic image of the totality of our thoughts, and the singleness thereof as interpreted in our complicated, tangled and thwarted lives.

It may have been your habit of mind to consider drama as occasional; episodic; an artful presentation merely, as set forth on a stage within an isolated house called a theatre; and more or less well done, more or less inane, as the case might be. That is but a little truth. The broader, unescapable truth, is that you are ever in the midst of a drama; a drama in the open. You are both spectator and actor therein. It is the drama of the Great City. This drama is unfolded within the action of the greater drama of Land and People. The drama of Land and People is in turn enfolded within the greater drama of the nations and peoples of the Earth. This latter drama is but the tidal continuation of the still greater drama of history; and the urge of it all sets forth the stupendous and pitiful drama of Man,—moving passionately through the ages, and as passionately moving today; ever-seeking, ever-thwarted Man! It is this great drama of the soul of man that we are slowly to unfold. It is the background, the vista, the ever pressing drift, now nearing culmination for weal or woe, on which we must set our gaze, and concentrate our hearts and minds. It is the one drama! and in it man (the spirit and summation of mankind) the sole actor, has moved and moves in solitude through the great wilderness and teeming world of nature, through darkness and light, ever, in a darkling dream, seeking to know man, seeking to know God,—and tragically unaware! unaware!

And thus, in the drama of the Great City, are enfolded lesser and lesser dramas,—dramas growing ever acuter, more poignant, more intimate, as they grow ever, but in seeming, only, smaller and less significant; dramas innumerable in the open, dramas of the day and the night. The lesser drama keys to the greater drama, the greater a key to the lesser, and the least. Dramas, without end, within a roof and a wall. Terrible and subtle tragedies behind closed doors; behind the door the breath of Life has blown to, to hold in tight the sordid and calloused soul—the wrecker of thousands of his fellow-men; to hold in tight the terrible, the solitary drama of one, bitterly alone behind the door that Life has blown to in disgust with man.—A flash! and it is done! A drama of the wretched home: —Enter the man, drunk unto mania, surly, irritable. A surging word of reproach; an oath and a blow; a woman prostrate, huddled screaming children; a maudlin interval; and then a man, outstretched, snoring on the floor in the night stillness, in the sanctuary of one home, behind the closed door, behind the veil where we are told we cannot enter because there is no trail and all are safe in solitude.

But there is a trail. It leads from the forlorn home direct to the workingman's saloon; and there it parts in two straight lines, running, one to the brewer, the other to the rectifier—both poisoners, both cowards—(they both struck the woman). From the wife beater, beaten wife, children, brewer and rectifier run lines straight as the crow flies to you and me (we also brutalized the man, struck the woman, terrified and degraded the children), and from us, they run straight to every man, woman and child in the land—and come back to us; and between all the people in the land they cross-connect, and connect us in endless combinations.

Have you deemed the inter-relations of human life and civilization impossible of precise definition? Have you agreed to be thwarted? and that the aggregate of human life is a mere blur, a smear, all grays except a few bright spots for the favored,—and that there is no simple definite meaning underlying it all?

Do you think there is no center of gravity? No definite direction of urge, merely because the man on the street seems commonplace to you, and you to him? He, the practical man; you, the practical man—inane dreamers both—visionaries, spending your lives dreaming difficulties and hence creating them—never dreaming a solution.

Awake! The hour is drawing near when all this must be changed—or we undone!

Wake! Be a man! Do you really deem it incredible that all these varied, endlessly flowing and intermingling pictures and dramas, have sprung, and can and now do spring from a single thought all men have held in common, and have not ceased to hold? Do you really believe that violent opposites cannot contain the same truth? Do you really consider differences more significant than similarities? Have you been betrayed by words, not knowing the meaning of words?

Are you then the closet-philosopher, who has spun a theory of thought, but has not gone abroad among men in the world of stress—where he might clearly see that acts, and *acts alone* identify thoughts. Where he might see the mind, the heart, the soul of man clearly, indubitably set forth in the actual pictures and the actual dramas of man's individual and collective life? Open to the view of all—even to the dull, dreaming, inconsequential, frivolous philosopher of abstractions!

Why should we bother with the rubbish of abstractions when we have the palpitating living thing? Why should we take a tortuous and obscure way, which never arrives, when there is a clear way straight from deed to man?

Awake! Let your heart expand until you become aware that you are not alone! Until you become aware that between you and every human there is a thread of thought connecting all together. Binding all—brain to brain, heart to heart, soul to soul, body to body, life to life. A thread more ethereal than gossamer, stronger than steel. A thread we cannot break, a living thread from whose band there is no escape—and yet a thread which may transmit a new universal impulse that shall prove our salvation.

Had you thought it possible really to isolate yourself from your fellows? To evade and deny the tie? To evade and deny your responsibility, your manhood? You cannot! Along these delicate threads, these live wires, I will pass like a current, and, entering intimately into your secret depths, will shift your ballast; and you will feel the awakening shock of an enlarging consciousness as I bring you to an even keel.

I will search your mind as never mind has been searched. I will search your heart as never heart has been searched. I will search your soul as never soul has been searched. To me you are no secret. To know you I have merely to look at any other man, high or low, rich or poor, in the ditch or on the throne of the vicar of God on earth. And if I look at a thousand men, I shall see but yourself in a thousand occupations or situations, the same You—called by a thousand other names. So shall I place you, at last, squarely before yourself and before all—in the open, and in secret, whoever you are, wherever you are, and whenever you are. And I shall set humanity square before you in the open, and in the secret longing. Square in the daylight—face to face!

As we walk together in the heart of the Great City, is there aught greeting our eyes to suggest or even hint the nearby presence of a noble Lake, the teeming prairies, green and radiant, half-encircling the Great and gloomy City? Do you think the picture of the City one thing, the picture of the fair broad water and land another thing? The drama of the City one thing, the drama of the open another?—the drama of the open air, the open sky, the open waters and the open land! Do you perhaps deem them paradoxical? No. Undeceive yourself! Open your eyes! The two pictures are but parts of a larger; the two dramas but responsive and coordinate scenes of a greater, simultaneous drama:—Picture and drama the same; and, together, merged into one living image, which marks us, as with a fateful and monitory finger; and then moves to the one thought within it from which the mirage of a seeming paradox has come forth to obscure the City and the open.

Spare your explanations, your excuses, practical, sentimental, historical, scientific, benevolent and what not withal. I have listened to the chatter for many a year. Patiently I have read on page after page of many a book, endlessly, concerning an exquisite and delicately rapturous difference between tweedledum and tweedledee; knowing well, in decency that the real proposition (so deftly set aside) had nothing to do with either tweedledum or tweedledee, but vitally concerned you and me! Over and over I have seen the hair split into a thousandth part, and, meanwhile, I have seen simple men DO!!—simple things—and do them well!

Thus have I come to know to my sorrow and waste of time the inanity of the wise, pious, wordy, over-educated poseurs—and their joint and several inefficiency. By way of compensation I have learned their lesson.

But they are busier than they opine. I shall show you in picture and drama their color, form and movements. I shall show you just how, why and where they fit into the scheme of the little dramas and the great drama. We shall run along the live wires reaching to them, and binding them to us all in the fierce, disconsolate and impassioned stress of real life. That life, calling, calling,—calling!

So, too, in the drama, shall appear the man on the street. He *says* he would not do certain things. But in the great drama I shall point him out to you in the act of killing by thought, by word, by deed, by indifference, by indirection. We shall run along his wire like Nemesis! Because he is a liar, a thief, a scoundrel and an assassin—and because he has declared his religion to be his most precious possession—Because he has been benevolent and charitable with the loot of his murders. I shall show him to you sitting silent, or wandering like a madman. And in the great moving picture I shall point out to you, as therein clearly set forth in sharpest definition, just what the word "practical" means, as used by him; just what his word "business" signifies; and just what "economy," as he understands it, signifies for him, for you, for me, and for every man, woman and child on earth. No doubt he lies; sometimes even to himself. But the lies, the hypocrisy, the turpitude, the concealments, avail not. For, unwittingly, the man on the street, he who is no dreamer, no visionary, who believes himself no artist, no poet, is painting on the great picture, his great and little share, and revealing there, with a precision unattainable by him in conscious speech, the startling truth concerning himself and us all—where we may see.

What a curious notion men have, concerning themselves, their thoughts, their sayings, their doings; with what a curious hebetude they minimize and maximize their parts in the roaring farce, the vaudeville, the melodrama, the tragedy of the Great City and the far-flung Land. How like semi-mechanical figures they go this way and that, not dreaming their dream is come true; not surmising that daily, as a sheer reality, it mocks them, jeers them, warns them, ridicules them—and seduces them into dreaming anew!—And yet no one laughs!

Think of a civilization, a city, a land in which men are honest at their peril, and speak truth at their risk!—And yet no one laughs! No one smiles.

Think! of a civilization in which the predatory, the relentless, the parasite, the saintly, the feudally benevolent pull the wool over our eyes—knowing us for the sheep we are!—And no one laughs! Preacher and teacher pulling the wool over our eyes—and their own. All of us eagerly pulling the feudal wool over our own eyes—And not a smile!—all serious and fanatic, in a vast silence, and emptiness of sympathy. Truly our feudal denial of reality has at last undermined not only our sense of human tenderness, but even our sense of humor. Thus no one weeps at the dream come true. . . .

Have you ever stopped to reflect that the education you have received in school, college, University, and are still receiving in the greater school of practical life has been and is Feudal?! with all the manifold inversions of human thought that that word, that reality, contains and breeds? No, of course you have not. How do I know? *Results!!*—results set clearly forth in the pictures and dramas you have made and are making!—you who are no artist, no poet!—Yet have the power to paint most startling pictures, and create most revolting and heart-rending dramas! I don't bother to look at you, or to talk to *you;* I look at the insane, the destitute, the criminal, the vicious, the corrupt, the restless, the tuberculous, the anaemic, the outcast, the criminal rich, the financial rottenness, the political rottenness, the poisoning packer, the treacherous lawyer, the unscrupulous business man, the timid and hypocritical priest and preacher, that you have created and are sanctioning this day!—out of your feudal thought. . . . No wonder you have so heavy a countenance as you walk the streets of the Great City—alone, bitterly alone, helplessly alone amidst the shoals of faces, among the half-humans, the feudal humans—who are moving swiftly or slowly towards nothing whatsoever but graves. Because brutally they have struck kindly and smiling Nature in the face—in return for her smile. No wonder you cannot see these faces, ghostly and pictorial as they are, dramatic as they are, eloquent as they are of the feudal thought you and they have held and hold in common—and which your forebears and theirs held in common—The feudal thought which wears out the heart, unbalances the mind, devastates the soul and wrecks the hopes of mankind. That feudal thought which has brought hitherto civilizations to decay; and is now, swiftly disintegrating and inflaming our own. That! is our Crisis! That is what our Crisis means! That is what makes a terrible reversal, revulsion and cataclysmic revolution, not only possible, probable, but imminent. That is what renders imperative the prompt liberation and diffusion of the aspiring spirit and the kindliness of Democracy. That spirit, so long thwarted and denied utterance, that it has accumulated intensive explosive power within the subconsciousness of men. That is what the printing press, land lines and ocean cables mean, in the last analysis. That is what the teaching of the Nazarene means in the last analysis. Our hour is on the wing. Democracy is at last about to be born. Whether in anguish, alarm and terror, or in peace, reasonableness and joy—remains to be seen. But one thing is palpable: our equilibrium is unstable. It is trembling delicately in its balance. And, soon, we are going —one way or the other. It is high time that you get busy thinking about realities. It is high time you begin to understand what this prosperity of ours means *under the surface;* in the pictures and dramas, in the open;—(and in yourself)! *This* is the thought you will want to take with you into your sanctuary of one, behind the veil. This is the thought that will cause the feudal mighty to dissolve as though they never had been. You had better get busy forgetting your "practical difficulties!" and learn how simple, how masterful, thought and act can become, when you will them to become so. How quickly problems can be solved when we make up our minds that they shall be solved.

It is then equally no wonder you deem benevolence and charity sweet and lovely things; no wonder you do not see that these two fetid-sweet feudal words are but the names of two ghastly, grinning skeletons in the ring of our grim and ponderous dance of death; and that you and your kind, (all of us—feudal) are but phantoms joining with them, hand in hand, clattering, running and clamoring around and about dazed and momentarily terrorized manhood; and that all the fine words, all the fine deceptions, are but a weird and sombre song of the Modern Crucifixation. No wonder you cannot see that what you call Business is the name of another such phantom; and the laws of trade—as you call them—others; Industry—as you call it—another; and society as you call it—another; the rich man—another; and the poor man—another. Can you not hear them all?—like the murmur of a keen wintry wind driving through a bare forest—singing the song of the Great City? Can you not hear it? It is roaring on, day in, day out; night in, night out; in the churches, in the asylums, in the jails; in the mansions, in the shanties; in the pest house, in the hospitals, in the police stations; in the mills, the factories, the ditch, the marts of trade; in the hotels, the theatres, the boarding houses; in the sweat shops, the rear of saloons, in the private office, in the newspaper sanctuary, in political committee rooms:—Everywhere—anywhere! Ceaselessly!—Here in a whisper—there it passes in a wink, a nod, a tip, a sign—there amid clangor and clamor, and bustle and hustle, buying and selling, hooting and yelling—There it is! For you to see! For you to hear!—in the Great City! In the Great City where you and I are walking side by side, looking into the faces of the passers-by; observing the traffic in the streets, and over the streets, and along the streets; dropping in here and there and everywhere, by day and by night, only to hear the same song with its endless, teeming variations in pitch and key and intonation and volume —in smooth flow, in rabid discord—in fine words and ribald words and crude words—in pious prayers and in strings of oaths—It is always the same, always with the same refrain—The Dance of Death and the Song of Death! For we are indeed a busy people—none busier—We have no time—we are greatly occupied—And business is business—so we say.

5. LOUIS D. BRANDEIS

*The Workingman and American Democracy**

Louis Dembitz Brandeis was born in Louisville, Kentucky, on November 13, 1856, the son of Jewish immigrants from Prague. Educated in the local schools, he studied in Dresden, Germany, for a time and graduated from the Harvard Law School in 1877. He entered practice in Boston where he remained for almost forty years. He was active in corporation organization and became intimately familiar with the developing structure of American business. But he was also concerned with the problems of labor and realized that modern industry raised deep issues of social justice. He became a Zionist out of the hope that a Jewish settlement in Palestine would be a laboratory for experiment with those issues. In 1916, President Wilson appointed him Associate Justice of the Supreme Court. Confirmed after a sharp battle in the Senate, Brandeis was a prominent member of that bench until his retirement in 1939. At first, he and Justice Oliver W. Holmes were in a persistent minority; but he served long enough to see many of his views prevail in the 1930's. He died on October 5, 1941.

Mr. Chairman, my special interest in this subject arises from a conviction that in the first place the workingmen, and in the second the members of the community generally, can attain the ideals of our American democracy only through an immediate increase and perhaps a constant increase in the productivity of man. We hear a great deal about the inequality

* "Testimony of Mr. Louis D. Brandeis," United States Commission on Industrial Relations, *Final Report and Testimony* (Washington, 1916), I, pp. 991–7.

in the distribution of wealth and in the proceeds and the profits derived from industry. Such inequality exists; and it is clear that, even if there were a perfectly fair distribution, our ideals could not be attained unless we succeeded in greatly increasing the productivity of man; and to my mind the greatest objection from one standpoint to the inequality to-day is that it tends to discourage effort and therefore suppresses productivity. The progress that we have made in improving the condition of the workingmen during the last century, and particularly during the last 50 years, has been largely due to the fact that the intervention or the introduction of machinery has gone so far in increasing the productivity of the individual man. The misfortune in connection with the introduction of machinery and the revolution that came with it is, or was, that when that introduction of a method of increasing the productivity of man was made labor did not get the share to which it was entitled. With the advent of the new science of management has come the next great opportunity for increasing labor's share in production; and it seems to me, therefore, of the utmost importance not only that the science should be developed and should be applied as far as possible, but that it should be applied in cooperation with the representatives of organized labor in order that labor may now in this new movement get its proper share.

Now, I take it that the whole of this science of management is nothing more than an organized effort, pursued intensively, to eliminate waste. The expert tells us how this may be done. The experts make the individual detailed study, which is an essential of the elimination of waste; but, after all, the fundamental problems are social and industrial. It is, in the process of eliminating waste and increasing the productivity of man to adopt those methods which will insure the social and industrial essentials, fairness in the development, fairness in the distribution of the profits, and that encouragement to the workingman, which can not come without fairness.

Now, I take it that in order to accomplish this result it is absolutely essential that the unions should be represented in the process. In the first place, the question comes up—must come up—in applying the results of scientific management, in determining the very basis and standard on which any system is to rest, as to what is the proper time in which a certain operation shall be performed. Now, that subject of what is the proper time is a question in which representatives of the workers distinctly ought to have a voice. No matter how far you may go into scientific investigation, there must always come in the question of the human element, as to how hard a man ought to work, how fast he ought to work, and how fast he can work consistently with health. Now, in that question there ought to be an opportunity for the full protection of the men who work, and that properly can be done only through representatives of organized labor.

In the next place—the first bears, of course, upon the adopting of what is the standard—but the next thing comes in applying some matter, some incentive, as you may call it, or a reward of a fair division of the profits resulting from the introduction of the new system. Now, what is fair? What is the amount which ought to go to labor is a subject which can not be determined by any scientific investigation. It is a matter for the exercise of judgment, judgment as to what not only shall be the best and the proper incentive but judgment as to what is just, what is consistent with the interests of the community, all of the conditions which surround introduction, and all of the conditions which concern the pursuit of business under these new conditions, just as those which concern the conduct of business under the old conditions, demand that labor should have its representatives in the solution of these problems. When labor is given such a representation I am unable to find anything in scientific management which is not strictly in accord with the interests of labor, because it is nothing more than fair, through the application of these methods which have been pursued in other branches of science, to find out the best and the most effective way of accomplishing the result. It is not making men work harder. The very effort of it is to make them work less hard, to accomplish more by what they do, and eliminate all unnecessary motions; to educate them so as to make them most effective; to give special effort and special assistance to those who at the time of the commencement of their work are mostly in need of assistance because they are least competent.

Now, the advance in the condition of the workingman is attained by each and every one of the purposes which scientific management and which the apostles of scientific management set before themselves. Whatever there is in the application of the principles of scientific management to a business that may expose the workingman to danger, that is to be guarded against and will be guarded against by a proper representation.

So that as I view the problem it is only one of making the employer recognize the necessity of the participation of representatives of labor in the introduction and carrying forward of the work, and on the other hand bringing to the workingman and the representatives of organized labor the recognition of the fact that there is nothing in scientific management itself which is inimical to the interests of the workingman, but merely perhaps the practices of certain individuals, of certain employers, or concerns who have been engaged in it.

I have felt that this presented a very great opportunity for organized labor. It seemed to me absolutely clear, as scientific management rested upon fundamental principles of advance in man's productivity, of determining what the best way was of doing a thing instead of the poor way, of a complete co-ordination and organization of the various departments of business, that the introduction of scientific management in our businesses was certain to come; that those who oppose introduction altogether were undertaking a perfectly impossible task; and that if organized labor took the position of absolute opposition, instead of taking the position of insisting upon their proper part in the introduction of this system, and the conduct of the business under it, organized labor would lose its greatest opportunity and would be defeating the very purpose for which it exists. . . .

It seems to me that the elements of difficulty in introduction are largely due to the fact that there is hostility to the introduction, and that if organized labor or the representatives of labor should welcome and cooperate in the introduction a greater part of these difficulties would be removed. Of course, there are a good many difficulties that must stop—I mean matters that involve a very great study—difficult in the sense of problems to be solved. They will exist under any circumstances—the problems of finding out how you want to do a thing; when you know how you ought to do it, how you ought to bring a man to do it the way he ought to do it. Those are problems which are inherent and have to be worked out and require most intensive application and patience. But the whole of the work, it seems to me, would be greatly aided by a spirit of helpfulness instead of the reverse. . . .

There is a question of tact, there is a question of consideration, there is a question of the recognition of prejudice and feelings and of the possibility of misunderstanding which a man of tact and a man accustomed to dealing with labor or to dealing with men generally must recognize. But if it is done in the right way, the stop watch can not, it seems to me, be objected to by labor, because it is the greatest possible protection to labor. What labor has suffered from in the past and is constantly suffering from now is the ignoring of facts, either because they are not known or because they are known to some persons and not to labor. There is nothing, as I view it, in the situation, the whole social industrial structure, that labor wants so much as knowledge. It wants not only to know itself but it wants others to know it; and any means that may be adopted, whether it be the stop watch or the photograph or any other means, that could absolutely establish the fact as to what is being done, how long it takes to do it, what the unit is of doing the particular thing—all those are in the interest of labor, because they are in the interest of truth. Of course, there is a question, as I have said, of tact in dealing with the subject. . . .

We are fortunately getting to the point where the unions, as they are developing stability and strength, are recognizing that they, like other people, must employ experts. They are taking, consequently, in selecting for their important work men who are not members of their unions, just as employers must select professional men to perform particular duties. They have found in many instances that some men were available and were as loyal to their cause as anybody could possibly be to a cause. That is the situation which presents itself. The expert who is to be selected may be selected by the unions with quite as much intelligence and with quite as much certainty of loyal service as if it were by the employer; and there are very many relations in life where the selection, for instance, of an expert accountant is to be made by the various parties at interest, and where experts are constantly being employed by parties who have different interests to conserve by joint arrangements. I see no difficulty whatever in making that selection in such a case as this. . . .

I think it is perfectly possible and probable that scientific management has been introduced in so many shops where the workmen have been well treated, and certainly where their wages have been very largely increased by the process, but it is not safe, and as a broad social proposition we ought to insist upon the other thing. It is contrary to all our ideas of democracy, and particularly of industrial democracy. . . .

To my mind one of the greatest advantages of the introduction of scientific management is to make the so-called incompetent man useful. The man who is extraordinary needs no help from anyone under any system. He advances—of course, not as far as he might. He might waste considerable of a great ability; but the man of great ability does not need any help from the community as such, or from a system as such. . . .

One man out of five might be able to perform a particular work, or one man out of 10 or 20 a particular work, and there ought to be work for him to do, and work that he could do more effectively than he would ordinarily do it.

Of course, it is the essence of scientific management to pick your man for a particular work, just as important and essential as it is to pick your tool for a machine for a particular work—that is, to treat human beings as you treat a machine—intelligently—and not put a round man in a square hole.

But in the evidence which we have on the subject of scientific management, one of the interesting and hopeful things is that by which seemingly the most incompetent and most impossible persons were made by patient instruction to become effective workingmen and aid themselves and industry as a whole. . . .

Scientific management . . . recognizes the conservation of man and it affords the very greatest incentive to the conservation of man, because it takes raw material and makes it a perfect and finished article.

It would be absolutely suicidal for any manager to develop his men and then kill them. That is the way you could take unskilled labor and kill it at the start, but under scientific management the manager has put an immense amount of money in his investment. It would tend also to the stabilizing of labor, because men want to keep their health when they have been trained; so all the fundamental ideas of scientific management are in accord with our social desires for labor, but it needs a protection. Nobody ought to be absolute; everybody ought to be protected from arbitrariness and wrong decisions by the representations of others who are being affected. . . .

It seems to me that the time has come when that should be one of the specific demands of society and of the labor unions, and that the conception of day labor is entirely unsocial and is entirely uneconomical; it is distinctly contrary to the whole conception of scientific management, because it involves such waste as you can find in any possible department of industry. . . .

It seems to me that we are so far away in this country, and probably in any country, from satisfying the possible wants of the community, that there is no fear of overproduction in its proper sense. It all comes to the question of what people can afford to buy, and whether it be steel or whether it be many of the other things, if they could be produced in a way so that they themselves would thereafter be productive; that is, at less cost, that the demand would be there for them, and that there is practically no such thing as there not being potential demand enough for all that we can produce. . . .

Society and labor should demand continuity of employment, and when we once get to a point where workingmen are paid throughout the year, as the officers of a corporation are paid throughout the year, and the higher employees are paid throughout the year, everyone will recognize that a business can not be run profitably unless you keep it running, because if you have to pay, whether your men are working or not, your men will work.

It seems to me that industry has been allowed to develop chaotically, mainly because we have accepted irregularity of employment as if it was something inevitable. It is no more inevitable than insistence upon payment for a great many of the overhead charges in a business, whether the business is in daily operation or is not. . . .

I think there would be a good deal left for unionism to do, and I do not think the time will come when there will not be, as long as there is a wage system in existence. That is, this other thing we have been discussing now, the question of the regularity of employment; that is a subject as to which the unions have taken practically no steps up to the present time, and it is a matter which in some ways is infinitely more important than a great many as to which they have. That subject would occupy the unions, I think, for a very long time to come.

Again, I do not feel that we have reached the limit of the shorter day; certainly not in some employments; nor do I think that we have reached the limit of the higher wage; certainly we have not reached the limit of the best conditions of employment in many industries.

All of these subjects are subjects which must be taken up, and should be taken up, by the representatives of the men and women who are particularly interested. There will be work for unions to do as long as there is a wage system. . . .

It seems to me that the intensive study of businesses and of the elimination of wage in business must result in regularizing business. Every man who has undertaken to study the problem of his business in the most effective way has come to recognize that what he must do is to keep the business running all the time, keep it full. If it is a retail business, he makes it his effort to make other days in the week than Saturday a great day; he tries to take periods of the year when people do not naturally buy and make them buy, in the off seasons, in order to keep his plant going during the period in which ordinarily and in other places of business it loses money. Now, that effort must proceed in every business, to try by means of invention, and invention involving large investment, to make the business run throughout the year; that is, to regularize the work, avoid the congestion of the extra-busy season, and avoiding the dearth in what has been a slack season.

Now, scientific management must develop regularly; therefore, in developing regularity it will tend to eliminate unemployment. Of course, it also will naturally tend to eliminate that other unemployment, which comes from lack of work to do, because if we are right in supposing that there is plenty of consumptive power but not enough ability to buy the things, then we may be able to produce them cheaply enough and people will want them and will take them.

6. THORSTEIN VEBLEN

*Devout Observances**

Thorstein B. Veblen was born in 1857, the sixth of twelve children whose parents had immigrated from Norway in 1847. He grew up in Norwegian communities in Wisconsin and Minnesota and studied at Carleton College where he felt the influence of the economist John Bates Clark. There followed periods of graduate study at Johns Hopkins and Yale, but Veblen was unable to locate a teaching post and was compelled to spend several years farming in Stacyville, Iowa. At the age of thirty-four he secured a teaching fellowship at Cornell and then moved to Chicago. His advancement was slow despite a solid record of publication and his unconventional behavior created difficulties. He taught at Stanford, the University of Missouri, and the New School for Social Research in New York; yet he did not fit any conventional academic mold. He died in 1929. He left behind a body of work which went beyond the technicalities of economics to the critical observations of a shrewd outsider on the basic elements of his society. See also Joseph Dorfman, Thorstein Veblen and His America *(New York, 1947); David Riesman,* Thorstein Veblen *(New York, 1960).*

In the discussion of the sporting temperament, it has appeared that the sense of an animistic propensity in material things and events is what affords the spiritual basis of the sporting man's gambling habit. For the economic purpose, this sense of propensity is substantially the same psychological

* Thorstein Veblen, *Theory of the Leisure Class* (New York, 1945), pp. 294–331.

element as expresses itself, under a variety of forms, in animistic beliefs and anthropomorphic creeds. So far as concerns those tangible psychological features with which economic theory has to deal, the gambling spirit which pervades the sporting element shades off by insensible gradations into that frame of mind which finds gratification in devout observances. As seen from the point of view of economic theory, the sporting character shades off into the character of a religious devotee. Where the betting man's animistic sense is helped out by a somewhat consistent tradition, it has developed into a more or less articulate belief in a preternatural or hyperphysical agency, with something of an anthropomorphic content. And where this is the case, there is commonly a perceptible inclination to make terms with the preternatural agency by some approved method of approach and conciliation. This element of propitiation and cajoling has much in common with the crasser forms of worship—if not in historical derivation, at least in actual psychological content. It obviously shades off in unbroken continuity into what is recognized as superstitious practice and belief, and so asserts its claim to kinship with the grosser anthropomorphic cults.

The sporting or gambling temperament, then, comprises some of the substantial psychological elements that go to make a believer in creeds and an observer of devout forms, the chief point of coincidence being the belief in an inscrutable propensity or a preternatural interposition in the sequence of events. For the purpose of the gambling practice the belief in preternatural agency may be, and ordinarily is, less closely formulated, especially as regards the habits of thought and the scheme of life imputed to the preternatural agent; or, in other words, as regards his moral character and his purposes in interfering in events. With respect to the individuality or personality of the agency whose presence as luck, or chance, or hoodoo, or mascot, etc., he feels and sometimes dreads and endeavours to evade, the sporting man's views are also less specific, less integrated and differentiated. The basis of his gambling activity is, in great measure, simply an instinctive sense of the presence of a pervasive extraphysical and arbitrary force or propensity in things or situations, which is scarcely recognised as a personal agent. The betting man is not infrequently both a believer in luck, in this naïve sense, and at the same time a pretty staunch adherent of some form of accepted creed. He is especially prone to accept so much of the creed as concerns the inscrutable power and the arbitrary habits of the divinity which has won his confidence. In such a case he is possessed of two, or sometimes more than two, distinguishable phases of animism. Indeed, the complete series of successive phases of animistic belief is to be found unbroken in the spiritual furniture of any sporting community. Such a chain of animistic conceptions will comprise the most elementary form of an instinctive sense of luck and chance and fortuitous necessity at one end of the series, together with the perfectly developed anthropomorphic divinity at the other end, with all intervening stages of integration. Coupled with these beliefs in preternatural agency goes an instinctive shaping of conduct to conform with the surmised requirements of the lucky chance on the one hand, and a more or less devout submission to the inscrutable decrees of the divinity on the other hand.

There is a relationship in this respect between the sporting temperament and the temperament of the delinquent classes; and the two are related to the temperament which inclines to an anthropomorphic cult. But the delinquent and the sporting man are on an average more apt to be adherents of some accredited creed, and are also rather more inclined to devout observances, than the general average of the community. It is also noticeable that unbelieving members of these classes show more of a proclivity to become proselytes to some accredited faith than the average of unbelievers. This fact of observation is avowed by the spokesmen of sports, especially in apologising for the more naïvely predatory athletic sports. Indeed, it is somewhat insistently claimed as a meritorious feature of sporting life that the habitual participants in athletic games are in some degree peculiarly given to devout practices. And it is observable that the cult to which sporting men and the predaceous delinquent classes adhere, or to which proselytes from these classes commonly attach themselves, is ordinarily not one of the so-called higher faiths, but a cult which has to do with a thoroughly anthropomorphic divinity. Archaic, predatory human nature is not satisfied with abstruse conceptions of a dissolving personality that shades off into the concept of quantitative causal sequence, such as the speculative, esoteric creeds of Christendom impute to the First Cause, Universal Intelligence, World Soul, or Spiritual Aspect. As an instance of a cult of the character which the habits of mind of the athlete and the delinquent require, may be cited that branch of the church militant known as the Salvation Army. This is to some extent recruited from the lower-class delinquents, and it appears to comprise also, among its officers especially, a larger proportion of men with a sporting record than the proportion of such men in the aggregate population of the community.

College athletics afford a case in point. It is contended by exponents of the devout element in college life—and there seems to be no ground for disputing the claim—that the desirable athletic material afforded by any student body in this country is at the same time predominantly religious; or that it is at least given to devout observances to a greater degree than the average of those students whose interest in athletics and other college sports is less. This is what might be expected on theoretical grounds. It may be remarked, by the way, that from one point of view this is felt to reflect credit on the college sporting life, on athletic games, and on those persons who occupy themselves with these matters. It happens not infrequently that college sporting men devote themselves to the religious propaganda, either as a vocation or as a by-occupation; and it is observable that when this happens they are likely to become propagandists of some one of the more anthropomorphic cults. In their teaching they are apt to insist chiefly on the personal relation of status which subsists between an anthropomorphic divinity and the human subject.

This intimate relation between athletics and devout observance among college men is a fact of sufficient notoriety; but it has a special feature to which attention has not been called, although it is obvious enough. The religious zeal which pervades much of the college sporting element is especially prone to express itself in an unquestioning devoutness and a naïve and complacent submission to an inscrutable Providence. It therefore by preference seeks affiliation with some one of those lay religious organisations which occupy themselves with the spread of the exoteric forms of the faith,—as, *e.g.*, the Young Men's Christian Association or the Young People's Society for Christian Endeavour. These lay bodies are organised to further "practical" religion; and as if to enforce the argument and firmly establish the close relationship between the sporting temperament and the archaic devoutness, these lay religious bodies commonly devote some appreciable portion of their energies to the furtherance of athletic contests and similar games of chance and skill. It might even be said that sports of this kind are apprehended to have some efficacy as a means of grace. They are apparently useful as a means of proselyting, and as a means of sustaining the devout attitude in converts once made. That is to say, the games which give exercise to the animistic sense and to the emulative propensity help to form and to conserve that habit of mind to which the more exoteric cults are congenial. Hence, in the hands of the lay organisations, these sporting activities come to do duty as a novitiate or a means of induction into that fuller unfolding of the life of spiritual status which is the privilege of the full communicant alone.

That the exercise of the emulative and lower animistic proclivities are substantially useful for the devout purpose seems to be placed beyond question by the fact that the priesthood of many denominations is following the lead of the lay organisations in this respect. Those ecclesiastical organisations especially which stand nearest the lay organisations in their insistence on practical religion have gone some way towards adopting these or analogous practices in connection with the traditional devout observances. So there are "boys' brigades," and other organisations, under clerical sanction, acting to develop the emulative proclivity and the sense of status in the youthful members of the congregation. These pseudo-military organisations tend to elaborate and accentuate the proclivity to emulation and invidious comparison, and so strengthen the native facility for discerning and approving the relation of personal mastery and subservience. And a believer is eminently a person who knows how to obey and accept chastisement with good grace.

But the habits of thought which these practices foster and conserve make up but one-half of the substance of the anthropomorphic cults. The other, complementary element of devout life—the animistic habit of mind—is recruited and conserved by a second range of practices organised under clerical sanction. These are the class of gambling practices of which the church bazaar or raffle may be taken as the type. As indicating the degree of legitimacy of these practices in connection with devout observances proper, it is to be remarked that these raffles, and the like trivial opportunities for gambling, seem to appeal with more effect to the common run of the members of religious organisations than they do to persons of a less devout habit of mind.

All this seems to argue, on the one hand, that the same temperament inclines people to sports as inclines them to the anthropomorphic cults, and on the other hand that the habituation to sports, perhaps especially to athletic sports, acts to develop the propensities which find satisfaction in devout observances. Conversely; it also appears that habituation to these observances favours the growth of a proclivity for athletic sports and for all games that give play to the habit of invidious comparison and of the appeal to luck. Substantially the same range of propensities finds expression in both these directions of the spiritual life. That barbarian human nature in which the predatory instinct and the animistic standpoint predominate is normally prone to both. The predatory habit of mind involves an accentuated sense of personal dignity and of the relative standing of individuals. The social structure in which the predatory habit has been the dominant factor in the shaping of institutions is a structure based on status. The pervading norm in the predatory community's scheme of life is the relation of superior and inferior, noble and base, dominant and subservient persons and classes, master and slave. The anthropomorphic cults have come down from that stage of industrial development and have been shaped by the same scheme of economic differentiation,—a differentiation into consumer and producer,—and they are pervaded by the same dominant principle of mastery and subservience. The cults impute to their divinity the habits of thought answering to the stage of economic differentiation at which the cults took shape. The anthropomorphic divinity is conceived to be punctilious in all questions of precedence and is prone to an assertion of mastery and an arbitrary exercise of power—an habitual resort to force as the final arbiter.

In the later and maturer formulations of the anthropomorphic creed this imputed habit of dominance on the part of a divinity of awful presence and inscrutable power is chastened into "the fatherhood of God." The spiritual attitude and the aptitudes imputed to the preternatural agent are still such as belong under the régime of status, but they now assume the patriarchal cast characteristic of the quasi-peaceable stage of culture. Still it is to be noted that even in this advanced phase of the cult the observances in which devoutness finds expression consistently aim to propitiate the divinity by extolling his greatness and glory and by professing subservience and fealty. The act of propitiation or of worship is designed to appeal to a sense of status imputed to the inscrutable power that is thus approached. The propitiatory formulas most in vogue are still such as carry or imply an invidious comparison. A loyal attachment to the person of an anthropomorphic divinity endowed with such an archaic human nature implies the like archaic propensities in the devotee. For the purposes of economic theory, the relation of fealty, whether to a physical or to an extraphysical person, is to be taken as a variant of that personal subservience which makes up so large a share of the predatory and the quasi-peaceable scheme of life.

The barbarian conception of the divinity, as a warlike chieftain inclined to an overbearing manner of government, has been greatly softened through the milder manners and the soberer habits of life that characterise those cultural phases which lie between the early predatory stage and the present. But even after this chastening of the devout fancy, and the consequent mitigation of the harsher traits of conduct and character that are currently imputed to the divinity, there still remains in the popular apprehension of the divine nature and temperament a very substantial residue of the barbarian conception. So it comes about, for instance, that in characterising the divinity and his relations to the process of human life, speakers and writers are still able to make effective use of similes borrowed from the vocabulary of war and of the predatory manner of life, as well as of locutions which involve an invidious comparison. Figures of speech of this import are used with good effect even in addressing the less warlike modern audiences, made up of adherents of the blander variants of the creed. This effective use of barbarian epithets and terms of comparison by popular speakers argues that the modern generation has retained a lively appreciation of the dignity and merit of the barbarian virtues; and it argues also that there is a degree of congruity between the devout attitude and the predatory habit of mind. It is only on second thought, if at all, that the devout fancy of modern worshippers revolts at the imputation of ferocious and vengeful emotions and actions to the object of their adoration. It is a matter of common observation that sanguinary epithets applied to the divinity have a high æsthetic and honorific value in the popular apprehension. That is to say, suggestions which these epithets carry are very acceptable to our unreflecting apprehension.

> Mine eyes have seen the glory of the coming of the Lord;
> He is trampling out the vintage where the grapes of wrath are stored;
> He hath loosed the fateful lightning of his terrible swift sword;
> His truth is marching on.

The guiding habits of thought of a devout person move on the plane of an archaic scheme of life which has outlived much of its usefulness for the economic exigencies of the collective life of to-day. In so far as the economic organisation fits the exigencies of the collective life of to-day, it has outlived the régime of status, and has no use and no place for a relation of personal subserviency. So far as concerns the economic efficiency of the community, the sentiment of personal fealty, and the general habit of mind of which that sentiment is an expression, are survivals which cumber the ground and hinder an adequate adjustment of human institutions to the existing situation. The habit of mind which best lends itself to the purposes of a peaceable, industrial community, is that matter-of-fact temper which recognises the value of material facts simply as opaque items in the mechanical sequence. It is that frame of mind which does not instinctively impute an animistic propensity to things, nor resort to preternatural intervention as an explanation of perplexing phenomena, nor depend on an unseen hand to shape the course of events to human use. To meet the requirements of the highest economic efficiency under modern conditions, the world process must habitually be apprehended in terms of quantitative, dispassionate force and sequence.

As seen from the point of view of the later economic exigencies, devoutness is, perhaps in all cases, to be looked upon as a survival from an earlier phase of associated life—a mark of arrested spiritual development. Of course it remains true that in a community where the economic structure is still substantially a system of status; where the attitude of the average of persons in the community is consequently shaped by and adapted to the relation of personal dominance and personal subservience; or where for any other reason—of tradition or of inherited aptitude—the population as a whole is strongly inclined to devout observances; there a devout habit of mind in any individual, not in excess of the average of the community, must be taken simply as a detail of the prevalent habit of life. In this light, a devout individual in a devout community can not be called a case of reversion, since he is abreast of the average of the community. But as seen from the point of view of the modern industrial situation, exceptional devoutness—devotional zeal that rises appreciably above the average pitch of devoutness in the community—may safely be set down as in all cases an atavistic trait.

It is, of course, equally legitimate to consider these phenomena from a different point of view. They may be appreciated for a different purpose, and the characterisation here offered may be turned about. In speaking from the point of view of the devotional interest, or the interest of devout taste, it may, with equal cogency, be said that the spiritual attitude bred in men by the modern industrial life is unfavourable to a free development of the life of faith. It might fairly be objected to the later development of the industrial process that its discipline tends to "materialism," to the elimination of filial piety. From the æsthetic point of view, again, something to a similar purport might be said. But, however legitimate and valuable these and the like reflections may be for their purpose, they would not be in place in the present inquiry, which is exclusively concerned with the valuation of these phenomena from the economic point of view.

The grave economic significance of the anthropomorphic habit of mind and of the addiction to devout observances must serve as apology for speaking further on a topic which it can not but be distasteful to discuss at all as an economic phenomenon in a community so devout as ours. Devout observances are of economic importance as an index of a concomitant variation of temperament, accompanying the predatory habit of mind and so indicating the presence of industrially disserviceable traits. They indicate the presence of a mental attitude which has a certain economic value of its own by virtue of its influence upon the industrial serviceability of the individual. But they are also of importance more directly, in modifying the economic activities of the community, especially as regards the distribution and consumption of goods.

The most obvious economic bearing of these observances is seen in the devout consumption of goods and services. The consumption of ceremonial paraphernalia required by any cult, in the way of shrines, temples, churches, vestments, sacrifices, sacraments, holiday attire, etc., serves no immediate material end. All this material apparatus may, therefore, without implying depreciation, be broadly characterised as items of conspicuous waste. The like is true in a general way of the personal service consumed under this head; such as priestly education, priestly service, pilgrimages, fasts, holidays, household devotions, and the like. At the same time the observances in the execution of which this consumption takes place serve to extend and protract the vogue of those habits of thought on which an anthropomorphic cult rests. That is to say, they further the habits of thought characteristic of the régime of status. They are in so far an obstruction to the most effective organisation of industry under modern circumstances; and are, in the first instance, antagonistic to the development of economic institutions in the direction required by the situation of to-day. For the present purpose, the indirect as well as the direct effects of this consumption are of the nature of a curtailment of the community's economic efficiency. In economic theory, then, and considered in its proximate consequences, the consumption of goods and effort in the service of an anthropomorphic divinity means a lowering of the vitality of the community. What may be the remoter, indirect, moral effects of this class of consumption does not admit of a succinct answer, and it is a question which can not be taken up here.

It will be to the point, however, to note the general economic character of devout consumption, in comparison with consumption for other purposes. An indication of the range of motives and purposes from which devout consumption of goods proceeds will help toward an appreciation of the value both of this consumption itself and of the general habit of mind to which it is congenial. There is a striking parallelism, if not rather a substantial identity of motive, between the consumption which goes to the service of an anthropomorphic divinity and that which goes to the service of a gentleman of leisure—a chieftain or patriarch—in the upper class of society during the barbarian culture. Both in the case of the chieftain and in that of the divinity there are expensive edifices set apart for the behoof of the person served. These edifices, as well as the properties which supplement them in the service, must not be common in kind or grade; they always show a large element of conspicuous waste. It may also be noted that the devout edifices are invariably of an archaic cast in their structure and fittings. So also the servants, both of the chieftain and of the divinity, must appear in the presence clothed in garments of a special, ornate character. The characteristic economic feature of this apparel is a more than ordinarily accentuated conspicuous waste, together with the secondary feature—more accentuated in the case of the priestly servants than in that of the servants or courtiers of the barbarian potentate—that this court dress must always be in some degree of an archaic fashion. Also the garments worn by the lay members of the community when they come into the presence, should be of a more expensive kind than their everyday apparel. Here, again, the parallelism between the usage of the chieftain's audience hall and that of the sanctuary is fairly well marked. In this respect there is required a certain ceremonial "cleanness" of attire, the essential feature of which, in the economic respect, is that the garments worn on these occasions should carry as little suggestion as may be of any industrial occupation or of any habitual addiction to such employments as are of material use.

This requirement of conspicuous waste and of ceremonial cleanness from the traces of industry extends also to the apparel, and in a less degree to the food, which is consumed on sacred holidays; that is to say, on days set apart—tabu—for the divinity or for some member of the lower ranks of the preternatural leisure class. In economic theory, sacred holidays are obviously to be construed as a season of vicarious leisure performed for the divinity or saint in whose name the tabu is imposed and to whose good repute the abstention from useful effort on these days is conceived to inure. The characteristic feature of all such seasons of devout vicarious leisure is a more or less rigid tabu on all activity that is of human use. In the case of fast-days the conspicuous abstention from gainful occupations and from all pursuits that (materially) further human life is further accentuated by compulsory abstinence from such consumption as would conduce to the comfort or the fulness of life of the consumer.

It may be remarked, parenthetically, that secular holidays are of the same origin, by slightly remoter derivation. They shade off by degrees from the genuinely sacred days, through an intermediate class of semi-sacred birthdays of kings and great men who have been in some measure canonised, to the deliberately invented holiday set apart to further the good repute of some notable event or some striking fact, to which it is intended to do honour, or the good fame of which is felt to be in need of repair. This remoter refinement in the employment of vicarious leisure as a means of augmenting the good repute of a phenomenon or datum is seen at its best in its very latest application. A day of vicarious leisure has in some communities been set apart as Labour Day. This observance is designed to augment the prestige of the fact of labour, by the archaic, predatory method of a compulsory abstention from useful effort. To this datum of labour-in-general is imputed the good repute attributable to the pecuniary strength put in evidence by abstaining from labour.

Sacred holidays, and holidays generally, are of the nature of a tribute levied on the body of the people. The tribute is paid in vicarious leisure, and the honorific effect which emerges is imputed to the person or the fact for whose good repute the holiday has been instituted. Such a tithe of vicarious leisure is a perquisite of all members of the preternatural leisure class and is indispensable to their good fame. *Un saint qu'on ne chôme pas* is indeed a saint fallen on evil days.

Besides this tithe of vicarious leisure levied on the laity, there are also special classes of persons—the various grades of priests and hierodules—whose time is wholly set apart for a similar service. It is not only incumbent on the priestly class to abstain from vulgar labour, especially so far as it is lucrative or is apprehended to contribute to the temporal well-being of mankind. The tabu in the case of the priestly class goes farther and adds a refinement in the form of an injunction against their seeking worldly gain even where it may be had without debasing application to industry. It is felt to be unworthy of the servant of the divinity, or rather unworthy the dignity of the divinity whose servant he is, that he should seek material gain or take thought for temporal matters. "Of all contemptible things a man who pretends to be a priest of God and is a priest to his own comforts and ambitions is the most contemptible."

There is a line of discrimination, which a cultivated taste in matters of devout observance finds little difficulty in drawing, between such actions and conduct as conduce to the fulness of human life and such as conduce to the good fame of the anthropomorphic divinity; and the activity of the priestly class, in the ideal barbarian scheme, falls wholly on the hither side of this line. What falls within the range of economics falls below the proper level of solicitude of the priesthood in its best estate. Such apparent exceptions to this rule as are afforded, for instance, by some of the mediæval orders of monks (the members of which actually laboured to some useful end), scarcely impugn the rule. These outlying orders of the priestly class are not a sacerdotal element in the full sense of the term. And it is noticeable also that these doubtfully sacerdotal orders, which countenanced their members in earning a living, fell into disrepute through offending the sense of propriety in the communities where they existed.

The priest should not put his hand to mechanically productive work; but he should consume in large measure. But even as regards his consumption it is to be noted that it should take such forms as do not obviously conduce to his own comfort or fulness of life; it should conform to the rules governing vicarious consumption, as explained under that head in an earlier chapter. It is not ordinarily in good form for the priestly class to appear well fed or in hilarious spirits. Indeed, in many of the more elaborate cults the injunction against other than vicarious consumption by this class frequently goes so far as to enjoin mortification of the flesh. And even in those modern denominations which have been organised under the latest formulations of the creed, in a modern industrial community, it is felt that all levity and avowed zest in the enjoyment of the good things of this world is alien to the true clerical decorum. Whatever suggests that these servants of an invisible master are living a life, not of devotion to their master's good fame, but of application to their own ends, jars harshly on our sensibilities as something fundamentally and eternally wrong. They are a servant class, although, being servants of a very exalted master, they rank high in the social scale by virtue of this borrowed light. Their consumption is vicarious consumption; and since, in the advanced cults, their master has no need of material gain, their occupation is vicarious leisure in the full sense. "Whether therefore ye eat, or drink, or whatsoever ye do, do all to the glory of God."

It may be added that so far as the laity is assimilated to the priesthood in the respect that they are conceived to be servants of the divinity, so far this imputed vicarious character attaches also to the layman's life. The range of application of this corollary is somewhat wide. It applies especially to such movements for the reform or rehabilitation of the religious life as are of an austere, pietistic, ascetic cast,—where the human subject is conceived to hold his life by a direct servile tenure from his spiritual sovereign. That is to say, where the institution of the priesthood lapses, or where there is an exceptionally lively sense of the immediate and masterful presence of the divinity in the affairs of life, there the layman is conceived to stand in an immediate servile relation to the divinity, and his life is construed to be a performance of vicarious leisure directed to the enhancement of his master's repute. In such cases of reversion there is a return to the unmediated relation of subservience, as the dominant fact of the devout attitude. The emphasis is thereby thrown on an austere and discomforting vicarious leisure, to the neglect of conspicuous consumption as a means of grace.

A doubt will present itself as to the full legitimacy of this characterisation of the sacerdotal scheme of life, on the ground that a considerable proportion of the modern priesthood depart from the scheme in many details. The scheme does not hold good for the clergy of those denominations which have in some measure diverged from the old established schedule of beliefs or observances. These take thought, at least ostensibly or permissively, for the temporal welfare of the laity, as well as for their own. Their manner of life, not only in the privacy of their own household, but often even before the public, does not differ in an extreme degree from that of secular-minded persons, either in its ostensible austerity or in the archaism of its apparatus. This is truest for those denominations that have wandered the farthest. To this objection it is to be said that we have here to do not with a discrepancy in the theory of sacerdotal life, but with an imperfect conformity to the scheme on the part of this body of clergy. They are but a partial and imperfect representative of the priesthood, and must not be taken as exhibiting the sacerdotal scheme of life in an authentic and competent manner. The clergy of the sects and denominations might be characterised as a half-caste priesthood, or a priesthood in process of becoming or of reconstitution. Such a priesthood may be expected to show the characteristics of the sacerdotal office only as blended and obscured with alien motives and traditions, due to the disturbing presence of other factors than those of animism and status in the purposes of the organisations to which this non-conforming fraction of the priesthood belongs.

Appeal may be taken direct to the taste of any person with a discriminating and cultivated sense of the sacerdotal proprieties, or to the prevalent sense of what constitutes clerical decorum in any community at all accustomed to think or to pass criticism on what a clergyman may or may not do without blame. Even in the most extremely secularised denominations, there is some sense of a distinction that should be observed between the sacerdotal and the lay scheme of life. There is no person of sensibility but feels that where the members of this denominational or sectarian clergy depart from traditional usage, in the direction of a less austere or less archaic demeanour and apparel, they are departing from the ideal of priestly decorum. There is probably no community and no sect within the range of the Western culture in which the bounds of permissible indulgence are not drawn appreciably closer for the incumbent of the priestly office than for the common layman. If the priest's own sense of sacerdotal propriety does not effectually impose a limit, the prevalent sense of the proprieties on the part of the community will commonly assert itself so obtrusively as to lead to his conformity or his retirement from office.

Few if any members of any body of clergy, it may be added, would avowedly seek an increase of salary for gain's sake; and if such avowal were openly made by a clergyman, it would be found obnoxious to the sense of propriety among his congregation. It may also be noted in this connection that no one but the scoffers and the very obtuse are not instinctively grieved inwardly at a jest from the pulpit; and that there are none whose respect for their pastor does not suffer through any mark of levity on his part in any conjuncture of life, except it be levity of a palpably histrionic kind—a constrained unbending of dignity. The diction proper to the sanctuary and to the priestly office should also carry little if any suggestion of effective everyday life, and should not draw upon the vocabulary of modern trade or industry. Likewise, one's sense of the proprieties is readily offended by too detailed and intimate a handling of industrial and other purely human questions at the hands of the clergy. There is a certain level of generality below which a cultivated sense the proprieties in homiletical discourse will not permit a well-bred clergyman to decline in his discussion of temporal interests. These matters that are of human and secular consequence simply, should properly be handled with such a degree of generality and aloofness as may imply that the speaker represents a master whose interest in secular affairs goes only so far as to permissively countenance them.

It is further to be noticed that the non-conforming sects and variants whose priesthood is here under discussion, vary among themselves in the degree of their conformity to the ideal scheme of sacerdotal life. In a general way it will be found that the divergence in this respect is widest in the case of the relatively young denominations, and especially in the case of such of the newer denominations as have chiefly a lower middle-class constituency. They commonly show a large admixture of humanitarian, philanthropic, or other motives which can not be classed as expressions of the devotional attitude; such as the desire of learning or of conviviality, which enter largely into the effective interest shown by members of these organisations. The non-conforming or sectarian movements have commonly proceeded from a mixture of motives, some of which are at variance with that sense of status on which the priestly office rests. Sometimes, indeed, the motive has been in good part a revulsion against a system of status. Where this is the case the institution of the priesthood has broken down in the transition, at least partially. The spokesman of such an organisation is at the outset a servant and representative of the organisation, rather than a member of a special priestly class and the spokesman of a divine master. And it is only by a process of gradual specialisation that, in succeeding generations, this spokesman regains the position of priest, with a full investiture of sacerdotal authority, and with its accompanying austere, archaic and vicarious manner of life. The like is true of the breakdown and redintegration of devout ritual after such a revulsion. The priestly office, the scheme of sacerdotal life, and the schedule of devout observances are rehabilitated only gradually, insensibly, and with more or less variation in details, as the persistent human sense of devout propriety reasserts its primacy in questions touching the interest in the preternatural,—and, it may be added, as the organisation increases in wealth, and so acquires more of the point of view and the habits of thought of a leisure class.

Beyond the priestly class, and ranged in an ascending hierarchy, ordinarily comes a superhuman vicarious leisure class of saints, angels, etc.,—or their equivalents in the ethnic cults.

These rise in grade, one above another, according to an elaborate system of status. The principle of status runs through the entire hierarchical system, both visible and invisible. The good fame of these several orders of the supernatural hierarchy also commonly requires a certain tribute of vicarious consumption and vicarious leisure. In many cases they accordingly have devoted to their service sub-orders of attendants or dependents who perform a vicarious leisure for them, after much the same fashion as was found in an earlier chapter to be true of the dependent leisure class under the patriarchal system.

It may not appear without reflection how these devout observances and the peculiarity of temperament which they imply, or the consumption of goods and services which is comprised in the cult, stand related to the leisure class of a modern community, or to the economic motives of which that class is exponent in the modern scheme of life. To this end a summary review of certain facts bearing on this relation will be useful.

It appears from an earlier passage in this discussion that for the purpose of the collective life of to-day, especially so far as concerns the industrial efficiency of the modern community, the characteristic traits of the devout temperament are a hindrance rather than a help. It should accordingly be found that the modern industrial life tends selectively to eliminate these traits of human nature from the spiritual constitution of the classes that are immediately engaged in the industrial process. It should hold true, approximately, that devoutness is declining or tending to obsolescence among the members of what may be called the effective industrial community. At the same time it should appear that this aptitude or habit survives in appreciably greater vigour among those classes which do not immediately or primarily enter into the community's life process as an industrial factor.

It has already been pointed out that these latter classes, which live by, rather than in, the industrial process, are roughly comprised under two categories: (1) the leisure class proper, which is shielded from the stress of the economic situation; and (2) the indigent classes, including the lower-class delinquents, which are unduly exposed to the stress. In the case of the former class an archaic habit of mind persists because no effectual economic pressure constrains this class to an adaptation of its habits of thought to the changing situation; while in the latter the reason for a failure to adjust their habits of thought to the altered requirements of industrial efficiency is innutrition, absence of such a surplus of energy as is needed in order to make the adjustment with facility, together with a lack of opportunity to acquire and become habituated to the modern point of view. The trend of the selective process runs in much the same direction in both cases.

From the point of view which the modern industrial life inculcates, phenomena are habitually subsumed under the quantitative relation of mechanical sequence. The indigent classes not only fall short of the modicum of leisure necessary in order to appropriate and assimilate the more recent generalisations of science which this point of view involves, but they also ordinarily stand in such a relation of personal dependence or subservience to their pecuniary superiors as materially to retard their emancipation from habits of thought proper to the régime of status. The result is that these classes in some measure retain that general habit of mind the chief expression of which is a strong sense of personal status, and of which devoutness is one feature.

In the older communities of the European culture, the hereditary leisure class, together with the mass of the indigent population, are given to devout observances in an appreciably higher degree than the average of the industrious middle class, wherever a considerable class of the latter character exists. But in some of these countries, the two categories of conservative humanity named above comprise virtually the whole population. Where these two classes greatly preponderate, their bent shapes popular sentiment to such an extent as to bear down any possible divergent tendency in the inconsiderable middle class, and imposes a devout attitude upon the whole community.

This must, of course, not be construed to say that such communities or such classes as are exceptionally prone to devout observances tend to conform in any exceptional degree to the specifications of any code of morals that we may be accustomed to associate with this or that confession of faith. A large measure of the devout habit of mind need not carry with it a strict observance of the injunctions of the Decalogue or of the common law. Indeed, it is becoming somewhat of a commonplace with observers of criminal life in European communities that the criminal and dissolute classes are, if anything, rather more devout, and more naïvely so, than the average of the population. It is among those who constitute the pecuniary middle class and the body of law-abiding citizens that a relative exemption from the devotional attitude is to be looked for. Those who best appreciate the merits of the higher creeds and observances would object to all this and say that the devoutness of the low-class delinquents is a spurious, or at the best a superstitious devoutness; and the point is no doubt well taken and goes directly and cogently to the purpose intended. But for the purpose of the present inquiry these extra-economic, extra psychological distinctions must perforce be neglected, however valid and however decisive they may be for the purpose for which they are made.

What has actually taken place with regard to class emancipation from the habit of devout observance is shown by the latter-day complaint of the clergy,—that the churches are losing the sympathy of the artisan classes, and are losing their hold upon them. At the same time it is currently believed that the middle class, commonly so called, is also falling away in the cordiality of its support of the church, especially so far as regards the adult male portion of that class. These are currently recognised phenomena, and it might seem that a simple reference to these facts should sufficiently substantiate the general position outlined. Such an appeal to the general phenomena of popular church attendance and church membership may be sufficiently convincing for the proposition here advanced. But it will still be to the purpose to trace in some detail the course of events and the particular forces which have wrought this change in the spiritual attitude of the more advanced industrial communities of to-day. It will serve to illustrate the manner in which economic causes work towards a secularisation of men's habits of thought. In this respect the American community should afford an exceptionally convincing illustration, since this community has been the least trammelled by external circumstances of any equal important industrial aggregate.

After making due allowance for exceptions and sporadic departures from the normal, the situation here at the present time may be summarised quite briefly. As a general rule the classes that are low in economic efficiency, or in intelligence, or both, are peculiarly devout,—as, for instance, the negro population of the South, much of the lower-class foreign population, much of the rural population, especially in those sections which are backward in education, in the stage of development of their industry, or in respect of their industrial contact with the rest of the community. So also such fragments as we possess of a specialised or hereditary indigent class, or of a segregated criminal or dissolute class; although among these latter the devout habit of mind is apt to take the form of a naïve animistic belief in luck and in the efficacy of shamanistic practices perhaps more frequently than it takes the form of a formal adherence to any accredited creed. The artisan class, on the other hand, is notoriously falling away from the accredited anthropomorphic creeds and from all devout observances. This class is in an especial degree exposed to the characteristic intellectual and spiritual stress of modern organised industry, which requires a constant recognition of the undisguised phenomena of impersonal, matter-of-fact sequence and an unreserved conformity to the law of cause and effect. This class is at the same time not underfed nor overworked to such an extent as to leave no margin of energy for the work of adaptation.

The case of the lower or doubtful leisure class in America—the middle class commonly so called—is somewhat peculiar. It differs in respect of its devotional life from its European counterpart, but it differs in degree and method rather than in substance. The churches still have the pecuniary support of this class; although the creeds to which the class adheres with the greatest facility are relatively poor in anthropomorphic content. At the same time the effective middle-class congregation tends, in many cases, more or less remotely perhaps, to become a congregation of women and minors. There is an appreciable lack of devotional fervour among the adult males of the middle class, although to a considerable extent there survives among them a certain complacent, reputable assent to the outlines of the accredited creed under which they were born. Their everyday life is carried on in a more or less close contact with the industrial process.

This peculiar sexual differentiation, which tends to delegate devout observances to the women and their children, is due, at least in part, to the fact that the middle-class women are in great measure a (vicarious) leisure class. The same is true in a less degree of the women of the lower, artisan classes. They live under a régime of status handed down from an earlier stage of industrial development, and thereby they preserve a frame of mind and habits of thought which incline them to an archaic view of things generally. At the same time they stand in no such direct organic relation to the industrial process at large as would tend strongly to break down those habits of thought which, for the modern industrial purpose, are obsolete. That is to say, the peculiar devoutness of women is a particular expression of that conservatism which the women of civilised communities owe, in great measure, to their economic position. For the modern man the patriarchal relation of status is by no means the dominant feature of life; but for the women on the other hand, and for the upper middle-class women especially, confined as they are by prescription and by economic circumstances to their "domestic sphere," this relation is the most real and most formative factor of life. Hence a habit of mind favourable to devout observances and to the interpretation of the facts of life generally in terms of personal status.

The logic, and the logical processes, of her everyday domestic life are carried over into the realm of the supernatural, and the woman finds herself at home and content in a range of ideas which to the man are in great measure alien and imbecile.

Still, the men of this class are also not devoid of piety, although it is commonly not piety of an aggressive or exuberant kind. The men of the upper middle class commonly take a more complacent attitude towards devout observances than the men of the artisan class. This may perhaps be explained in part by saying that what is true of the women of the class is true to a less extent also of the men. They are to an appreciable extent a sheltered class; and the patriarchal relation of status, which still persists in their conjugal life and in their habitual use of servants, may also act to conserve an archaic habit of mind and may exercise a retarding influence upon the process of secularisation which their habits of thought are undergoing. The relations of the American middle-class man to the economic community, however, are usually pretty close and exacting; although it may be remarked, by the way and in qualification, that their economic activity frequently also partakes in some degree of the patriarchal or quasi-predatory character. The occupations which are in good repute among this class, and which have most to do with shaping the class habits of thought, are the pecuniary occupations which have been spoken of in a similar connection in an earlier chapter. There is a good deal of the relation of arbitrary command and submission, and not a little of shrewd practice, remotely akin to predatory fraud. All this belongs on the plane of life of the predatory barbarian, to whom a devotional attitude is habitual. And in addition to this, the devout observances also commend themselves to this class on the ground of reputability. But this latter incentive to piety deserves treatment by itself and will be spoken of presently.

There is no hereditary leisure class of any consequence in the American community, except at the South. This Southern leisure class is somewhat given to devout observances; more so than any class of corresponding pecuniary standing in other parts of the country. It is also well known that the creeds of the South are of a more old-fashioned cast than their counterparts at the North. Corresponding to this more archaic devotional life of the South is the lower industrial development of that section. The industrial organisation of the South is at present, and especially it has been until quite recently, of a more primitive character than that of the American community taken as a whole. It approaches nearer to handicraft, in the paucity and rudeness of its mechanical appliances, and there is more of the element of mastery and subservience. It may also be noted that, owing to the peculiar economic circumstances of this section, the greater devoutness of the Southern population, both white and black, is correlated with a scheme of life which in many ways recalls the barbarian stages of industrial development. Among this population offences of an archaic character also are and have been relatively more prevalent and are less deprecated than they are elsewhere; as, for example, duels, brawls, feuds, drunkenness, horse-racing, cock-fighting, gambling, male sexual incontinence (evidenced by the considerable number of mulattoes). There is also a livelier sense of honour—an expression of sportsmanship and a derivative of predatory life.

As regards the wealthier class of the North, the American leisure class in the best sense of the term, it is, to begin with, scarcely possible to speak of an hereditary devotional attitude. This class is of too recent growth to be possessed of a well-formed transmitted habit in this respect, or even of a special home-grown tradition. Still, it may be noted in passing that there is a perceptible tendency among this class to give in at least a nominal, and apparently something of a real, adherence to some one of the accredited creeds. Also, weddings, funerals, and the like honorific events among this class are pretty uniformly solemnised with some especial degree of religious circumstance. It is impossible to say how far this adherence to a creed is a *bona fide* reversion to a devout habit of mind, and how far it is to be classed as a case of protective mimicry assumed for the purpose of an outward assimilation to canons of reputability borrowed from foreign ideals. Something of a substantial devotional propensity seems to be present, to judge especially by the somewhat peculiar degree of ritualistic observance which is in process of development in the upper-class cults. There is a tendency perceptible among the upper-class worshippers to affiliate themselves with those cults which lay relatively great stress on ceremonial and on the spectacular accessories of worship: and in the churches in which an upper-class membership predominates, there is at the same time a tendency to accentuate the ritualistic, at the cost of the intellectual features in the service and in the apparatus of the devout observances. This holds true even where the church in question belongs to a denomination with a relatively slight general development of ritual and paraphernalia. This peculiar development of the ritualistic element is no doubt due in part to a predilection for conspicuously wasteful spectacles, but it probably also in part indicates something of the devotional attitude of the worshippers. So far as the latter is true, it indicates a relatively archaic form of the devotional habit. The predominance of spectacular effects in devout observances is noticeable in all devout communities at a relatively primitive stage of culture and with a slight intellectual development. It is especially characteristic of the barbarian culture. Here there is pretty uniformly present in the devout observances a direct appeal to the emotions through all the avenues of sense. And a tendency to return to this naïve, sensational method of appeal is unmistakable in the upper-class churches of to-day. It is perceptible in a less degree in the cults which claim the allegiance of the lower leisure class and of the middle classes. There is a reversion to the use of coloured lights and brilliant spectacles, a freer use of symbols, orchestral music and incense, and one may even detect, in "processionals" and "recessionals" and in richly varied genuflexional evolutions, an incipient reversion to so antique an accessory of worship as the sacred dance.

This reversion to spectacular observances is not confined to the upper-class cults, although it finds its best exemplification and its highest accentuation in the higher pecuniary and social altitudes. The cults of the lower-class devout portion of the community, such as the Southern negroes and the backward foreign elements of the population, of course also show a strong inclination to ritual, symbolism, and spectacular effects; as might be expected from the antecedents and the cultural level of those classes. With these classes the prevalence of ritual and anthropomorphism are not so much a matter of reversion as of continued development out of the past. But the use of ritual and related features of devotion are also spreading in other directions. In the early days of the American community the prevailing denominations started out with a ritual and paraphernalia of an austere simplicity; but it is a matter familiar to every one that in the course of time these denominations have, in a varying degree, adopted much of the spectacular elements which they once renounced. In a general way, this development has gone hand in hand with the growth of the wealth and the ease of life of the worshippers and has reached its fullest expression among those classes which grade highest in wealth and repute.

The causes to which this pecuniary stratification of devoutness is due have already been indicated in a general way in speaking of class differences in habits of thought. Class differences as regards devoutness are but a special expression of a generic fact. The lax allegiance of the lower middle class, or what may broadly be called the failure of filial piety among this class, is chiefly perceptible among the town populations engaged in the mechanical industries. In a general way, one does not, at the present time, look for a blameless filial piety among those classes whose employment approaches that of the engineer and the mechanician. These mechanical employments are in a degree a modern fact. The handicraftsmen of earlier times, who served an industrial end of a character similar to that now served by the mechanician, were not similarly refractory under the discipline of devoutness. The habitual activity of the men engaged in these branches of industry has greatly changed, as regards its intellectual discipline, since the modern industrial processes have come into vogue; and the discipline to which the mechanician is exposed in his daily employment affects the methods and standards of his thinking also on topics which lie outside his everyday work. Familiarity with the highly organised and highly impersonal industrial processes of the present acts to derange the animistic habits of thought. The workman's office is becoming more and more exclusively that of discretion and supervision in a process of mechanical, dispassionate sequences. So long as the individual is the chief and typical prime mover in the process; so long as the obtrusive feature of the industrial process is the dexterity and force of the individual handicraftsman; so long the habit of interpreting phenomena in terms of personal motive and propensity suffers no such considerable and consistent derangement through facts as to lead to its elimination. But under the later developed industrial processes, when the prime movers and the contrivances through which they work are of an impersonal, nonindividual character, the grounds of generalisation habitually present in the workman's mind and the point of view from which he habitually apprehends phenomena is an enforced cognisance of matter-of-fact sequence. The result, so far as concerns the workman's life of faith, is a proclivity to undevout scepticism.

It appears, then, that the devout habit of mind attains its best development under a relatively archaic culture; the term "devout" being of course here used in its anthropological sense simply, and not as implying anything with respect to the spiritual attitude so characterised, beyond the fact of a proneness to devout observances. It appears also that this devout attitude marks a type of human nature which is more in consonance with the predatory mode of life than with the later-developed, more consistently and organically industrial life process of the community. It is in large measure an expression of the archaic habitual sense of personal status,—the relation of mastery and subservience,—and it therefore fits into the industrial scheme of the predatory and the quasi-peaceable culture, but does not fit into the industrial scheme of the present. It also appears that this habit persists with greatest tenacity among those classes in the modern communities whose everyday life is most remote from the mechanical processes of industry and which are the most conservative also in other respects; while for those classes that are habitually in immediate contact with modern industrial processes, and whose habits of thought are therefore exposed to the constraining force of technological necessities, that animistic interpretation of phenomena and that respect of persons on which devout observance proceeds are in process of obsolescence. And also—as bearing especially on the present discussion—it appears that the devout habit to some extent progressively gains in scope and elaboration among those classes in the modern communities to whom wealth and leisure accrue in the most pronounced degree. In this as in other relations, the institution of a leisure class acts to conserve, and even to rehabilitate, that archaic type of human nature and those elements of the archaic culture which the industrial evolution of society in its later stages acts to eliminate.

7. LOUISE IMOGEN GUINEY

*Homeland Poverty**

Louise Imogen Guiney was born on January 7, 1861 in Roxbury, a suburb of Boston. Her father was a native of County Tipperary in Ireland who had prospered as a lawyer in the New World. Wounds in the Civil War permanently shattered his health; and he died at the age of forty-two in 1877, but not before a strong attachment had developed between him and his adolescent daughter.

Louise attended a convent school from which she graduated at the age of eighteen. Bookish and a pious Catholic who was never to marry, she found no obvious career open to her in Boston, a community in which she stood apart from both the dominant Brahmin group and the mass of immigrant laborers. She supported herself by hack writing and research and then attracted some attention by a book of verses in 1884. Thereafter minor jobs in the postoffice and in the Boston Public Library brought her the modest income that permitted her to continue her writing.

The story here reprinted is one of the very few pieces of writing in which she touched upon the experience of her own group. Her "country of the mind" was cavalier England, remote, romantic and detached from the world about her. In 1901, she fulfilled a long-standing ambition when she moved to England and settled in Oxford where she lived in decent poverty until her death in 1920.

* Louise Imogen Guiney, "The Provider," *Lovers' Saint Ruth and Three Other Tales* (Boston, 1895), pp. 93–123.

THE PROVIDER

Nora cried out: "'Tis so pretty today!" The barefooted children were threading the slopes of Howth towards Raheny. Far-off, the city, with its lights and stretches of glorified evening water, was lying there lovely enough between the mountains and the sea. It was Nora's tenth birthday, and, to please her, they had been on the march all afternoon, their arms full of rock-born speedwell and primrose. " 'Tis so pretty!" echoed little Winny, with enthusiasm. But the boy looked abroad without a smile. "'T'd be prettier when things is right," he answered severely. Hughey was a man of culture; but his speech was the soft slipshod of the south. The three trudged on in silence, for Hughey was a personage to his small sisters; and Hughey in a mood was to be respected. He, alas, had been in a mood too long. He had carried Winny over the roughest places, and shown her Ireland's Eye, and, alongshore, the fishing-nets and trawls; he had given his one biscuit to be shared between them all; and lying in the velvet sward by the Druid stone, he had told them all he knew of the fairy-folk in their raths, for the seventieth time. But he was full of sad and bitter brooding the while, thinking of his mother, his poor mother, his precious mother, working too hard at home, for whom there never seemed to be any birthdays or out-of-door pleasures.

Hugh was nearly twelve now, and mature as the eldest child must always be among the poor. He could remember times in the county Wexford, before his father, who was of kin to half the gentry in the countryside, died; times when life had a very different outlook, and when his peasant mother, with short skirts and her sleeves rolled up, would go gayly between her great stone-flagged kitchen and the well or the turkey-hen's nest under the blackthorn hedge, singing, singing, like a lark. They had to leave that pleasant farm, and the thatched roof which had sheltered them from their fate, and move up to cloudier Dublin, to a stifling garret over a beer-shop; and it was a miserable change. Malachi O'Kinsella, the cheerful thriftless man, with his handsome bearing and his superfluous oratory, was gone; and his Hughey was too young to be of service to those he left behind. A fine monument, with *Glory be to God* on it, had to be put up over him in the old churchyard, two years ago; and there had been since the problem of schooling, feeding, and clothing Hughey, Nora, and Winny. Then Rose, three years old, fell into a lime-kiln, and was associated with the enforced luxury of a second funeral; and Dan, the baby, born after his father's death, was sickly, and therefore costly too; and now the rent had to be paid, and the morrow thought of, on just nothing a week! All of which this Hugh, with his acumen and quick sympathy, had found out. He worshipped his mother, in his shy, abstinent Irish way; his heart was bursting for her sake, though he but half knew it, with a sense of the mystery and wrong-headedness of human society.

That April Tuesday night, when the wildflowers were in a big earthen basin on the table, like streaks of moonlight and moon-shadow, and the girls were in bed, Hughey blew out his candle, shut up his penny *Gulliver*, and went over to the low chair in their one room, where his mother was crooning Dan to sleep on her breast. It shocked him to see how thin she was. Her age was but three-and-thirty; but it might have been fifty. She wore a faded black gown, of decent aspect once in a village pew; her thick eyelashes were burning wet. Outside and far below, were the polluted narrow cross-streets, full of flaring torches, and hucksters' hand-carts, and drunken voices; and beyond, loomed the Gothic bulk of Saint Patrick's, not a star above it.

"Mother! 't is not going to school any more Oi'll be." His tired, unselfish mother swallowed a great sigh, but said nothing. "Oi'll worruk for ye, mother; Oi'll be your man. Oi can do 't."

There was another and a longer pause; and then Moira O'Kinsella suddenly bent forward and kissed her first-born. Like all the unlettered class in Ireland, she adored learning from afar, and coveted it for her offspring. That he should give up his hope of "talkin' Latin" touched her to the quick. "God love ye, Hughey darlint! Phwat can a little bhoy do?" But she slept a happier woman for her knight's vow.

As for Hughey, there was no sleep for him. By the first white light he could see the two pathetic pinched profiles side by side, the woman's and the babe's, both set in the same startling flat oval of dark locks. The faces on the mattress yonder were so round and ruddy! They had not begun to think, as Hughey had; even scant dinners and no warmth in winter had not blighted one rose as yet in those country cheeks. Up to yesterday, he had somehow found his mother's plight bearable, thanks to the natural buoyancy of childhood, and the hope, springing up every week, that next week she would have a little less labor, a few more pence. Besides, it was spring; and in spring hearts have an irrational way of dancing, as if a fairy fiddler had struck up *Garryowen.* But now Hughey was sobered and desperate.

There was no breakfast but a crust apiece. The McCarthy grandmother, on the stairs, gave Nora, starting for school, some fresh water-cresses. Just then Mrs. O'Kinsella happened to open the door. Poor Nora had yielded to temptation and filled her mouth, and pretended, holding her head down, to be much concerned about a bruise on her knee. She could not look in her mother's honest eyes, ignorant as these were of any blame in Nora. Mrs. O'Kinsella went wearily to her charing, and seven-year-old Winny set up housekeeping with Dan, the primroses and a teapot-shaped fish-bone for their only toys. Hughey had already gone, nor was he at his desk in the afternoon, when his teacher and Nora looked vainly for him; nor did he return to his lodgings until after sundown. When he came, he brought milk with him, earned by holding a gentleman's horse at the Rotunda; and with that and some boiled potatoes, there was a feast. Hughey's vocation, it would appear, had not yet declared itself. He had haunted Stephen's Green and its sumptuous purlieus in vain. He had not been asked to join partners with Messrs. Pim, nor to accept a

Fellowship at Trinity. The next day's, the next month's history was no more heroic. There were so many of those bright, delicate-featured, ragged-shirted boys in Dublin, coming about on foggy mornings with propositions! The stout shopkeepers were sated with the spectacle of the unable and willing.

The days dragged. An affable policeman who had known Hughey's mother at home in New Ross, seeing him once gazing in a junk-shop door, finally presented him to the proprietor: "Toby, allow me t' inthroduce a good lad wants a dhrive at glory. Can ye tache um the Black Art, now? He can turrun his hand to most anythin', and his pomes, Oi hear, do be grand, for his age."

The junk-man, good-naturedly scanning Hughey, saw him burst into tears, and beat the air, though the giant of the law had passed on. That his chief and most secret sin should be mentioned aloud, to prejudice the world of commerce against him, was horrible. His mother had told on him! She must have found some lines on Winny's slate last Sunday, entitled *Drumalough: a Lament for the Fall of the Three Kings, Written at Midnight.* Worra, worra! Hughey was descended, on the paternal side, through a succession of ever-falling fortunes, from a good many more than three kings, and used to wonder where their crowns and sceptres were, not that he might pawn them, either. The O'Kinsellas were a powerful aboriginal sept in the old days, and lived in fortress castles, and playfully carried off cattle and ladies from their neighbors of the Pale. Malachi O'Kinsella's mother, a heroine of romance who ran away with a jockey lover, and never throve after, was of pure Norman blood, and most beautiful, with gray eyes, water-clear, like Hughey's own, and the same bronze-colored hair; and it was said she could play the harp that soft it would draw the hearing out of your head with ecstasy! Now the junk-man was fatherly, and presented Hughey, in default of a situation, with a consolatory coin; but foregoing events had been too trying for the boy's nerves: he dropped it, and fled, sobbing. He simply couldn't live where his po'try was going to rise up against him, and wail like a Banshee in the public ear. He charged, in his wrath and grief, across the crowded bridge, and down the line of quays east of it, straight into a fat, gray-headed, leather-aproned person directing a group of sailors unloading a boat.

This person, sent of Heaven with miraculous suddenness, and with musical distinctness, exclaimed: "'Aven't I been a-wishin' of 'im, and directly 'e runs into me harms! Crawl into that barrel, sonny, and if you 'old it steady, I'll 'eave you tuppence." Hughey, foreordained likewise, crawled in. When he came out, Mr. J. Everard Hoggett looked him over, from his moribund hat to his slight patrician ankle. "I likes a boy wot's 'andy, and 'as little to sy, like you." He resumed critically, "'E don't appear to be from any of 'Er Marjesty's carstles, 'e don't. Perhaps 'e might like to 'ang about 'ere, and earn three bob a week?" Hughey hugged his twopenny piece, blushed, trembled, twisted his legs in the brown trousers too big for him, and replied in gulps: "O sir! Yes, sir." Whereby his annals begin.

This perfectly amazing luck befell towards the end of May. Mr. Hoggett, going home, beckoned him, took him into a little eating-house, sat him down, paid for a huge order, and departed. "There's a couple o' lion cubs hinside wot ought to be your westcot, needs 'am and heggs. Fill 'em full; and mind you come to-morrow at a quarter to ight. I'll 'ave no lyzy lubbers alongside o' me." With which fierce farewell, and disdaining thanks, Mr. Hoggett faded wholly away.

Hughey, half-dazed, sat at a table alone, sniffing celestial fragrances from the rear, with the joy in his breast jumping like a live creature in a box. To quiet it, while he waited, he took up a torn journal which was lying on the nearest chair. At first, what he read seemed to have no meaning, but when some moments had passed, still odorous only, and non-flavorous, Hughey's collected and intelligent eye had taken in the dramatic political crisis, the stocks, the African news, the prospects of Irish literature, and the latest London wife-beating. On the advertisement page, one especial paragraph in sensational print rooted his attention. This was it:—

"SERVANTS AND APPRENTICES, ATTENTION! Here is the best Chance of your lives. It will Never come again. *Trade with us, and you lay the* FOUNDATION *of your* FORTUNE! With every sixpenny worth of goods bought of us on any Saturday night, we give a COUPON on the Ninth anti-Sassenach Bank of Belfast. *Fifty of these* entitle the Bearer at the end of the year to a gift of TEN POUNDS IN GOLD! ! Honesty the best Policy our motto. Best Material at Lowest Prices; come and see. *Do not Neglect your own* GOOD. McClutch & Gullim, Linendrapers, No. 19—— ——— St."

Hughey, the innocent prospective capitalist, took a stubby pencil from the only sound pocket in his habiliments, and began to figure on the margin of the paper; for he had an inspiration. "Mother would be thundherin' rich!" was what flashed into his mind. Before he had done with his emergency arithmetic, ham and eggs, with all their shining train, were set before him. With them, he gallantly swallowed his conscience, for Hughey, like a nobler Roman before him, was resolving to be gloriously false, and, for piety's sake, to trade his soul. He foresaw vaguely that he would not be allowed, out of his royal wages of three shillings, to spend full half every Saturday night, at McClutch and Gullim's; yet to do it was the imperative thing now, and that he felt impelled to do it was his own super-private business, and his warrant. Therefore would he keep his secret close, and make what excuse he might. He could not even think of asking advice; how should any one else be able to realize how he must act towards his mother? The angels had given her into his hands; and he knew at last what was to be done for her. She should be rich and gay, and have a coach, perhaps, like a real lady; and Danny should have a goat, and a sash with stripes in it, like the little twin Finnegans; and the Misses Honora and Winifrid O'Kinsella should walk abroad with parasols! Proper manœuvring now would fetch twenty-five pounds sterling next summer. But he would hide away what he bought, and never tell until the beatific hour when his mother should have the money, and the linen, and the truth about them, all together!

Hughey went home in a series of hops and whirls, like a kitten's. He brought a flood of riotous sunshine in with him. It was supper-time; the children had each a ha-penny bun, and some tea. Mrs. O'Kinsella was lying down, with an ache between her lungs and her spine, after a long day's lifting and scrubbing. She felt the good news, before the child spoke. "O mother! 't is the most illigant thing's happened: ye never heard the loike." Hughey's pale comely little face was radiant.

"Phwhere is ut, and phwhat d' ye get, dear?" Then Hughey screwed up his courage, and told his only, his masterly lie: "North Wall, mother; and a shillin' and six every week." "A shillin' and six!" shrieked Nora. "O Hughey!" But the critic for whose opinion he cared was not quite so enraptured. She smiled, and praised him, but took it too tamely, her son thought. However, he reflected that she little knew the felicities in store.

In the morning, his career began, and it maintained itself with vigor, inasmuch as by the autumn he was of real value to his employers. He had many duties and some trusts. His orders all came directly from the benevolent bluff Mr. Hoggett, or from his mild reflection and under-study, a small, bald, capable headclerk from the north, who was known as Jibtopsails; for what reason, Hughey could never divine, unless it was that his ears were uncommonly large and flapping. Jibtopsails sent him here and there with parcels and messages, and he had been faithful; he had made no grave mistake yet, nor had he been unpunctual. But every Saturday of his life saw him posing as a purchaser at 19— —— Street, where a hard-featured old woman, supposed mother of the supposed junior partner, served him always with the same ironically deferent, "Good day, sir; and what can I show you?" Jibtopsails inquired occasionally after the health of Hughey's family, particularly after Hughey had told him that Mrs. O'Kinsella was not so well as she used to be. For the rest, the sympathy of that gentle cynic made the child's blood run cold: he had such a paralyzing fear that Jibtopsails might call there at the house, and talk to his mother, and say something about three shillings a week! Kind people in the parish, if they knew, would bring her in wood, and coal, and wine; but again, in the hallucination of his jealous determined heart, the boy prayed passionately that they might not know, and that he alone should be the deliverer. The dread of his secret being found out, little by little made his life intolerable. He had grown older since he had that to cherish in his bosom, and it seemed less delicious than while as yet it was nothing but a dream.

His mother broke down, and could toil no longer. Mrs. Drogan, who lived downstairs, began to come up with her mending, and sit between the bed and the window. Nora was clever, for so young a girl; but she stumbled a great deal in her roomy charity boots, and had to be scolded for awkwardness by Mrs. Drogan, who had brought up sixteen rebels, and was disposed to command. As for Winny and Dan, they made a noise, and therefore had to be exiled to the street, foul and dangerous as it was, almost all day, while the invalid slept the sleep of utter exhaustion. It occurred often to Hughey, and with increasing force, that to secure a future good, he was doing a very vicious wrong; that it would be far better for his mother to have the money now, to provide comforts and make her well, than for her to do without it now, and be too feeble in consequence to enjoy it when it would come, all in a lump. Heavy and sharp was this dilemma to the little fellow, as he labelled the great bales, or set Mr. Hoggett's dusted ledgers back on their shelves. "Phwhat ought I be doin'?" he would groan aloud, when he was alone. If he confessed to his mother, and handed over hereafter the total of his wages, there was an end to the big income sprouting and budding wondrously at Belfast, the income which would be hers yet, with ever so little patience. But if he should not confess, and, meanwhile, if she should not recover,—what would all the world's wealth be then to poor Hughey?

October was damp and dispiriting; Mrs. O'Kinsella coughed more, but apparently suffered little. Hughey still brought her, week by week, his pittance of a shilling and sixpence. Ill as she was, her alert instinct divined that something ailed him; she pitied him, and worried about him, and kissed his tears away with a blessing, very often. Doctor Nugent was called in for the first time, one rainy noon. He told Mrs. Drogan, laconically, that his patient was going to die, and stopped her gesture of remonstrance. "Say nothing to those children of hers," he added, aside, on the threshold; "there is no immediate need of it, and the eldest looks melancholy enough without it."

But the eldest was at his elbow. With a still ardor painful to see, he raised himself close to the tall doctor, and whispered into his ear. "Phwhat wud save me mother? Wudn't money do it, MONEY?" The boy looked so thrilling, impressively earnest that the doctor rose to the occasion. "Perhaps! That is, a winter in France or Italy might delay the end. But dear me! how on earth—" His voice wavered, and he hurried down.

On the way back to the office, Hughey crossed Augier Street, and stalked into McClutch and Gullim's. He had business with the old woman, imminent business. Would the Ninth anti-Sassenach Bank of Belfast advance half of an annual interest? that is, would they allow him, Hugh O'Kinsella of Dublin, merchant's errand-boy, what was due on his receipts of purchases up to date? He found that circumstances over which he had no control prevented his waiting until May: please might he draw out the eleven odd pounds now? The old woman had recently had other queries of that nature, which proved that the victims were getting restless; that it would soon be advisable, in short, to strike camp, and betake herself and her nefarious concerns to Leeds or Manchester. Her sourness vented itself promptly on Hughey. Decidedly, the Ninth anti-Sassenach bank would do nothing of the sort; it was against the rules; it never advanced cash except in case of death, when coupons from McClutch and Gullim's would hold good for a life-insurance policy to the corpse's relatives. "And now g'long to the divil wid ye, ye limb!" concluded Mrs. Gullim, in a burst of vernacular indignation.

Hughey fairly reeled out to the pavement, with wheels humming in his brain, and a large triangular rock, sharper than knives and smeared with poison (a not unfamiliar rock, of late), lodged in the middle of his throat. As he turned down the windy North Wall, among the sleek cattle waiting for exportation, and pushed open the warehouse door by the Liffey, Jibtopsails took his pen from behind his capacious ear, and peered over his spectacles.

"*Cead mille failthe, Brian Boruihme!* and how is the royal fam——." He got no further; the young face opposite was so awry with the spirit's mortal anguish that Jibtopsails was truly sorry he had tried to be jocose. It was almost a first offence.

And now, with much introspection, and heart-searching, and resolve, Hughey's tragedy gathered itself together. On Sunday, after church, he had occasion to go out of town. As he wished to deal with Nora, he offered to give her a ride on the tram: a species of entertainment which she accepted with enthusiasm. When they were at the end of their route, they set forth on foot, up-hill, over two miles of exquisite moorland, to the house of the retired first mate of the Grace Greeley, who was summoned by the firm of Hoggett as witness in a lawsuit. Nora was in her usual spirits, and her brother tried to wait until they should show signs of flagging. O the heavenly freedom of the country! the pleasant smell of damp leaves! But Hughey's heart would not rise. As they passed the sheep-folds, the pretty huddled creatures made Nora laugh, standing still, agape, in her blue faded frock; and he grabbed her roughly by the arm, albeit his sad forbearing tone was not rough.

"D'ye love me at all, Nora?"

"That Oi do, Hughey O'Kinsella; and ye needn't be scrunchin' of me to foind ut out."

"Nora!"

"Phwhat is ut?"

"There's somethin' Oi do be bound to say to ye." A pause.

"Can ye keep a secret?"

"Shure, Oi can."

"'Tis turrible."

"Niver ye moind, Oi'll keep ut!" said the loyal other.

Hughey lifted his face to the sweet blowy autumn afternoon, took breath, and increased his pace. "Mother is loike to be doyin' soon. Maybe ye didn't hear o' that. But she cud live a hunderd year if ut wasn't so cruel poor we are. Oi've been a-thinkin' wan reason of ut is she has too many childher. 'Tis good little Rosy is with the saints. Childher all eats and wears clothes, and isn't much use. If mother wasn't ill, there'd be nothin' the matther wid me; we cud go on along, and Oi'd have power to do the beautiful things, Nora dear. Ye'd all be proud as paycocks o' me whin next the cuckoo'll be in the green bush down be the Barrow; only mother wud be undher the ground. So 't is long before that Oi must be doin' phwhat Oi'm meanin' to do. Now's the toime for her to be cured, and the toime for me to behave the usefullest to her is to-morrow, just afther Oi'm dead."

The younger child was bewildered, over-awed. "May the Lorrud have mercy upon your sowl, Hughey!" she murmured with vague solemnity, taking in the legendary word "dead" and nothing else. Her light feet ran unevenly beside his, up the slope and down the hollow, and over stiles and pasture-walls, bright with their withering vines. She was all ear when her brother began again, irrelevantly and more softly, on his tremendous theme, so old now to his thoughts that he was conscious of no solecism in the abrupt utterance of it. "Whin ye dhrown, ye niver look bad at a wake. A man kilt in the battle looks bad, but not a dhrowned man. 'T is grand to be a marthyr to your counthry; howsomiver, the guns is n't convanient, and Oi must hould to the wather. The rest Oi can't tell, becaze ye're a woman, and wud n't undhersthand; but there's pounds and pince in ut, and 't is the foine thing intoirely for mother." He turned upon her his most searching gaze. "Ye'll be constant and koind to her, now? Ye'll be runnin' and bringin' her a chair, and takin' the beef out o' your mouth for her as long as ye live? (Shure Oi forgot there's goin' to be tons o' beef for yez all.) Promus me, Nora." She looked at him, and her wide blue eyes filled; and presently she sank down all in a heap, her face in the grass, her heels in the air. It looked like revolt; but it was regret, or rather the utter helplessness of either. The boy never flinched. "Promus me, Nora." "Oh, Oi do, brother Hughey, Oi do!" she sobbed. He stood by her a moment, then with firmness followed the path out of sight, his slender withdrawing figure significant against the sky.

When he came back, the anxious Nora was on the road, whence she could see far and wide. Little was said as they returned home, through ways thickening with cabs and passers-by. But skirting Dean Swift's dark Cathedral, they heard the treble voices at evensong in the choir, and the grave sweetness of Tallis' old music seemed to thaw Hughey's blood. He drew his sister closer as they walked, and bent his curls over her. He had received a fresh illumination since he spoke last.

"You're what mother needs," he whispered, "and so's Dan, seein' he's no bigger than a fairy. But Oi'd be betther away, and so'd Winny, for the sake o' leavin' plenthy to eat and plenthy o' room. Ye'll give me Winny in her little coat whin Oi ax ye to-noight, will ye, Nora?" The child glanced up mournfully at her ruling genius, without a word, but with a look of supernatural submission. They went up the rickety stairs, arm in arm.

Mrs. O'Kinsella, who had had a trying day, had just said to Mrs. Drogan, rising with a view to supper for her husband: "Oi'm of that moind meself. Johanna Carr 'd be a widdy contint in her ould age, if she'd had childher, if she'd had a son loike Hughey. Me blessid darlint! he's gould an' dimonds. By the grace o' God Almighty, Oi cud bow me head if He tuk the rest away from me, but He cudn't part me and the bhoy, me and the bhoy." She began to cough again.

Her son asked to sit up late. "Oi'd be writin', mother," he pleaded. Her pride in him came to her poor thin cheeks. "'Tis a Bard ye'll be yet, loike the wans your father read about in the histhory!" Hughey knew he had been misunderstood; but trifles were trifles, and must be ignored, now that the hour of action had struck.

Having taken off his shoes, he sat down in the broken chair by the table, with his pencil, and the paper which Jibtopsails had given him. The inmates of the room were all unconscious in half an hour, except himself and Nora. She, in a fever of excitement, kept vigil, lying as usual since consumption had come openly under their roof, between Winny and the baby.

Winny, dirty, hungry, and tired out with dancing to a hurdy-gurdy, had fallen asleep in her clothes. Nora did not require her to undress. These were the three letters which Hughey wrote.

Mr. Everard Hoggett, Limited.

DEAR SIR: Thank you for being kind to me. I was fond of you. I hope you won't be out of a boy long. There do be a very honest boy named Mickey McGooley goes to my school I used to go to. He has a iron foot, but he is good-looking in the rest of him. I think he would come if you asked him. Please tell the other gentilmen I won't forget him either.

Your respeckful friend,

HUGH.

Ninth Anti-Sassenach Bank, Belfast, Ireland.

SIR: My mother she is named Mrs. M. O'Kinsella, will send you the papers from McClutch and Gullim. As I will be dead you pay my money please to her. I let you know now so that it will be all rite. It began last May 28th and stops Saturday, October 21st. Yours truly, hoping you will send it soon,

Yours,

H. O'KINSELLA.

11 — ST., DUBLIN.
October 22nd, 1893.

DEAR MOTHER: You must cheer up and not cough. You can go to France or somewhere. You will find a heap of lengths of linen stuff in a box under the steps of old Tom's shop. He does n't know about it. It is mine and the nicest they is, and if you don't be wanting it, you can sell it. Then you look in the lining of Danny's cap, and find some bank papers, and you send them to the Ninth anti-Sassenach Bank in Belfast and it will send you nigh twelve pound gold. You will find Winny and me by Richmond Bridge, and it will not be so expencive without us. I hope you won't be low for me, for Nora says she will be good. Dear mother, I dident know any other way to make you happy and well at this present. Goodbye from your loving son,

HUGH CORMAC FITZEUSTACE LE POER O'KINSELLA.

After that laborious signature, he folded and addressed the first two sheets, and after a plunge into the recesses of his pocket, stamped them. The last one he slipped beneath his mother's pillow. He looked at her wistfully, lying there on the brink of all compensation, at last! She turned over, and sighed feebly: "Go to bed, Hughey dear." He did not dare to kiss her, for fear she should become wide awake. Back into the shadow he shrank, and so remained a long time. A dim sense of defeat stole over him, like a draught through a crack, from a wind which pushes vainly without. But he had never in his life hugged any thought whose interest centred in himself, and immediately his whole being warmed again with the remembrance that his defeat meant victory for a life dearer to him than his own. When the great bell outside had struck two, he crept across the room.

"Is she ready, Nora?"

"She is, Hughey."

He stooped to the floor, and gathered the drowsy body in his arms. On the landing, one floor below, the little sister cried aloud. "No, no, no, no!" he crooned, in a passion of apprehension: "Brother will show Winny the bright moon."

They came safely to the street; the moon indeed was there, flooding the world with splendor. When Nora had buttoned Winny's coat, and the boy had posted his letters, they took her by either hand, and started.

Hughey had planned out his difficult campaign to the end, and his brain was quiet and clear. Passing through Church Street, he raised his hat with reverence, as he had always done since he came to Dublin, to a blank stone on the south side in the ancient yard of Saint Michan's; for under that stone, according to a tradition, Robert Emmett's sentinel dust reposes. There on the old Danish ground, at the crisis, Winny's fiery Gaelic temper came again to the fore. Struck with the solitude and the dark, the dread faces of unusual things, and jostled by the wind which pounced at her from its corner lair on the north bank of the river, she hung back and rebelled. "Let me go, let me—go! Hughey! Oh! . . ." The little silver lisp arose in very real, in irresistible alarm.

Never once, in all his mistaken planning, had Hughey paused to consider that she had a voice in the matter. If she were unwilling to die for his dearest, why, what right had he, Hughey, though scornful and disappointed because of it, to compel her? After all, she was only seven, and silly! He looked at Nora over the capped head between them. Then he fetched a deep, deep sigh, and the tears came to his eyelids, burned, and dried.

They went on, ever slower; and at Richmond Bridge Hughey spoke to Winny, as he felt that he could do at last, tenderly, and even with humorous understanding. "Now 't is the end o' your walk, an' ye'll trot home wid Nora, and niver moind me at all, dear. Some day she'll be tellin' ye phwhat ye missed." But to Nora herself he said softly:

"Take care o' mother, mavourneen."

"Oi will, Hughey."

She kissed him twice; her smooth cheek against his was cold as a shell. He made a gesture of dismissal, which she did not disobey; and he watched them go, without further sign. The two childish figures were swallowed by the blue-black shadows, and the pavement under their naked feet gave forth no receding sounds. Yet Hughey, bereft of them so quickly and utterly, listened, listened, tiptoeing to the central arch of the bridge.

The autumnal Sabbath breath of the slumbering capital floated in a faint white mist against the brick and stone. Every high point was alive with light: the masts in port, the roof of the King's Inns, the Park, the top of the Nelson monument, the Castle standard, the nigh summits of the gracious Wicklow hills. Below were the dim line of Liffey bridges, processional to the sea, and the sad friendly wash of the chilly water. Clear of any regret or self-pity, he would have his farewell grave and calm, and he would set out with the sigh of faith. So he knelt down, in prayer, for a moment, and with his eyes still closed, dropped forward.

In another eternal instant, he came into the air. He had a confused sense of being glad for Winny, and otherwise quite satisfied and thankful. There, next the wall, was a rotten abandoned raft, a chance of life within clutch; he saw it, and smiled. Then Hughey sank, and the black ebb-tide took him.

Nora's knowledge, meanwhile, was too torturing to be borne. No sooner had she left her brother than she caught the heavy little one into her slight arms, and ran. Breathless, and choked with sorrow, she told her mother all she knew, and roused the Drogans, who in turn called up the Smiths, the Fays, the Holahans, the McCarthys. From right and left the neighbors swarmed forth on a vain and too familiar trail: the Spirit of Poverty flying unmercifully ever to the rescue of her own, she

—"that would upon the rack of this rough world Stretch them out longer."

* * * * * * *

Two of Hughey's letters had to go undelivered: one belonging to a corporation which never existed, and one to a heartbroken woman who set sail for the Isles of Healing, before the dawn.

THE END.

8. FINLEY PETER DUNNE

*Observations by Mr. Dooley**

Finley Peter Dunne was born in Chicago in 1867, the son of comfortably situated Irish parents. After graduation from high school, he became a police and sports reporter, then moved on to feature and editorial writing. At the age of twenty-one, he was City Editor of the Chicago Times, after which he shifted among the other newspapers of the city. In 1892 he made his first effort at social commentary, coated with the humor of Irish dialect. His essays in the press and collected in books were widely read. Through the jocular phrases of Mr. Dooley, he expressed a compassionate, liberal view of the problems of his society. After the turn of the century, he moved to New York and, in 1906, joined Lincoln Steffens, Ida Tarbell, Ray Stannard Baker, and William A. White as editor of the American Magazine. *He died in 1936.*

THE IRISH QUESTION

"They was gr-reat ructions in th' House iv Commons th' other day," said Mr. Dooley.

"What about?" asked Mr. Hennessy.

"About our downthrodden land," said Mr. Dooley. "Not this wan, but that little green imrald island iv th' opprissed acrost th' sea. I can't make out what 'twas all about, on'y wan iv th' good lads ast th' Right Hon'rable Arthur James Balfour, a long-legged Scotchman with side whiskers, wud he or wud he not give a day to th' discussion iv th' state iv Ire-

* Finley Peter Dunne, *Dissertations* (New York, 1906), pp. 129–34, and *Observations* (New York, 1902), pp. 49–54.

land. He wud not, says th' Right Hon'rable Arthur James Balfour. Divvle th' day. 'Well, thin,' says th' good fellow with th' fine name iv O'Donnell, 'seein' that I can get no justice f'r me beloved counthry, I will, with th' kind permission iv th' Speaker, an' not angrily, but in a sperit iv parlyminthry propriety, step acrost th' hall, makin' a ginyflixion to th' Speaker on th' way over, shake me fist in ye'er face thus, an' lave th' room,' he says. An' he done it. Th' ol' oak hall iv Westminsther sildom has witnessed such a scene, but manny like it. Th' air was filled with cries iv 'Shame,' 'Splindid,' 'O'Donnell aboo,'' while the' Right Hon'rable Arthur James Balfour set in his chair, his face livid, but smilin', th' Speaker tugged narvously at his overskirt an' felt iv his frizzes, an' siveral iv th' more violent mimbers iv th' Irish party took off their hats an' put thim on again in token iv their rage. It was some minyits befure th' House raysumed its nap. Thus was another Irish riv'lution brought to a successful con-clusion.

" 'Twas a g-reat day f'r th' race, Hinnissy. I thought, whin I begun to read th' pa-aper an' see th' name O'Donnell: 'Well, here's where the Right Hon'rable Arthur James Balfour gets a good smack in th' eye.' They're a fightin' breed, th' O'Donnells, though niver a match f'r us, an' no mimber iv th' fam'ly that I iver knew cud get his fist within an inch iv a man's nose without lavin' it go two inches further. Says I to mesilf: 'Go it, O'Donnell, me boy. Eight to wan on ye.' But no! Ne'er a blow was sthruck. Th' race iv O'Donnells has changed. They're no longer th' burly boys with th' pike an' th' scythe. They're f'r riv'lution, but don't upset the tay-things. They no more attimpt to catch th' Speaker's eye with th' thumb. They're in favor iv freein' Ireland, but with th' permission iv th' comity on rules. It's right, too, Hinnissy. I'm opposed to vilence in anny form. We must be pathrites, but we must first iv all be gintlemen. Afther ye, me dear Alphonse.

"But whin I come to think iv it, I guess p'raps I'm wrong. Ye can't be a rivolutionist in a silk hat an' a long coat. Riv'lution is wurruk f'r th' shirtsleeves. A riv'lution can't be bound be th' rules iv the game because it's again' th' rules iv th' game. Put away th' tall hat, niver mind th' cups an' saucers, tell ma to pack up her things, an' take th' girls off to her mother's. Pah an' th' boys ar-re goin' to have a riv'lution.

"Th' Irish wud have no throuble with th' English if th' English were Irish. Th' trouble with Englishmen governin' Ireland is that they're English. An Englishman niver gets to know an Irishman. They don't speak th' same language. An Englishman can understand a German, a Turk, a Chinyman, a naygur, or an Indyan, but he don't know anny more what an Irishman is talkin' an' thinkin' about thin what th' angels in Hiven ar-re sayin'. What's th' use iv con-varsin' with him? Give him a belt in th' jaw. That's a language so gin'rally undhershtud that ye niver need a pocket ditchnry to make it out. An Irishman is always dhreamin' dhreams. If ye cud get into th' mind iv a hungry Irishman an' a hungry Englishman ye'd find th' Irishman was thinkin' about a banket iv th' gods with him in seat number wan singin' a song, an' th' Englishman was reflictin' on th' smell iv th' thripe down th' sthreet.

"An Englishman don't know they'se anny such things as wrongs in th' wurruld. He sets down in front iv his dinner an' says he to himsilf: 'What a jolly wurruld this is! What an awf'lly beastly jolly wurruld! Ivrybody is happy. Annybody that kicks does it f'r exercise. I can't see a spot where th' wurruld needs improvemint. It's such a complete job I must have done it mesilf. Very civil iv me. What th' doose is that man over there spoutin' pothry about? He's a loonytick. Put him out. Why, he's pintin' a gun at me. Well, p'raps I'd betther listen to him.'

"Mind ye, Hinnissy, I ain't in favor iv dinnymite. Far fr'm it. Even an Englishman was niver improved be bein' blown up. Or I'll put it this way: I'm in favor iv dinnymite, but not in favor iv its goin' off. They always ought to be a little iv it undher an Englishman's chair. Thin we cud go up to him an' say: 'Things is goin' badly in Ireland, an' somethin' must be done. Plaze to sign this pa-aper an' redhress our wrongs.' 'Wrongs?' says he. 'What ar-re wrongs?' he says. 'It wud take too long to explain,' says me. 'We will on'y say they'se a bunch iv joynt powdher undher ye'er chair that may go off anny minyit. Sign here.'

"I ain't a Feenyan, d'ye mind, though I was, an' I ain't a Clan-na-Gael, though ye can't prove it be me, but I niver in me life see annything done without they was a gun-play somewhere concealed in it. Hiven f'rbid that I shud want annything to happen to those dear cousins iv ours acrost th' sea. I wudden't bring a tear to th' blue eye iv Whitelaw Reid. I don't believe in too much foorce, but ye've always got to flavor th' porridge with it. I'd have a little constichoochinal agytation an' a little foorce, a sthreak iv wan an' a sthreak iv th' other, a polite request an' a punch in th' eye, an argymint an' a kick, a janial la-ad in parlymint with a mellow voice an' a good, ginteel accint, an' a boy in corduroys behind a rock in th' County Sligo to pint th' moral. I wud shoot off th' mouth wan day an' th' blundherbuss th' next. I'd have me frind Tay Pay stand up in parlymint an' say: 'Gintlemen, ye know I'm sthrongly again' th' use iv foorce. Th' name iv dinnymite fills me with abhorrence, an' th' explosion iv a fire-cracker gives me th' jumps. As a rale ol' English gintleman in a long coat to rale ol' English gintlemen in long coats, as between fellow-subjicks iv th' king, that dear, good man whom all revere, I plead with ye to do justice to th' fair land iv mine, which I often see on th' maps as I come down to th' House,' he says. 'Go to th' divvle,' says th' Right Hon'rable Arthur James Balfour. 'They ain't enough justice to go around amongst us now, an' why wud we be throwin' it away on a nice, polite people like ye,' he says. 'I f'rgot to add,' says Tay Pay, 'that a frind iv mine is settin' in th' gall'ry with a bag containin' about thirty pounds iv up-with-ye,' he says. 'He has just wrote me a note sayin' that his arm is tired, an' wud I mind if he tossed th' bag down to ye,' he says. 'I'm greatly grieved with th' action iv me fellow-counthryman, but his name is O'Brien, an' I can't conthrol him,' he says. 'So here I go f'r th' fire-escape,' he says; 'an',' he says, 'if ye'll bring th' pa-apers with ye,' he says, 'we might discuss th' terms iv th' settlemint as we climb down,' he says.

"That's my policy, Hinnissy, an' it's been th' policy iv all other gr-reat statesmen. Niver start a riv'lution without a gun. Niver ask a man f'r annything unless ye can make him think ye're li'ble to take it, annyhow. My wrongs ar-re my wrongs, an' it's little ye mind thim until they begin to hurt ye. If I'm sick in me room up-stairs ye don't care, but whin I begin hollerin' an' jumpin' on th' flure an' knockin' th' plastherin' down on ye'er head ye'll sind f'r th' doctor. I'd have all th' mimbers iv parlymint wear black coats, but they ought to be ready to peel thim off at a minyit's notice an' show up ready f'r business in red shirts.

"F'r, Hinnissy, Ireland 'll nivor get annything fr'm England but a threaty iv peace."

"I wondher will England iver free Ireland?" asked Mr. Hennessy.

"Niver," said Mr. Dooley. "What talk have ye? No wan wants it that way. England will niver free Ireland, but some day, if we make it inthrestin' enough f'r her she'll have to free England iv Ireland. An' that 'll be all right."

IMMIGRATION

"Well, I see Congress has got to wurruk again," said Mr. Dooley.

"The Lord save us fr'm harm," said Mr. Hennessy.

"Yes, sir," said Mr. Dooley, "Congress has got to wurruk again, an' manny things that seems important to a Congressman 'll be brought up befure thim. 'Tis sthrange that what's a big thing to a man in Wash'nton, Hinnissy, don't seem much account to me. Divvle a bit do I care whether they dig th' Nicaragoon Canal or cross th' Isthmus in a balloon; or whether th' Monroe docthrine is enfoorced or whether it ain't; or whether th' thrusts is abolished as Teddy Rosenfelt wud like to have thim or encouraged to go on with their neefaryous but magnificent entherprises as th' Prisidint wud like; or whether th' water is poured into th' ditches to reclaim th' arid lands iv th' West or th' money f'r thim to fertilize th' arid pocket-books iv th' conthractors; or whether th' Injun is threated like a depindant an' miserable thribesman or like a free an' indepindant dog; or whether we restore th' merchant marine to th' ocean or whether we lave it to restore itsilf. None iv these here questions inthrest me, an' be me I mane you an' be you I mane ivrybody. What we want to know is, ar-re we goin' to have coal enough in th' hod whin th' cold snap comes; will th' plumbin' hold out, an' will th' job last.

"But they'se wan question that Congress is goin' to take up that you an' me are intherested in. As a pilgrim father that missed th' first boats, I must raise me claryon voice again' th' invasion iv this fair land be th' paupers an' arnychists iv effete Europe. Ye bet I must—because I'm here first. 'Twas diff'rent whin I was dashed high on th' stern an' rockbound coast. In thim days America was th' refuge iv th' oppressed iv all th' wurruld. They cud come over here an' do a good job iv oppressin' thimsilves. As I told ye I come a little late. Th' Rosenfelts an' th' Lodges bate me be at laste a boat lenth, an' be th' time I got here they was stern an' rockbound thimsilves. So I got a gloryous rayciption as soon as I was towed off th' rocks. Th' stars an' sthripes whispered a welcome in th' breeze an' a shovel was thrust into me hand an' I was pushed into a sthreet excyvatin' as though I'd been born here. Th' pilgrim father who bossed th' job was a fine ol' puritan be th' name iv Doherty, who come over in th' Mayflower about th' time iv th' potato rot in Wexford, an' he made me think they was a hole in th' breakwather iv th' haven iv refuge an' some iv th' wash iv th' seas iv opprission had got through. He was a stern an' rockbound la-ad himsilf, but I was a good hand at loose stones an' wan day—but I'll tell ye about that another time.

"Annyhow, I was rayceived with open arms that sometimes ended in a clinch. I was afraid I wasn't goin' to assimilate with th' airlyer pilgrim fathers an' th' instichoochions iv th' counthry, but I soon found that a long swing iv th' pick made me as good as another man an' it didn't require a gr-reat intellect, or sometimes anny at all, to vote th' dimmycrat ticket, an' befure I was here a month, I felt enough like a native born American to burn a witch. Wanst in a while a mob iv intilligint collajeens, whose grandfathers had bate me to th' dock, wud take a shy at me Pathrick's Day procission or burn down wan iv me churches, but they got tired iv that befure long; 'twas too much like wurruk.

"But as I tell ye, Hinnissy, 'tis diff'rent now. I don't know why 'tis diff'rent but 'tis diff'rent. 'Tis time we put our back again' th' open dure an' keep out th' savage horde. If that cousin iv ye'ers expects to cross, he'd betther tear f'r th' ship. In a few minyits th' gates 'll be down an' whin th' oppressed wurruld comes hikin' acrost to th' haven iv refuge, they'll do well to put a couplin' pin undher their hats, f'r th' Goddess iv Liberty 'll meet thim at th' dock with an axe in her hand. Congress is goin' to fix it. Me frind Shaughnessy says so. He was in yisterdah an' says he: ''Tis time we done something to make th' immigration laws sthronger,' says he. 'Thrue f'r ye, Miles Standish,' says I; 'but what wud ye do?' 'I'd keep out th' offscourin's iv Europe,' says he. 'Wud ye go back?' says I. 'Have ye'er joke,' says he. ' 'Tis not so seeryus as it was befure ye come,' says I. 'But what ar-re th' immygrants doin' that's roonous to us?' I says. 'Well,' says he, 'they're arnychists,' he says; 'they don't assymilate with th' counthry,' he says. 'Maybe th' counthry's digestion has gone wrong fr'm too much rich food,' says I; 'perhaps now if we'd lave off thryin' to digest Rockyfellar an' thry a simple diet like Schwartzmeister, we wudden't feel th' effects iv our vittels,' I says. 'Maybe if we'd season th' immygrants a little or cook thim thurly, they'd go down betther,' I says.

" 'They're arnychists, like Parsons,' he says. 'He wud've been an immygrant if Texas hadn't been admitted to th' Union,' I says. 'Or Snolgosh,' he says. 'Has Mitchigan seceded?' I says. 'Or Gittoo,' he says. 'Who come fr'm th' effete monarchies iv Chicago, west iv Ashland Av'noo,' I says. 'Or what's-his-name, Wilkes Booth,' he says. 'I don't know what he was—maybe a Boolgharyen,' says I. 'Well, annyhow,' says he, 'they're th' scum iv th' earth.' 'They may be that,' says I; 'but we used to think they was th' cream iv civilization,' I says. 'They're off th' top annyhow. I wanst believed 'twas th' best men iv Europe come here, th' la-ads that was too sthrong and indepindant to be kicked around be a boorgomasther at home an' wanted to dig out f'r a place where they cud get a chanst to make their way to th' money. I see their sons fightin' into politics an' their daughters tachin' young American idee how to shoot too high in th' public school, an' I thought they was all right. But I see I was wrong. Thim boys out there towin' wan heavy foot afther th' other to th' rowlin' mills is all arnychists. There's warrants out f'r all names endin' in 'inski, an' I think I'll board up me windows, f'r,' I says, 'if immygrants is as dangerous to this counthry as ye an' I an' other pilgrim fathers believe they are, they'se enough iv thim sneaked in already to make us aborigines about as inflointial as the prohibition vote in th' Twinty-ninth Ward. They'll dash again' our stern an' rock-bound coast till they bust it,' says I.

"'But I ain't so much afraid as ye ar-re. I'm not afraid iv me father an' I'm not afraid iv mesilf. An' I'm not afraid iv Schwartzmeister's father or Hinnery Cabin Lodge's grandfather. We all come over th' same way, an' if me ancestors were not what Hogan calls rigicides, 'twas not because they were not ready an' willin', on'y a king niver come their way. I don't believe in killin' kings, mesilf. I niver wud've sawed th' block off that curly-headed potintate that I see in th' pitchers down town, but, be hivins, Presarved Codfish Shaughnessy, if we'd begun a few years ago shuttin' out folks that wudden't mind handin' a bomb to a king, they wudden't be enough people in Mattsachoosetts to make a quorum f'r th' Anti-Impeeryal S'ciety,' says I. 'But what wud ye do with th' off-scourin' iv Europe?' says he. 'I'd scour thim some more,' says I.

"An' so th' meetin' iv th' Plymouth Rock Assocyation come to an end. But if ye wud like to get it together, Deacon Hinnissy, to discuss th' immygration question, I'll sind out a hurry call f'r Schwartzmeister an' Mulcahey an' Ignacio Sbarbaro an' Nels Larsen an' Petrus Gooldvink, an' we 'll gather to-night at Fan-neilnoviski Hall at th' corner iv Sheridan an' Sigel sthreets. All th' pilgrim fathers is rayquested f'r to bring interpreters."

"Well," said Mr. Hennessy, "divvle th' bit I care, on'y I'm here first, an' I ought to have th' right to keep th' bus fr'm bein' overcrowded."

"Well," said Mr. Dooley, "as a pilgrim father on me gran' nephew's side, I don't know but ye're right. An' they'se wan sure way to keep thim out."

"What's that?" asked Mr. Hennessy.

"Teach thim all about our instichoochions befure they come," said Mr. Dooley.

9. JOHN A. RYAN

*Faith and Social Order**

John A. Ryan was born near Vermillion, Minnesota, in 1869, the eldest son of a family of eleven. His parents were Irish immigrants who had managed to acquire a farm after some years of labor in the United States. His father was a member of the Farmers' Alliance and was undoubtedly influenced by Ignatius Donnelly who lived nearby. John was destined for the priesthood and after studying at St. Thomas Seminary was ordained in 1898 by Archbishop Ireland. After further study at Catholic University, Ryan taught moral theology at the Seminary in St. Paul and after 1915 in Catholic University. Caught up in the liberal Catholic movement of the last decades of the nineteenth century and influenced by progressive ideas, he was eager to have the state intervene in social reform. He argued in favor of public ownership of utilities, a progressive income tax, and the regulation of speculation. He favored the child labor amendment and was active in the National Catholic Welfare Conference and its Social Action Department. He died in 1945. See also Francis L. Broderick, Right Reverend New Dealer *(New York, 1963).*

May 15 is the anniversary of two great Papal Encyclicals. The first was issued by Pope Leo XIII, forty-five years ago. The title of the Latin version is *Rerum Novarum;* the English translation is entitled "On the Condition of Labor." The purpose and viewpoint of this Encyclical are clearly indicated in the following sentence: "At this moment the condition of the

* John A. Ryan, *The Message of the Encyclicals for America Today* (Washington, 1936).

working population is the question of the hour; and nothing can be of higher interest to all classes of the state than that it should be rightly and reasonably decided." Almost half a century has elapsed since Pope Leo wrote these words, but the labor question is still a long way from a right and reasonable solution.

Exactly forty years after the appearance of *Rerum Novarum*, Pope Pius XI issued the Encyclical which in Latin is entitled *Quadragesimo Anno;* in English, "On Reconstructing the Social Order." In it the Holy Father defends, confirms, and develops the economic and ethical doctrines contained in *Rerum Novarum,* and sets forth a specific program for a new social order. The economic system recommended by the Pope is neither capitalism nor collectivism. It is genuine economic democracy and it offers the only permanent solution of our economic problems.

I would strongly advise the readers of this pamphlet to study the Pope's plan of economic reconstruction in the Encyclical itself and in the pamphlet entitled "Organized Social Justice," published by the National Catholic Welfare Conference. In the present pamphlet I shall deal only with specific statements which fall under the head of reform rather than reconstruction.

There are scores of declarations in these two Encyclicals which contain pertinent messages for present-day America. I have selected five for brief discussion. They deal with our bad distribution of wealth and income; with just wages; with the just rewards of capital; with labor unions; and with cooperation between capital and labor. Taken together these five declarations show what we must do in order to get out of the depression and attain genuine prosperity.

Concerning the bad distribution, Pope Pius XI says: "The immense number of propertyless wage earners on the one hand and the superabundant riches of the fortunate few on the other is an unanswerable argument that the earthly goods, so abundantly produced in this age of industrialism, are far from rightly distributed and equitably shared among the various classes of men. Every effort, therefore, must be made that, at least in future, a just share only of the fruits of production be permitted to accumulate in the hands of the wealthy and that an ample sufficiency be supplied to the workingmen."

The unjust distribution to which the Pope calls attention in the foregoing sentences is particularly striking in the United States. Here are a few of the most significant figures. They are taken from the Brookings Institution volume on "America's Capacity to Consume." In 1929, the richest one-tenth of one per cent of American families received as large a share of the product as the poorest forty-two per cent. In other words, 36,000 families at the top of the income scale obtained as much as eleven and one-half million families at the bottom.

Occasionally it is still asserted that while the rich are getting richer, the poor are getting richer likewise. This statement may not be technically untrue, but it is highly misleading. From the year 1900 onward, the incomes of the higher-income classes increased faster than those of the lower-income groups. This is shown in the Brookings Institution volume, "America's Capacity to Consume." The disproportionate growth was particularly striking between 1922 and 1929. Basing his conclusions upon two tables compiled from the data published by the U. S. Treasury Department concerning the incomes of those who make federal income tax reports, Professor Arthur B. Adams, of the University of Oklahoma, says in his recent book, "National Economic Security":

> A close study of these two tables furnishes convincing evidence that during the twenties practically all the increase in the national money income went to those who received incomes large enough to make income tax reports to the Federal government, and the larger the individual income the more rapidly did it increase from year to year. . . .
>
> Examination of the trend of wages and profits during this same period shows that from year to year a decreasing percentage of the national income was paid out as wages and an increasing percentage of it was paid out as profits, interest, rents, royalty, and other property payments. . . .

This bad distribution was the main cause of the depression. For at least a quarter of a century before the year 1929, too much of the national product had been distributed in the form of profits and interest and too little in the form of wages to labor and prices to the farmers. As a consequence, too much of the national income was invested in new capital goods. Too much was saved and too little spent. The product could not all be sold because labor and the farmers had not been receiving enough income to buy as much as they wanted to buy. The receivers of large profits and interest would not buy more because they did not want nor need to buy more. According to the recent volumes published by the Brookings Institution on income and economic progress, our productive plant could have produced twenty per cent more than it did produce in the supposedly busy year of 1929. Nor is this all. In that year, fifteen billion dollars were saved, but only five of these fifteen billions were able to find a profitable place in new instruments of production. The other ten billion dollars were wasted in worthless securities and various other forms of speculation. Had this sum of ten billion dollars not been saved; had it gone to the farmers in the form of higher prices and to labor in the form of higher wages, our industries could have been kept going at one hundred per cent instead of at eighty per cent capacity. Since the distribution was not made, our productive plant was twenty per cent idle, and at least two and a half million persons were out of employment in the allegedly prosperous year of 1929.

The unjust distribution condemned by the Pope not only prevents the majority of our people from living decently, but compels our industries to operate far below their full capacity. Until this intolerable distribution is radically corrected, we cannot achieve complete business recovery.

The second declaration that I have in mind concerns just wages. Pope Pius demands that the workers be given "ample sufficiency." And he defines "ample sufficiency" in the following terms: the laborer's wages must be "sufficient for the support of himself and of his family"; "sufficient to meet adequately ordinary domestic needs"; sufficient to enable him "to bear the family burden with greater ease and security"; sufficient to free him from "hand to mouth uncertainty"; sufficient to "support life's changing fortunes"; sufficient to make "some little provision for those who remain after him"; sufficient "to acquire a certain moderate ownership."

These specifications show that Pope Pius demanded something more than a bare living wage, something more than the minimum means of a day-to-day livelihood. To comply with these specifications would probably require more than the $2,000 income which, at 1929 prices, the Brookings Institution estimates as "sufficient to supply only basic necessities." Yet in 1929, sixty per cent of the total number of American families were below this standard. In effect, the Pope calls for a revolutionary change in the present distribution.

The third declaration of *Quadragesimo Anno* which I desire to cite is that "the distribution of created goods must be brought into conformity with the demands of the common good and social justice." This is the Pope's answer to the question, "how much of the product should go to the capitalist?" Only as much as is required by the common good. Therefore, if an interest rate of two per cent, or even one per cent, will induce men to provide all the capital that the community needs, the capitalist has no right to claim more than two per cent. This principle is tremendously important for the maintenance of prosperity. In his most recent volume, entitled, "The General Theory of Employment, Interest and Money," the eminent British economist, John Maynard Keynes, insists again and again that the rate of interest must be reduced if industry is to function with anything like a reasonable degree of efficiency. Unless the rate of interest is reduced, he maintains, the industrial systems of the great capitalist countries will never be able to operate at full capacity or to provide full employment.

Lower interest rates are likewise required in order to bring justice to the workers. Labor cannot obtain a larger share of the product unless capital receives a smaller share, a smaller proportion, than in the past. The only way to reduce the share of capital is by reducing the rate of interest. A considerable reduction in the interest charges upon industry would make possible at least five beneficent changes in our economy: first, higher wages for labor; second, lower prices to consumers; third, increased demand for goods; fourth, a decreased capacity for oversaving and excessive investment by the well-to-do and the rich; and, fifth, a reduction in our intolerable burden of mortgages and all other kinds of debts. All these benefits and reforms are implicit in the Pope's principle that capital's share of the product must be brought into conformity with "the demands of the common good and social justice."

The fourth papal statement to be considered is found in Pope Leo's Encyclical, "On the Condition of Labor." It reads thus: "Speaking summarily, we may lay it down as a general and perpetual law that workmen's associations should be so organized and governed as to furnish the best and most suitable means for attaining what is aimed at; that is to say, for helping each individual member to better his condition to the utmost, in body, mind, and property." This comprehensive principle implicitly condemns the company union, the non-union shop and all the other devious devices by which labor is deprived of the opportunity to organize effectively and to bargain collectively. This comprehensive principle implicitly approves the Wagner-Connery Labor Disputes Act. Independent and effective labor unions are necessary not only for the protection of the workers but for a rational organization of industrial society. By this time it should be abundantly clear that the first step toward industrial peace and industrial justice is adequate cooperation between capital and labor. Unless employees have their own independent unions they cannot cooperate intelligently or effectively with the representatives of the employers.

The last statement that I shall present deals specifically with this matter of employer and employee cooperation. When employers are really unable to pay decent wages they should, says Pius XI in *Quadragesimo Anno* join forces with their employees "to overcome all difficulties and obstacles; and let them be aided in this wholesome endeavor by the wise measures of public authority."

According to this recommendation, labor, employers and the public should unite to abolish the evil of insufficient wages. Precisely this kind of cooperation existed under the National Recovery Administration. Unfortunately, it was ended by the Supreme Court. A few months ago a new attempt was made to explore the possibilities of common action by capital, labor and the government, in the conferences held under the chairmanship of Major George L. Berry at the direction of the President of the United States. Greatly to be lamented is the fact that almost all of the most important directors of industry who were invited to join in this endeavor refused to participate. Apparently the great majority of our most powerful industrialists do not desire to cooperate; they prefer to dominate. Moreover, they ignore the fundamental realities of our economic situation. They talk vaguely and expansively about the necessity of restoring confidence and stimulating new investments. Very few of them seem to have grasped the elementary facts that we already have too much investment and too much productive plant, that industry needs not more factories but more sales of goods and that we cannot have more sales until more purchasing power is put into the hands of the masses.

The outlook for cooperation between industry, labor and the government is discouraging because the dominant and dominating elements of business still believe in the old order and are still opposed to intervention by the government for social justice. Last December the National Association of Manufacturers at convention in New York adopted this brazen proposition: "Control of the individual by government is limited to the minimum essential for the protection of individual rights and the safety of the nation." At its annual meeting in Washington the latter part of April, the United States Chamber of Commerce passed the following resolution:

> The true function of government is to maintain equality of opportunity for all, to preserve the sanctity of contracts, and to assume those collective activities which society must conduct as a whole. When government attempts by legislative means or executive fiat to impose upon business, rules of conduct pertain-

ing to such matters as wages, hours, conditions and terms of employment, or other restrictive measures interfering with the free play of economic forces, it retards both the material and spiritual progress of the nation.

These statements by the two most powerful business associations in our country enable us to see why very little of a helpful character is to be expected from organized business in the struggle for social justice and a better economic order. The voices of great and enlightened industrialists, such as Filene and Dennison, as well as the opinions of thousands of smaller business men, are overwhelmed or overawed by the dominating reactionaries. Humane and helpful business opinion is, for the most part, silent and ineffectual.

The refusal of our greatest industrial leaders to unite on equal terms with labor and the government in the effort to substitute industrial order and justice for industrial anarchy and injustice, together with their antiquated economic thinking, constitute the most deadly obstacle to the attainment of prosperity and social justice. Yet these men could and should be our leaders in the struggle for a better economic order. Let us hope that they will not much longer maintain their present unwise attitude and temper. Let us hope that they will at an early date cease to emulate those Bourbons who learned nothing, forgot nothing and finally lost everything. Let us hope that they will take to heart the warning of the Holy Father, that unless serious, energetic and prompt efforts be made to reform existing conditions, the peace and tranquillity of human society cannot be "effectively defended against the forces of revolution."

The five statements that I have quoted from the Encyclicals are at once a comprehensive description of our economic maladies and an indication of the way to complete business recovery. We must have a better distribution of the product, ample living wages for all workers, a smaller return to capital, effective organization of labor and adequate cooperation between business, labor and the government.

10. THEODORE DREISER

*The Threat of Poverty**

Theodore Dreiser was born in 1871, the eighth child of a restless family of German origin. His father, a Catholic, had come from Germany in 1844; his mother was the daughter of a Moravian farmer. They were never well off, and the young man was early depressed by the misfortunes of his sisters. He held various jobs as a farmhand and laborer, with intermittent spells of education in high school and at the University of Indiana. He became a reporter and worked briefly on Chicago, Pittsburgh, and St. Louis newspapers before coming east to New York where he found a job on the World. *His fiction was controversial. Even his most successful novel,* An American Tragedy, *shocked its readers by its realistic portrayal of characters and its bitter observations of the life of his time. Here and elsewhere he dealt with the theme of the outsider, challenged by the hostility of society. See also Robert H. Elias,* Theodore Dreiser *(New York, 1949); F. O. Matthiessen,* Theodore Dreiser *(New York, 1951).*

Minnie's flat, as the one-floor resident apartments were then being called, was in a part of West Van Buren Street inhabited by families of labourers and clerks, men who had come, and were still coming, with the rush of population pouring in at the rate of 50,000 a year. It was on the third floor, the front windows looking down into the street, where, at night, the lights of grocery stores were shining and children were playing. To Carrie, the sound of the little bells upon the horse-cars, as they tinkled in and out of hearing, was as pleasing as

* Theodore Dreiser, *Sister Carrie* (New York, 1907), pp. 12–27.

it was novel. She gazed into the lighted street when Minnie brought her into the front room, and wondered at the sounds, the movement, the murmur of the vast city which stretched for miles and miles in every direction.

Mrs. Hanson, after the first greetings were over, gave Carrie the baby and proceeded to get supper. Her husband asked a few questions and sat down to read the evening paper. He was a silent man, American born, of a Swede father, and now employed as a cleaner of refrigerator cars at the stock-yards. To him the presence or absence of his wife's sister was a matter of indifference. Her personal appearance did not affect him one way or the other. His one observation to the point was concerning the chances of work in Chicago.

"It's a big place," he said. "You can get in somewhere in a few days. Everybody does."

It had been tacitly understood beforehand that she was to get work and pay her board. He was of a clean, saving disposition, and had already paid a number of monthly instalments on two lots far out on the West Side. His ambition was some day to build a house on them.

In the interval which marked the preparation of the meal Carrie found time to study the flat. She had some slight gift of observation and that sense, so rich in every woman—intuition.

She felt the drag of a lean and narrow life. The walls of the rooms were discordantly papered. The floors were covered with matting and the hall laid with a thin rag carpet. One could see that the furniture was of that poor, hurriedly patched together quality sold by the instalment houses.

She sat with Minnie, in the kitchen, holding the baby until it began to cry. Then she walked and sang to it, until Hanson, disturbed in his reading, came and took it. A pleasant side to his nature came out here. He was patient. One could see that he was very much wrapped up in his offspring.

"Now, now," he said, walking. "There, there," and there was a certain Swedish accent noticeable in his voice.

"You'll want to see the city first, won't you?" said Minnie, when they were eating. "Well, we'll go out Sunday and see Lincoln Park."

Carrie noticed that Hanson had said nothing to this. He seemed to be thinking of something else.

"Well," she said, "I think I'll look around to-morrow. I've got Friday and Saturday, and it won't be any trouble. Which way is the business part?"

Minnie began to explain, but her husband took this part of the conversation to himself.

"It's that way," he said, pointing east. "That's east." Then he went off into the longest speech he had yet indulged in, concerning the lay of Chicago. "You'd better look in those big manufacturing houses along Franklin Street and just the other side of the river," he concluded. "Lots of girls work there. You could get home easy, too. It isn't very far."

Carrie nodded and asked her sister about the neighbourhood. The latter talked in a subdued tone, telling the little she knew about it, while Hanson concerned himself with the baby. Finally he jumped up and handed the child to his wife.

"I've got to get up early in the morning, so I'll go to bed," and off he went, disappearing into the dark little bedroom off the hall, for the night.

"He works way down at the stock-yards," explained Minnie, "so he's got to get up at half-past five."

"What time do you get up to get breakfast?" asked Carrie.

"At about twenty minutes of five."

Together they finished the labour of the day, Carrie washing the dishes while Minnie undressed the baby and put it to bed. Minnie's manner was one of trained industry, and Carrie could see that it was a steady round of toil with her. . . .

When she awoke at eight the next morning, Hanson had gone. Her sister was busy in the dining-room, which was also the sitting-room, sewing. She worked, after dressing, to arrange a little breakfast for herself, and then advised with Minnie as to which way to look. The latter had changed considerably since Carrie had seen her. She was now a thin, though rugged, woman of twenty-seven, with ideas of life coloured by her husband's, and fast hardening into narrower conceptions of pleasure and duty than had ever been hers in a thoroughly circumscribed youth. She had invited Carrie, not because she longed for her presence, but because the latter was dissatisfied at home, and could probably get work and pay her board here. She was pleased to see her in a way but reflected her husband's point of view in the matter of work. Anything was good enough so long as it paid—say, five dollars a week to begin with. A shop girl was the destiny prefigured for the newcomer. She would get in one of the great shops and do well enough until—well, until something happened. Neither of them knew exactly what. They did not figure on promotion. They did not exactly count on marriage. Things would go on, though, in a dim kind of way until the better thing would eventuate, and Carrie would be rewarded for coming and toiling in the city. It was under such auspicious circumstances that she started out this morning to look for work.

Before following her in her round of seeking, let us look at the sphere in which her future was to lie. In 1889 Chicago had the peculiar qualifications of growth which made such adventuresome pilgrimages even on the part of young girls plausible. Its many and growing commercial opportunities gave it widespread fame, which made of it a giant magnet, drawing to itself, from all quarters, the hopeful and the hopeless—those who had their fortune yet to make and those whose fortunes and affairs had reached a disastrous climax elsewhere. It was a city of over 500,000, with the ambition, the daring, the activity of a metropolis of a million. Its streets and houses were already scattered over an area of seventy-five square miles. Its population was not so much thriving upon established commerce as upon the industries which prepared for the arrival of others. The sound of the hammer engaged upon the erection of new structures was everywhere heard. Great industries were moving in. The huge railroad corporations which had long before recognised the prospects of the place had seized upon vast tracts of land for transfer and shipping purposes. Street-car lines had been extended far out into the open country in anticipation of rapid growth. The city had laid miles and miles of streets and sewers through regions where, perhaps, one solitary house stood out alone—a pioneer of the populous ways to be.

There were regions open to the sweeping winds and rain, which were yet lighted throughout the night with long, blinking lines of gas-lamps, fluttering in the wind. Narrow board walks extended out, passing here a house, and there a store, at far intervals, eventually ending on the open prairie.

In the central portion was the vast wholesale and shopping district, to which the uninformed seeker for work usually drifted. It was a characteristic of Chicago then, and one not generally shared by other cities, that individual firms of any pretension occupied individual buildings. The presence of ample ground made this possible. It gave an imposing appearance to most of the wholesale houses, whose offices were upon the ground floor and in plain view of the street. The large plates of window glass, now so common, were then rapidly coming into use, and gave to the ground floor offices a distinguished and prosperous look. The casual wanderer could see as he passed a polished array of office fixtures, much frosted glass, clerks hard at work, and genteel business men in "nobby" suits and clean linen lounging about or sitting in groups. Polished brass or nickel signs at the square stone entrances announced the firm and the nature of the business in rather neat and reserved terms. The entire metropolitan centre possessed a high and mighty air calculated to overawe and abash the common applicant, and to make the gulf between poverty and success seem both wide and deep.

Into this important commercial region the timid Carrie went. She walked east along Van Buren Street through a region of lessening importance, until it deteriorated into a mass of shanties and coal-yards, and finally verged upon the river. She walked bravely forward, led by an honest desire to find employment and delayed at every step by the interest of the unfolding scene, and a sense of helplessness amid so much evidence of power and force which she did not understand. These vast buildings, what were they? These strange energies and huge interests, for what purposes were they there? She could have understood the meaning of a little stone-cutter's yard at Columbia City, carving little pieces of marble for individual use, but when the yards of some huge stone corporation came into view, filled with spur tracks and flat cars, transpierced by docks from the river and traversed overhead by immense trundling cranes of wood and steel, it lost all significance in her little world.

It was so with the vast railroad yards, with the crowded array of vessels she saw at the river, and the huge factories over the way, lining the water's edge. Through the open windows she could see the figures of men and women in working aprons, moving busily about. The great streets were wall-lined mysteries to her; the vast offices, strange mazes which concerned far-off individuals of importance. She could only think of people connected with them as counting money, dressing magnificently, and riding in carriages. What they dealt in, how they laboured, to what end it all came, she had only the vaguest conception. It was all wonderful, all vast, all far removed, and she sank in spirit inwardly and fluttered feebly at the heart as she thought of entering any one of these mighty concerns and asking for something to do—something that she could do—anything. . . .

Once across the river and into the wholesale district, she glanced about her for some likely door at which to apply. As she contemplated the wide windows and imposing signs, she became conscious of being gazed upon and understood for what she was—a wage-seeker. She had never done this thing before, and lacked courage. To avoid a certain indefinable shame she felt at being caught spying about for a position, she quickened her steps and assumed an air of indifference supposedly common to one upon an errand. In this way she passed many manufacturing and wholesale houses without once glancing in. At last, after several blocks of walking, she felt that this would not do, and began to look about again, though without relaxing her pace. A little way on she saw a great door which, for some reason, attracted her attention. It was ornamented by a small brass sign, and seemed to be the entrance to a vast hive of six or seven floors. "Perhaps," she thought, "they may want some one," and crossed over to enter. When she came within a score of feet of the desired goal, she saw through the window a young man in a grey checked suit. That he had anything to do with the concern, she could not tell, but because he happened to be looking in her direction her weakening heart misgave her and she hurried by, too overcome with shame to enter. Over the way stood a great six-story structure, labelled Storm and King, which she viewed with rising hope. It was a wholesale dry goods concern and employed women. She could see them moving about now and then upon the upper floors. This place she decided to enter, no matter what. She crossed over and walked directly toward the entrance. As she did so, two men came out and paused in the door. A telegraph messenger in blue dashed past her and up the few steps that led to the entrance and disappeared. Several pedestrians out of the hurrying throng which filled the sidewalks passed about her as she paused, hesitating. She looked helplessly around, and then, seeing herself observed, retreated. It was too difficult a task. She could not go past them.

So severe a defeat told sadly upon her nerves. Her feet carried her mechanically forward, every foot of her progress being a satisfactory portion of a flight which she gladly made. Block after block passed by. Upon street-lamps at the various corners she read names such as Madison, Monroe, La Salle, Clark, Dearborn, State, and still she went, her feet beginning to tire upon the broad stone flagging. She was pleased in part that the streets were bright and clean. The morning sun, shining down with steadily increasing warmth, made the shady side of the streets pleasantly cool. She looked at the blue sky overhead with more realisation of its charm than had ever come to her before.

Her cowardice began to trouble her in a way. She turned back, resolving to hunt up Storm and King and enter. On the way she encountered a great wholesale shoe company, through the broad plate windows of which she saw an enclosed executive department, hidden by frosted glass. Without this enclosure, but just within the street entrance, sat a grey-haired gentleman at a small table, with a large open ledger before him. She walked by this institution several times hesitating, but, finding herself unobserved, faltered past the screen door and stood humbly waiting.

"Well, young lady," observed the old gentleman, looking at her somewhat kindly, "what is it you wish?"

"I am, that is, do you—I mean, do you need any help?" she stammered.

"Not just at present," he answered smiling. "Not just at present. Come in some time next week. Occasionally we need some one."

She received the answer in silence and backed awkwardly out. The pleasant nature of her reception rather astonished her. She had expected that it would be more difficult, that something cold and harsh would be said—she knew not what. That she had not been put to shame and made to feel her unfortunate position, seemed remarkable.

Somewhat encouraged, she ventured into another large structure. It was a clothing company, and more people were in evidence—well-dressed men of forty and more, surrounded by brass railings.

An office boy approached her.

"Who is it you wish to see?" he asked.

"I want to see the manager," she said.

He ran away and spoke to one of a group of three men who were conferring together. One of these came towards her.

"Well?" he said coldly. The greeting drove all courage from her at once.

"Do you need any help?" she stammered.

"No," he replied abruptly, and turned upon his heel.

She went foolishly out, the office boy deferentially swinging the door for her, and gladly sank into the obscuring crowd. It was a severe setback to her recently pleased mental state.

Now she walked quite aimlessly for a time, turning here and there, seeing one great company after another, but finding no courage to prosecute her single inquiry. High noon came, and with it hunger. She hunted out an unassuming restaurant and entered, but was disturbed to find that the prices were exorbitant for the size of her purse. A bowl of soup was all that she could afford, and, with this quickly eaten, she went out again. It restored her strength somewhat and made her moderately bold to pursue the search.

In walking a few blocks to fix upon some probable place, she again encountered the firm of Storm and King, and this time managed to get in. Some gentlemen were conferring close at hand, but took no notice of her. She was left standing, gazing nervously upon the floor. When the limit of her distress had been nearly reached, she was beckoned to by a man at one of the many desks within the near-by railing.

"Who is it you wish to see?" he inquired.

"Why, any one, if you please," she answered. "I am looking for something to do."

"Oh, you want to see Mr. McManus," he returned. "Sit down," and he pointed to a chair against the neighbouring wall. He went on leisurely writing, until after a time a short, stout gentleman came in from the street.

"Mr. McManus," called the man at the desk, "this young woman wants to see you."

The short gentleman turned about towards Carrie, and she arose and came forward.

"What can I do for you, miss?" he inquired, surveying her curiously.

"I want to know if I can get a position," she inquired.

"As what?" he asked.

"Not as anything in particular," she faltered.

"Have you ever had any experience in the wholesale dry goods business?" he questioned.

"No, sir," she replied.

"Are you a stenographer or typewriter?"

"No, sir."

"Well, we haven't anything here," he said. "We employ only experienced help."

She began to step backward toward the door, when something about her plaintive face attracted him.

"Have you ever worked at anything before?" he inquired.

"No, sir," she said.

"Well, now, it's hardly possible that you would get anything to do in a wholesale house of this kind. Have you tried the department stores?"

She acknowledged that she had not.

"Well, if I were you," he said, looking at her rather genially, "I would try the department stores. They often need young women as clerks."

"Thank you," she said, her whole nature relieved by this spark of friendly interest.

"Yes," he said, as she moved toward the door, "you try the department stores," and off he went.

At that time the department store was in its earliest form of successful operation, and there were not many. The first three in the United States, established about 1884, were in Chicago. Carrie was familiar with the names of several through the advertisements in the "Daily News," and now proceeded to seek them. The words of Mr. McManus had somehow managed to restore her courage, which had fallen low, and she dared to hope that this new line would offer her something. Some time she spent in wandering up and down, thinking to encounter the buildings by chance, so readily is the mind, bent upon prosecuting a hard but needful errand, eased by that self-deception which the semblance of search, without the reality, gives. At last she inquired of a police officer, and was directed to proceed "two blocks up," where she would find "The Fair."

The nature of these vast retail combinations, should they ever permanently disappear, will form an interesting chapter in the commercial history of our nation. Such a flowering out of a modest trade principle the world had never witnessed up to that time. They were along the line of the most effective retail organisation, with hundreds of stores coördinated into one and laid out upon the most imposing and economic basis. They were handsome, bustling, successful affairs, with a host of clerks and a swarm of patrons. Carrie passed along the busy aisles, much affected by the remarkable displays of trinkets, dress goods, stationery, and jewelry. Each separate counter was a show place of dazzling interest and attraction. She could not help feeling the claim of each trinket and valuable upon her personally, and yet she did not stop. There was nothing there which she could not have used—nothing which she did not long to own. The dainty slippers and stockings, the delicately frilled skirts and petticoats, the laces, ribbons, haircombs, purses, all touched her with individual desire, and she felt keenly the fact that not any of these things were in the range of her purchase. She was a work-seeker, an outcast without employment, one whom the average employee could tell at a glance was poor and in need of a situation.

It must not be thought that any one could have mistaken her for a nervous, sensitive, high-strung nature, cast unduly upon a cold, calculating, and unpoetic world. Such certainly she was not. But women are peculiarly sensitive to their adornment.

Not only did Carrie feel the drag of desire for all which was new and pleasing in apparel for women, but she noticed too, with a touch at the heart, the fine ladies who elbowed and ignored her, brushing past in utter disregard of her presence, themselves eagerly enlisted in the materials which the store contained. Carrie was not familiar with the appearance of her more fortunate sisters of the city. Neither had she before known the nature and appearance of the shop girls with whom she now compared poorly. They were pretty in the main, some even handsome, with an air of independence and indifference which added, in the case of the more favoured, a certain piquancy. Their clothes were neat, in many instances fine, and wherever she encountered the eye of one it was only to recognise in it a keen analysis of her own position—her individual shortcomings of dress and that shadow of *manner* which she thought must hang about her and make clear to all who and what she was. A flame of envy lighted in her heart. She realised in a dim way how much the city held—wealth, fashion, ease—every adornment for women, and she longed for dress and beauty with a whole heart.

On the second floor were the managerial offices, to which after some inquiry, she was now directed. There she found other girls ahead of her, applicants like herself, but with more of that self-satisfied and independent air which experience of the city lends; girls who scrutinised her in a painful manner. After a wait of perhaps three-quarters of an hour, she was called in turn.

"Now," said a sharp, quick-mannered Jew, who was sitting at a roll-top desk near the window, "have you ever worked in any other store?"

"No, sir," said Carrie.

"Oh, you haven't," he said, eyeing her keenly.

"No, sir," she replied.

"Well, we prefer young women just now with some experience. I guess we can't use you."

Carrie stood waiting a moment, hardly certain whether the interview had terminated.

"Don't wait!" he exclaimed. "Remember we are very busy here."

Carrie began to move quickly to the door.

"Hold on," he said, calling her back. "Give me your name and address. We want girls occasionally."

When she had gotten safely into the street, she could scarcely restrain the tears. It was not so much the particular rebuff which she had just experienced, but the whole abashing trend of the day. She was tired and nervous. She abandoned the thought of appealing to the other department stores and now wandered on, feeling a certain safety and relief in mingling with the crowd.

In her indifferent wandering she turned into Jackson Street, not far from the river, and was keeping her way along the south side of that imposing thoroughfare, when a piece of wrapping paper, written on with marking ink and tacked up on the door, attracted her attention. It read, "Girls wanted—wrappers & stitchers." She hesitated a moment, then entered.

The firm of Speigelheim & Co., makers of boys' caps, occupied one floor of the building, fifty feet in width and some eighty feet in depth. It was a place rather dingily lighted, the darkest portions having incandescent lights, filled with machines and work benches. At the latter laboured quite a company of girls and some men. The former were drabby-looking creatures, stained in face with oil and dust, clad in thin, shapeless, cotton dresses and shod with more or less worn shoes. Many of them had their sleeves rolled up, revealing bare arms, and in some cases, owing to the heat, their dresses were open at the neck. They were a fair type of nearly the lowest order of shop-girls—careless, slouchy, and more or less pale from confinement. They were not timid, however; were rich in curiosity, and strong in daring and slang.

Carrie looked about her, very must disturbed and quite sure that she did not want to work here. Aside from making her uncomfortable by sidelong glances, no one paid her the least attention. She waited until the whole department was aware of her presence. Then some word was sent around, and a foreman, in an apron and shirt sleeves, the latter rolled up to his shoulders, approached.

"Do you want to see me?" he asked.

"Do you need any help?" said Carrie, already learning directness of address.

"Do you know how to stitch caps?" he returned.

"No, sir," she replied.

"Have you ever had any experience at this kind of work?" he inquired.

She answered that she had not.

"Well," said the foreman, scratching his ear meditatively, "we do need a stitcher. We like experienced help, though. We've hardly got time to break people in." He paused and looked away out of the window. "We might, though, put you at finishing," he concluded reflectively.

"How much do you pay a week?" ventured Carrie, emboldened by a certain softness in the man's manner and his simplicity of address.

"Three and a half," he answered.

"Oh," she was about to exclaim, but checked herself and allowed her thoughts to die without expression.

"We're not exactly in need of anybody," he went on vaguely,

looking her over as one would a package. "You can come on Monday morning, though," he added, "and I'll put you to work."

"Thank you," said Carrie weakly.

"If you come, bring an apron," he added.

He walked away and left her standing by the elevator, never so much as inquiring her name.

11. HENRY SUZZALLO

*The Teaching Profession**

Henry Suzzallo was born in San José, California, the eighth of nine children of immigrant parents from Ragusa (now Dubrovnik), Yugoslavia. Although his family was poor, Henry attracted the notice of two local businessmen, Emile and Jesse Levy, who helped him to an education. A brilliant academic record at Stanford led him into the San Francisco public school system in which he became Deputy Superintendent within a few years. He taught at Stanford and at Teachers College before becoming President of the University of Washington in 1915. A political falling-out with the Governor led to his resignation in 1926; and four years later Suzzallo became President of the Carnegie Foundation for the Advancement of Teaching. His concern with the professional quality of education emerges in the address that follows.

THE NATURE OF THE DISTINCTION

. . . However worthy and respectable every useful work may be . . . there are some which carry wider responsibility, and call for larger knowledge and skill, greater power of initiative, and increased capacity for co-operation. These, as history proves, are more readily classified as professions. But there seems to be no justification for the assumption that one particular work, such as law, is inevitably to be included among the professions, and that another, such as business, is just as inevitably to be excluded. Law may cease to be professional in its

* Henry Suzzallo, "The Reorganization of the Teaching Profession," National Education Association, *Journal of Proceedings and Addresses of the Fifty-First Annual Meeting* (Ann Arbor, 1913), pp. 364–71.

practice, and business may attain professional ideals; which is to say that the manner in which a service is rendered is quite as important as the situations with which it deals.

Every traditional profession, therefore, must conform to certain standards of workmanship if it is to maintain its place; and every form of service which aspires to professional status must reconstruct its practice so that these special standards gain a larger recognition than is now current. The public esteem given to the existing professions is not a perpetual grant; it is conferred only for an indeterminate period of good behavior.

COMPARATIVE STUDY OF PROFESSIONAL STANDARDS

What, then, are the important standards which determine professional practice? A careful survey of the accepted policies and ethical codes of existing professions reveals many detailed variations, but they all agree in implying that there are certain positive characteristics which all types of professional life possess. These qualities are corroborated in a negative way by recognized types of unprofessional conduct, and by the current arguments offered for considering business and the trades nonprofessional in their present status.

FOUR QUALITIES OF PROFESSIONAL SERVICE

The fundamental qualities which seem to characterize work done in a professional spirit are: (1) Professional work must always be performed as a social service. (2) It requires an expert knowledge and technic. (3) It must be practiced with a resource and initiative adequate to meet changing needs. (4) It is a co-operation that takes account of the interests of all human factors involved. Tersely stated, professional work is: (1) a social servantship, (2) an expert service, (3) a mastery of crises, (4) an ethical co-operation.

PUBLIC EDUCATION A SOCIAL SERVANTSHIP

It is because the professions, traditional and modern, usually exercise a great influence upon fundamental social rights and standards of high value that they have their enlarged importance. The incidental effects of professional practice on social welfare are usually more important than the fact that the individual practitioner does or does not enjoy a prosperous livelihood. Hence every member of a profession is asked to pursue his work as one primarily for public service and secondarily for earning his living. If his work is dominated by a sense of personal financial gain and loss, he is likely to make it a business rather than a profession. When we say "business is business," we usually mean that we have failed to meet some moral obligation that society would prefer to have us keep. This may be fairly tolerable in business; it is intolerable in a profession, because the social and human considerations that are involved are too precious to be set aside. The lawyer unavoidably deals with the constitutional rights of life, liberty, property, and the pursuit of happiness; the doctor, with the natural gifts of health, efficiency, and physical life; the minister, with that religious faith or optimism which guarantees an effective confidence in an orderly and moral universe; the teacher, with all the potentialities of childhood, the gifts of natural and institutional life. From one point of view, there is not a single unprofessional practice that is not a result of ignoring or violating some such fundamental personal or social consideration. A doctor having the necessary skill ought not to let men die of neglect because they cannot pay. Neither should a lawyer let the innocent go to jail merely because they are too poor to pay a fee. The professional sins of teachers and ministers are of another sort. They are a conscienceful people. They fall short because they do not see their full social duty, rather than because, seeing it, they will not render service.

For these reasons the teaching and other professions should be dominated by a consciousness of social conditions and ends.

Their work should be regarded as primarily an expression of unselfish social service.

In a rough way, society tries to protect itself against an abuse of these large powers which are incident to the earnings of a livelihood in professional service. It demands more general culture preliminary to the study and practice of a profession. This means that it requires that the professional practitioner, because of his peculiar powers and temptations, must be given a fundamental knowledge of those values, ideals, and traditions which are fundamental to our social life. Hence the boy may go to a trade, or a business, at the close of the elementary school, but he may not start his work as a teacher, lawyer, doctor, or nurse before he has passed thru the high school at least. The secondary school means a broader and more intensive view of life in general than the elementary school. Professional work is not merely more scientific and complex than nonprofessional service—it has intimate connections with the fundamental values of life. It ramifies to such an extent that it touches all the important aspects of our civilization. Hence the need for a wider, more intensive general education, which will foster a knowledge of, and a reverence for, human rights and institutions.

But a wide basis in general education is not an adequate quaranty that such influential work will be done in that professional spirit which guarantees the conservation of fundamental rights and essential values. Professional training must itself be socialized, so that the bearing of particular practices on general welfare will always be obvious to the practitioner.

In this connection it is often said that the teaching profession lacks an adequate social consciousness. It is too frequently academic rather than vital in its approach to important matters bearing on the training of children for life. It is more often bookish than social in its interpretations of the place of knowledge. Hence the social world moves on, and the profession remains devoted to old knowledge and old needs preserved by the isolation of the school. When at last the school reacts against our overconservative traditionalism, the schoolmaster's devotions are likely to be caught by a new social demand more forceful than real. We do not know the social world either by direct experience or thru social science, and we are either halting or defective in our responses to a changing civilization.

But the overconservative or overfaddistic tendencies just mentioned are not more pathetic failures than the new enthusiasms of many teachers for organization on an economic basis. Pensions, tenure, and pay are vital questions, but they cannot and should not be made the prime basis of teachers' associations. To do so is to focus our professional vigor on personal return rather than on impersonal service. The prime end of teachers' organizations should be to make more efficient our social servantship. To the extent that the economic status of teachers affects their efficiency, and because teachers are human beings with certain economic and personal rights of their own, all these financial difficulties are a legitimate concern. But service, not selfishness, must be the dominant ideal.

PUBLIC EDUCATION AN EXPERT SERVICE

As teachers we are set aside to perform a more or less specialized duty. We should not have schools if homes could do the work as well. Teachers must have more power about their business than ordinary laymen. Otherwise we are not expert in our workmanship. The authority with which we speak should be based, not upon mere years of service, but on superior intelligence and skill in doing our work. In a world full of intelligent people, we shall have to stir ourselves to keep ahead in a work which has so much to do with life in general, a field in which all men play some part. To be expert necessitates definite technical powers along several lines.

The teacher's chief business is to intermediate between childhood and society. He must get children over into social life successfully else they will be failures. He must carry civilization over from books and constitutions into human beings or it will become a dead letter. Successful life is made up of *knowing* the facts of life and *reacting* appropriately to them. The teacher must first be a wholesome and successful social human being who knows life in terms of (a) superior command over its essential facts and conditions (scholarship), and (b) superior attitudes toward them (socialized character). But this only provides the superior man out of whom the teacher is to be made. The second requirement is that he should have expert power to transmit truth and attitude. This requires (a) superior conscious methods for teaching truth (pedagogy), and (b) superior unconscious methods for transmitting values, attitudes, standards, or ideals (personality). The ideal of expert service lays down these standards; therefore: (1) Every teacher should have an adequate cultural resource for his work. The elementary teacher should have a high-school education; the secondary teacher a college training, etc. (2) Every teacher must have a professional course in general and special methods of teaching coupled with some scientific knowledge of the educational psychology and educational sociology basic to their interpretation and application. (3) Every teacher must acquire an interest in, and command over, the fundamental problems and purposes of modern social life thru personal contact with, and extensive study of, social affairs. (4) Every teacher must react upon the situations of school life and classroom instruction with sincere and wholesome reactions that will be true to the larger aspirations of the outside world.

The supervising and administrative officials need all these expert powers of the teacher of children, if not in terms of a practical and active power, at least in terms which guarantee ready appreciation and constructive criticism. And they require more. In our modern school systems there are gathered about the teaching function many other functions, such as school organization, school administration, and school management. In all of these, the modern superintendent is obliged to have power superior to that of his teaching staff, his board of education, or the laymen of his community.

When we look at the profession as we know it and apply

these standards, our defects seem large. We are appalled by the large number of certificated teachers who have had little more general education than that of the grade of school in which they teach, and no special professional training for their particular task. We feel less confidence in our practical leaders when we realize that they are for the most part graduate-teachers who have had no additional special training for their new obligations save the apprenticeship served in the practical school of trial and error. This was well enough when our men could grow up with the school system, but the time has passed when we can rely upon the gifted few who emerge; we must make provision for the systematic training of the many who will fill the posts of lesser and greater responsibilities. We cannot raise our standards for training teachers without raising those for training the supervisory staff. The work of public education must be made expert from top to bottom, if we would have the public respect and support. In no other way can we check that rebellion now beginning which arrays grade teachers against their official leaders.

PUBLIC EDUCATION A MASTERY OF CRISES

We might be richly endowed with the spirit of social service, expert in teaching children and administering the schools, and still lack the power needed to make us effective. Our adjustment is not a fixed one. The problems with which efficiency must deal constantly change. The conditions underlying teaching and administration vary because we have new selections of children and new problems of civilization to deal with. These variables create a constant succession of new difficulties that challenge our resourcefulness. They are the educational crises, personal and social, in which something important is at stake.

A man who spends his life in the ever-repeating and monotonous business of working the lever of a machine in a shoe factory has little opportunity to meet new problems. It is not normal for him to be facing and solving new situations, mental crises that require resource and thought. The very nature of his situation makes it impossible for him to become what every professional workman is—a master of crises.

No such limiting situation exists in teaching. The teacher is master of the school, unless he makes of it a machine which masters him. Every child is in a degree different from every other, and so with every class, and with every day with the same class. Always there is some new ignorance, doubt, hope, or discouragement to be coped with. Here the resource and tact of the teacher are called for fully. He must know and think. It is precious human stuff in trouble with which he deals.

As a lawyer is called in to redeem a client from a situation which jeopardizes his legal rights, as a doctor protects health, as a minister faces down the danger of shattered faith, so the teacher conserves the power of childhood, conquers the deadening touch of error and discouragement, fosters intellectual courage and the passion for goodness. The teacher is in short a minister to the intellectual, moral, and spiritual crises of childhood.

At least it should be so, if teaching is rightly practiced. If our teaching becomes such a monotonous drill and grind that the child feels it to be of little moment to him, then teaching is not a professional service. Schools cannot become "locksteps" and "machines" and at the same time render professional service.

The crucial nature of all teaching of the young is frequently missed because we are dealing with children and not with adults. Teaching is a "calling," tho the pupil does not personally "call" us into his life. We foresee his needs and serve them. Because childhood's troubles are solved situations to the adult it does not follow that they are not important to the child. Children's troubles are very real to them. To deny a child's curiosity as it pokes around the world may be to commit him to slow intellectual starvation. Harshly to hush up his play and his garrulousness is to cripple his ultimate power to act, express, and control himself. And then it is also true that childhood's troubles come close together, as they do not in an adult's world. A child is only a babe ushered into a great confusing universe. Nothing is old to him; everything is new. The very commonness of new problems in his life hides their crucial nature from us, who look for new problems to appear only now and then. Only as we approach childhood with the traits of full sympathy and versatile imagination can we serve little children, and make them men and women of the power "they were born to be."

The essence of efficient teaching is to be found in the modern gospel of reverencing the student's personality. In ever-variable teaching methods, rather than in a uniform and fixed use of device, is true mastery over childhood to be found. No greater teacher, no moderately efficient one, will forever crave a rigidly fixed school system, an unchanged course of study, the same subject, or the same grade. He will be happy for the adventure of meeting new problems, glad to hear a call to his resources, for these redeem teaching from deadening sameness and make of it a real and free art at once effective and congenial.

The spirit of mastery over varying needs, which should characterize classroom teaching, should also characterize every public-school function which has been differentiated from teaching. It should be present in the organization, administration, and supervision of schools, tho, sad to relate, it seldom is. It is the business of the school administrator to aid rather than hinder the growth of this spirit in the teacher, as it is his emphatic business to remold the structure of the school system to meet changing social conditions and aspirations of his community. Every school superintendent should aim to master the difficulties of the civilization in which he lives to the degree that the right education of men and women will contribute.

Yet it can scarcely be said that we have gracefully welcomed the doctrine that teaching as a professional work is a constant progressive adjustment to changing needs. Teachers teach the same old subjects in the same old way when they ought to be teaching many kinds of children in different ways. They still shudder when the superintendent hints at change in the course of study or methods of teaching. Superintendents still impose a deadening uniformity on teachers and children which kills the individualities and enthusiasms of both and ignores differing social conditions and psychological needs. And how slow we all are to perceive what our own social time and place require. The industrial leaders of our country have beaten three times on the doors of our elementary schools asking for the early development of those fundamental interests and skills that the vocation will later call for and specialize; once in terms of drawing, again in terms of manual training, now in terms of industrial arts. We have only begun to hear. Shall our minds not be quickened to the changing needs of our own times so that school organization and school teaching may be remolded again and again to the new efficiencies required? We cannot remain stubbornly conservative, become wildly radical, or affect a feeble responsiveness, and still do our full professional duty. We must be open of mind to changing circumstances, flexible in technic, scientific in point of view, and eager and masterful in our ministry to new educational problems, if we are to play our professional part in the world's great task.

TEACHING AN ETHICAL CO-OPERATION

The time has passed when we can trust that the spirit of service, expert workmanship, resourcefulness, and initiative will be adequately generated and distributed in the teaching profession by any such loose organization as we have had in the past. The leadership of the rare few and the spontaneous co-operation of unusually progressive minorities will still be needed; but we must make more efficient use of them. During the past fifty years every large private interest has learned the worth of corporate organization. The public interest in clean politics, the fair conduct of business, or efficient public schools is entitled to the massive power of a similar support. We can capitalize the isolated demands of those interested in spiritual and social welfare just as readily as we can gather the scattered savings of many men, prosperous in a small way. In public education the time has come when we must organize the forces that favor an efficient public education. First, we must organize the 500,000 American teachers who have a professional obligation to serve the public in maintaining good schools. Second, we must associate with them every layman who has enough surplus interest and energy to be specially devoted to the schools. I stress this association of citizens with professional teachers, for, unlike law and medicine, public-school teaching is a state matter. We need the counsel and the influence of laymen who have an interest in our democracy and our schools. We cannot make progress without consciousness of general needs, or without the support of public opinion.

At present teachers and laymen do not adequately understand and support each other. Worse, the teachers themselves do not understand each other. It can scarcely be said that the paltry ten or twelve thousand now included in the existing national association are an adequate representation of the whole group of public-school teachers. The various state associations are themselves not sufficiently inclusive. They enroll from one to eight thousand members who are more or less transient in their interest and membership, the geographical location of meetings and the administrative zeal of the officers being the chief factors in enrollment. These state associations have no direct connection with the national association; and no existing method of co-operation among the state associations is effective.

Both state and national associations are organizations with a merely occasional purpose. The chief function of the permanent officers is to arrange for the annual meetings, at which the main business of members is to listen to addresses. Such organizations usually have no power over practical educational affairs in the interim, and even the resolutions of such meetings have few consequences.

The result of this situation is plain. Bodies of laymen usually have more direct influence upon educational legislation than groups of professional teachers. We find it difficult to unify our own opinions in the face of small disagreements within the profession, for sheer lack of that machinery of association and communication which insures adequate information, intelligent discussion, and approximate unity of opinion. We are powerless to enforce our standards of right and wrong upon the public. Of this we have many evidences. The influence of partisan and personal politics still interfers with a full rendering to the public of an expert educational service. Teachers and books are still selected, in many places, by boards of eduation rather than superintendents. Many teachers still split their fees for the first month's work with teachers' agencies, the chief purpose of which is commercial, not professional. Some textbook and supply houses still exploit the public schools for their own ends.

The teacher or superintendent who stands against these influences encounters a pernicious hostility. Without the backing of an organized profession for his professional ideals of public service he is, in backward and indifferent communities, as likely as not to lose his position. Thereafter, that one failure to hold his position is, in matters of reappointment or promotion with boards of education, a presumption of incompetency rather than of superior training and standards. Thus the present status of professional organization permits a handicap to be placed upon superior courage and idealism in maintaining high standards of service.

12. CARL SANDBURG

*Heroes among the Plain People**

Carl Sandburg was born in Galesburg, Illinois, in 1878, the son of Swedish immigrants. His father was a blacksmith and Carl had to work as a milk-wagon driver, barbershop porter, and a house painter, but managed to attend Lombard College in his native city. After some travel he became secretary to the Mayor of Milwaukee and then held a variety of writing jobs. His poetry reflected the Middle Western environment in which he was raised and expressed a concern for the dignity of the common man to which the 1930's were particularly sensitive. He won the Pulitzer Prize for poetry in 1950. See also H. L. Golden, Carl Sandburg *(Cleveland, 1961); Richard Crowder,* Carl Sandburg *(New York, 1964).*

"The people is a myth, an abstraction."
And what myth would you put in place
    of the people?
And what abstraction would you exchange
    for this one?
And when has creative man not toiled
    deep in myth?
And who fights for a bellyful only and
    where is any name worth remembering
    for anything else than the human ab-
    straction woven through it with in-
    visible thongs?

* Carl Sandburg, *The People, Yes* (New York, 1936), pp. 30, 34–7, 72–5.

"Precisely who and what is the people?"
Is this far off from asking what is grass?
what is salt? what is the sea? what is
loam?
What are seeds? what is a crop? why must
mammals have milk soon as born or they
perish?
And how did that alfalfaland governor
mean it: "The common people is a mule
that will do anything you say except
stay hitched"? . . .

The people, yes, the people,
Everyone who got a letter today
And those the mail-carrier missed,
The women at the cookstoves preparing meals,
in a sewing corner mending, in a basement
laundering, woman the homemaker,
The women at the factory tending a stitching
machine, some of them the mainstay of the
jobless man at home cooking, laundering,
Streetwalking jobhunters, walkers alive and keen,
sleepwalkers drifting along, the stupefied and
hopeless down-and-outs, the game fighters
who will die fighting,
Walkers reading signs and stopping to study
windows, the signs and windows aimed
straight at their eyes, their wants,
Women in and out of doors to look and feel, to
try on, to buy and take away, to order and
have it charged and delivered, to pass by on
account of price and conditions,
The shopping crowds, the newspaper circulation,
the bystanders who witness parades, who
meet the boat, the train, who throng in
wavelines to a fire, an explosion, an accident—
The people, yes—

Their shoe soles wearing holes in stone steps, their
hands and gloves wearing soft niches in banisters of granite, two worn foot-tracks at the
general-delivery window,
Driving their cars, stop and go, red light, green
light, and the law of the traffic cop's fingers,
on their way, loans and mortgages, margins to
cover,
Payments on the car, the bungalow, the radio, the
electric icebox, accumulated interest on loans
for past payments, the writhing point of
where the money will come from,
Crime thrown in their eyes from every angle,
crimes against property and person, crime in
the prints and films, crime as a lurking
shadow ready to spring into reality, crime as
a method and a technic,
Comedy as an offset to crime, the laughmakers,
the odd numbers in the news and the movies,
original clowns and imitators, and in the best
you never know what's coming next even
when it's hokum,
And sports, how a muff in the seventh lost yesterday's game and now they are learning to
hit Dazzy's fadeaway ball and did you hear
how Foozly plowed through that line for a
touchdown this afternoon?
And daily the death toll of the speed wagons; a
cripple a minute in fenders, wheels, steel and
glass splinters; a stammering witness before a
coroner's jury, "It happened so sudden I
don't know what happened."
And in the air a decree: life is a gamble; take a
chance; you pick a number and see what you
get: anything can happen in this sweepstakes:
around the corner may be prosperity or the
worst depression yet: who knows? nobody:

you pick a number, you draw a card, you
shoot the bones.
In the poolrooms the young hear, "Ashes to
ashes, dust to dust, If the women don't get
you then the whiskey must," and in the
churches, "We walk by faith and not by sight,"
Often among themselves in their sessions of candor
the young saying, "Everything's a racket,
only the gyp artists get by."
And over and beyond the latest crime or comedy
always that relentless meal ticket saying
dont-lose-me, hold your job, glue your mind
on that job or when your last nickel is gone
you live on your folks or sign for relief,
And the terror of these unknowns is a circle of
black ghosts holding men and women in toil
and danger, and sometimes shame, beyond
the dreams of their blossom days, the days
before they set out on their own.
What is this "occupational disease" we hear
about? It's a sickness that breaks your health
on account of the work you're in. That's all.
Another kind of work and you'd have been
as good as any of them. You'd have been
your old self.
And what is this "hazardous occupation"? Why
that's where you're liable to break your neck
or get smashed on the job so you're no good
on that job any more and that's why you
can't get any regular life insurance so long as
you're on that job.
These are heroes then—among the plain people—
Heroes, did you say? And why not? They
give all they've got and ask no questions and
take what comes and what more do you
want?
On the street you can see them any time, some
with jobs, some nothing doing, here a down-

and-out, there a game fighter who will die
fighting. . . .

"So you want to divide all the money there is
and give every man his share?"
"That's it. Put it all in one big pile and split
it even for everybody."
"And the land, the gold, silver, oil, copper, you want
that divided up?"
"Sure—an even whack for all of us."
"Do you mean that to go for horses and cows?"
"Sure—why not?"
"And how about pigs?"
"Oh to hell with you—you know I got a couple of
pigs."

In the night and the mist these voices:
What is mine is mine and I am going to keep it.
What is yours is yours and you are welcome to keep it.
You will have to fight me to take from me what is mine.
Part of what is mine is yours and you are welcome to it.
What is yours is mine and I am going to take it from you.
In the night and the mist
the voices meet
as the clash of steel on steel
Over the rights of possession and control and the points:
what is mine? what is yours?
and who says so?

The poor were divided into
the deserving and the undeserving
and a pioneer San Franciscan lacked words:
"It's hard enough to be poor
but to be poor and undeserving . . ."
He saw the slumborn illborn wearyborn
from fathers and mothers the same
out of rooms dank with rot

and scabs, rags, festerings, tubercles, chancres,
the very doorways quavering,
"What's the use?"

"I came to a country,"
said a wind-bitten vagabond,
"where I saw shoemakers barefoot
saying they had made too many shoes.
I met carpenters living outdoors
saying they had built too many houses.
Clothing workers I talked with,
bushelmen and armhole-basters,
said their coats were on a ragged edge
because they had made too many coats.
And I talked with farmers, yeomanry,
the backbone of the country,
so they were told,
saying they were in debt and near starvation
because they had gone ahead like always
and raised too much wheat and corn
too many hogs, sheep, cattle.
When I said, 'You live in a strange country,'
they answered slow, like men
who wouldn't waste anything, not even language:
'You ain't far wrong there, young feller.
We're going to do something, we don't know what.'"
The drowning man in the river
answered the man on the bridge:
"I don't want to die,
I'll lose my job in the molding room of
the Malleable Iron and Castings Works."
And the living man on the bridge
hotfooted to the molding room foreman
of the Malleable Iron and Castings Works
and got a short answer:
"You're ten minutes late. The man who
pushed that fellow off the bridge
is already on the job."

"What do you want?" a passing stranger asked
 a County Kerry farmer.
"What is it I'm wantin'? Me byes and girruls
 is gone. The rain has rotted the prathies.
 The landlord has taken me pig for the rint.
 All I'm wantin' is the Judgment Day."

"The poor of the earth hide themselves together," wrote Job
 meaning in those days too they had a shantytown.
"As wild asses in the wilderness they must go forth, to seek
 food as their task," wrote Job meaning then too they carried the banner and hoped to connect with board and clothes somehow.
"In a field not theirs they harvest," wrote Job as though in
 Judea then the frontier was gone, as now in America instead of free homesteads the signs say: No Trespassing.
"The weaklings groan and the souls of the wounded cry for
 help," wrote Job taking special notice of those "forced to garner the vineyard of the wicked one," mentioning footless wanderers of Bible times as though the devices of men then too had an edge against the propertyless.

In the Sunflower State 1928 Anno Domini
a Jayhawker sunburnt and gaunt
drove to a loading platform
and took what he got for his hogs
and spoke before two other hog raisers:
 "Everything's lopsided.
"I raise hogs and the railroads and the banks take them away
 from me and I get hit in the hind end.
"The more hogs I raise the worse my mortgages look.
"I try to sleep and I hear those mortgages gnawing in the night
 like rats in a corn crib.
"I want to shoot somebody but I don't know who.
"We'll do something. You wait and see.
"We don't have to stand for this skin game if we're free Ameri-
 cans."

"Get off this estate."
"What for?"
"Because it's mine."
"Where did you get it?"
"From my father."
"Where did he get it?"
"From his father."
"And where did he get it?"
"He fought for it."
"Well, I'll fight you for it."

13. FIORELLO H. LA GUARDIA

*A Youth in Arizona**

Fiorello H. LaGuardia was born in 1882 in Prescott, Arizona, where his father was an army bandmaster, having come from Italy as accompanist to the singer Patti. Fiorello went to Europe as a young man and held various jobs in the American consulates in Budapest, Trieste, and Fiume before returning to New York in 1906. He studied law at night while acting as an interpreter in Ellis Island and was admitted to the bar in 1910. He lived in Greenwich Village and his first clients were laborers. Entering Republican politics, he was elected to Congress in 1916 but resigned to enlist in the army at the outbreak of war. He served in Congress until his election as Mayor of New York in 1932. His own background and his masterful command of a variety of languages gave him immediate contact with the heterogeneous population of the city; and he proved a dynamic and vigorous executive. He died in 1947. See also Arthur Mann, La Guardia *(Philadelphia, 1959).*

What I saw and heard and learned in my boyhood days in Arizona made lasting impressions on me. Many of the things on which I have such strong feelings—feelings which some of my opponents have regarded as unreasonable obsessions—were first impressed on my mind during those early days, and the knowledge I acquired then never left me. On some of those things I believe I am so right in my attitude that I remain uncompromising.

For instance, there is the professional politician. Though I

* Fiorello H. La Guardia, *The Making of an Insurgent* (Philadelphia, 1948), pp. 22–31.

have been in politics for well over forty years, I loathe the professional politician. I have never been a regular. I have fought political machines and party politics at every opportunity. This attitude had its origin in the loudly dressed, slick and sly Indian agents, political appointees, I saw come into Arizona. The first time I ever heard the word politician was at Fort Huachuca, when I was still a small child. The word was applied to those Indian agents. I learned afterwards that they got the jobs because they were small-fry ward heelers. I saw hungry Indians, and the little Indian kids watched us while we munched a Kansas apple or ate a cookie Mother baked. I knew, even as a child, that the government in Washington provided food for all those Indians, but that the "politicians" sold the rations to miners and even to general stores, robbing the Indians of the food the government provided for them. That was my first contact with "politicians."

I had my first experience with a lobby when I was about twelve. My father received a letter from someone in Washington stating that the pay of band leaders could be increased to $100 a month. The pay was then $60 a month. The letter also stated that band leaders could become commissioned officers. I can see the gleam in Dad's eye to this day as he fancied himself adorned with shoulder straps. It all seemed so easy: just sign the agreement to pay one month's salary when the bill became the law, and no further obligation except to send $50 for necessary expenses.

Even as a kid I could not understand this. Why the expenses? There were hints in the letter that it was necessary to see certain Representatives and Senators, and that there were disbursements to be met. It was rather crude. But this technique of the 'nineties didn't differ so much from the technique of our own 'forties. I don't know why, but I felt instinctively that it was wrong. And Mother was on my side. I figured it out that if the men in the various regiments at our post sent in this money, it would amount to $2,250. That was a lot of money in those days. "It's a fake, a swindle," I shouted, and when I ran out of adjectives in denouncing the scheme to my father, I resorted to what to me has always been the most odious thing you could say about people: "They're a bunch of politicians." Father, a musician, who never bothered with politics, was soon talked out of joining the plan. The band leaders of the Army are still waiting for those shoulder straps some of them sent their money to get.

My Arizona days made a lasting impression on me of the "tinhorn" and his ways. Professional gamblers in the West were known as "tinhorns." To me they have been "tinhorns" ever since. But there is one thing that could be said about the professional gambler of over a half century ago in the West; if he was alive, it was a fair assumption that he had not been caught gypping. Gamblers and saloonkeepers were an important part of pioneer Western life, but they were never a reputable part of the community. I remember very well how it used to be said that a gambler or a saloonkeeper could not join the Masons or the Elks. Gamblers were tolerated and patronized but not accepted. If a "tinhorn" in the West was caught cheating, he would never play another game—and there was no coroner's inquest. When I became Mayor of New York, I did my best to make life unpleasant for "tinhorns." They did not have to worry about being shot when caught red-handed, but they were made to fear the law.

My first attempt at applied mathematics—I must have been fourteen or fifteen then—was to figure out the percentage against the player in a crap game, a faro game and what was then called "policy," now known as "the numbers" and other fancy names as well as the old name "policy." Nearly every saloon in Prescott, Arizona, had its gambling department, mainly crap, faro and some Chinese game. There was, of course, a good deal of poker played—not under professional auspices. These games must have been exciting, according to the stories we kids would hear: the guns were laid on the table at easy reach, and of course the games were on the level.

Then "policy" came to town. I remember Mother telling me that it was the same as Lotto, which was sponsored in her native Trieste by the city or the state. Mother would play a ten-cent policy slip almost every week. If she had an exceptional dream, she would risk a quarter. She never won. No one else I knew ever won. The game did not last very long in Prescott and folded up after a few months. I figured it out then as nothing but petty larceny from the pockets of the poor, and showed my mother how she couldn't win.

I was astonished when I finally returned to New York to live in 1906 to find the great influence there of professional gamblers, numbers monarchs, and big "bookies," among others, with close political and judicial connections. They also had many, many friends among the press. I do not mean the reporters. It is easy for this scum of society, these economic vermin, to make friends when they are able to take bets and pay cash if the influential one "happens" to win, and to give unlimited credit if Mr. Big Shot happens to lose. They are no good. They never were any good in Prescott, or New York, and they never will be any good anywhere.

Another early impression that made its mark on my mind was gained from watching the railroad being built between Ashfork, Prescott and Phoenix. There was no machinery used then. It was all manpower and draft animals. The laborers were all immigrants, mostly Mexicans and Italians. If a laborer was injured, he lost his job. If he was killed, no one was notified, because there was no record of his name, address or family. He just had a number. As construction moved on, it left in its wake the injured, the jobless, the stranded victims. Even as a young boy, this struck me as all wrong, and I thought about it a great deal. The more I thought about it, the less able was I to make sense out of that kind of situation. Years later, when I studied law, I learned about such things as "assumed risk," "the fellow servant rule," "contributory negligence," and other similar principles of law, all for the benefit of the employer. I still thought they were all wrong, and later, as a legislator, I did what little I could to have these antiquated eighteenth century rules of law changed. None of them are in use today. Employers' liability, workmen's compensation laws for injury, safeguards against accidents, sanitary and safety laws in factories and for other jobs, unemployment insurance have taken their place. It was this early glimpse of the condition of working people, of their exploitation and their utter lack of protection under the law, which prompted me to take an interest on their side in society. I hope I have made a contribution to progress in this respect.

I remember when the troops were called out to guard the property of the Atlantic & Pacific Railroad during the great Pullman strike of 1894. I was twelve years old then, and it was the first strike I ever knew. I was deeply interested. The whole thing had started with a small group of workers in the bedding department of the Pullman Company, and it spread until it became a general railroad strike throughout the entire country. Even then, as a boy, it occurred to me that surely there should be some way of settling labor disputes of this kind, and that the law should afford equal protection to both sides. I recognized the necessity for President Cleveland's order that there should be no interference with transportation of the United States mail. But I did not quite understand why it was unlawful for employees to inform other employees of grievances, or why they should be kept away from one another by a court mandate, enforced by bayonets of United States soldiers.

These memories were very helpful. It was nearly a life-time later, as a member of Congress, that I had the opportunity of taking part in preparing the Railways Labor Act and in the passage of the Norris-La Guardia Anti-injunction Act. The job is not yet completed. Satisfactory machinery for equitable and just settlement of labor disputes is still required. I do hope some day to see that job completed.

I also got my first glimpse of racial feeling born of ignorance, out there in Arizona. I must have been about ten when a street organ-grinder with a monkey blew into town. He, and particularly the monkey, attracted a great deal of attention. I can still hear the cries of the kids: "A dago with a monkey! Hey, Fiorello, you're a dago too. Where's your monkey?" It hurt. And what made it worse, along came Dad, and he started to chatter Neapolitan with the organ-grinder.

He hadn't spoken Italian in many years, and he seemed to enjoy it. Perhaps, too, he considered the organ-grinder a fellow musician. At any rate, he promptly invited him to our house for a macaroni dinner. The kids taunted me for a long time after that. I couldn't understand it. What difference was there between us? Some of their families hadn't been in the country any longer than mine.

I have heard Gilbert and Sullivan's *Pinafore* in almost every language, in many countries; and in the rendition of the song, "For He Is an Englishman," the traditional gesture mimicking the organ-grinder and the word "Eyetalian" always annoyed me.

Early in my first administration as Mayor, a traffic report by the Police Department showed that among the obstacles to free traffic was the nuisance of the street organ-grinder. It was with a great deal of gusto that I banned the organ-grinder from the streets of the City of New York. It caused some resentment among those who were sentimental about organ-grinders. One woman came up to me at a social function and berated me mildly for depriving her of her favorite organ-grinder. "Where do you live?" I asked. "Park Avenue," she said. "What floor?" "The fourteenth," she answered.

In addition to the fact that I never did like organ-grinders ever since my days of ridicule in Prescott when that one organ-grinder came to town, I felt that they made our traffic problem in New York more difficult. I was accused by some New Yorkers who liked them of having no sentimental feelings about organ-grinders, of having no soul, of oppressing the poor, of neglecting more important things to deprive old residents and young children of their pleasure. Some of my correspondents were genial and some were angry. Cornelia Otis Skinner, Beatrice Kauffman, Viola Irene Cooper were among the literary defenders of the hurdy-gurdy. Petitions were got up urging me to rescind the order. My answer to my critics was that there had been a time when the hurdy-gurdy was the only means of bringing music to many people. That was also the time before automobiles filled our streets. With the advent of the phonograph and the radio that time had passed. Free public concerts in parks, libraries, museums and other public places had given ample opportunity to hear music. But, more important, traffic conditions had changed. Children were endangered by trucks and other automobiles when they gathered in the middle of streets to hear and watch the organ-grinders. Also, the simple, sentimental hurdy-gurdy man had become a victim of a racket. My sentimental correspondents did not realize that the Italians' instruments were rented to them by padrones at exorbitant fees. Their licenses from the city were in reality licenses to beg. About a year before I banned the organ-grinders, I had terminated the contracts with musicians on city ferry boats on the grounds that these were merely licenses to beg issued by the city. Despite those reasons, which I gave to my correspondents in answer to their protests, the defenders of the hurdy-gurdy men kept on writing to me for over a year, and some of them warned me that they wouldn't vote again for a man without a soul.

The people of the territory of Arizona could not vote in national elections. They had a delegate in the House of Representatives who could talk for them, but who had no vote. In the McKinley-Bryan Presidential campaign of 1896, though the people of Arizona could not vote, there was a great deal of campaigning that year for the election of this territorial delegate and for local offices. Arizona, being in the silver belt, leaned toward the Democratic side. The Democrats were then considered the liberal party and the Republicans the conservatives. Like people in all newly settled territory, the people of Arizona leaned toward the so-called liberal side. I was going on fourteen years old now, and this exciting Presidential campaign was the first in which I was able to take interest.

It was during my boyhood in Arizona that I first learned about corrupt local government, and I got my political education from Pulitzer's New York *World*. We had two newspapers in Prescott, the *Journal Miner* and the Prescott *Courier*. These were typical Bret Harte Western newspapers, devoted mostly to local news. When the Sunday edition of the New York *World* arrived in Prescott on the following Friday or Saturday, I would rush to Ross's drugstore where it was on display. There I had looked at the first funny sections I had ever seen, featuring the Yellow Kid. From that comic strip came the expression "yellow journalism." I have enjoyed the comics ever since.

When I got home with the Sunday *World*, I would carefully read every word of the *World's* fight against the corrupt Tammany machine in New York. That was the period of the lurid disclosures made by the Lexow investigation of corruption in the Police Department that extended throughout the political structure of the city. The papers then were filled with stories of startling crookedness on the part of the police and the politicians in New York. Unlike boys who grew up in the city and who hear from childhood about such things as graft and corruption, the amazing disclosures hit me like a shock. I could not understand how the people of the greatest city in the country could put up with the vice and crime that existed there. A resentment against Tammany was created in me at that time, which I admit is to this day almost an obsession. But I did not become cynical or lose faith in government. I was certain that good people could eliminate bad people from public office. But as I grew older, my hatred of corrupt politicians and my feeling against dishonest and inefficient government increased with the years in proportion with my experience of it.

When I went to live in New York again after my return from Europe in 1906, Tammany was once more all-powerful. It was the era of "honest graft." When I had to choose a political party, my choice was easy. I joined the Republican Party. I was young and innocent. A party in the minority cannot help being good and pure. That seemed the only avenue I could choose at the time in order to carry out my boyhood dreams of going to work against corrupt government.

14. ARTHUR MEIER SCHLESINGER

*The American—a New Man**

Arthur Meier Schlesinger was born in Xenia, Ohio, in 1888, the son of immigrants from Germany. He studied at Ohio State University and at Columbia, then taught at Ohio State and Iowa before coming to Harvard in 1931. He gave a new direction to the study and writing of American social history and trained a generation of historians who broadened the understanding of the American past. Apart from being actively involved in professional activities, he also played a prominent role in political and social affairs until his death in 1965. His own background and his historical understanding turned his thought to the American national character, one important aspect of which he analyzes in the selection that follows. See also Arthur M. Schlesinger, In Retrospect *(New York, 1963).*

"WHAT, THEN, IS THE AMERICAN, THIS NEW MAN?"

The question which forms the title of this essay has never ceased to arouse interest since Crèvecœur posed it in the last years of the Revolution. If we can learn why the American has come to be what he is, how he reacts instinctively to life, wherein he differs from other peoples, we shall have gained a deep insight into the springs of national behavior. Crèvecœur's own answer, the considered opinion of a Frenchman long resident in the New World, may still be read with profit. The American, he said, "is either an European, or the descendant of

* Arthur M. Schlesinger, "What, Then, Is the American, This New Man?" *American Historical Review*, XLVIII (1942–1943), pp. 225–44; reprinted in *Paths to the Present* (Boston, 1964), pp. 3–23.

an European, hence that strange mixture of blood which you will find in no other country. . . . *He* is an American, who leaving behind him all his ancient prejudices and manners, receives new ones from the new mode of life he has embraced, the new government he obeys, and the new rank he holds. . . . From involuntary idleness, servile dependence, penury, and useless labour, he has passed to toils of a very different nature. —This is an American."

I

Crèvecœur, of course, was one of a long procession of Europeans who have tried to describe and appraise the American. Their writings, though of varying merit, possess the common advantage of presenting an outsider's point of view, free from the predilections and prepossessions which blur the American's vision of himself. Viewing the scene from a different background, they are also sensitive to national divergences of which the native-born are usually unaware. Though bias may influence the individual observer's judgment, the total number of visitors has been so great as to render far more significant their points of agreement.

The composite portrait that emerges deserves thoughtful consideration. The attributes most frequently noted have been a belief in the universal obligation to work; the urge to move from place to place; a high standard of average comfort; faith in progress; the eternal pursuit of material gain; an absence of permanent class barriers; the neglect of abstract thinking and of the aesthetic side of life; boastfulness; a deference for women; the prevalence of spoiled children; the general restlessness and hurry of life, always illustrated by the practice of fast eating; and certain miscellaneous traits such as overheated houses, the vice of spitting and the passion for rocking chairs and ice water.

This inventory, so far as it goes, reveals qualities and attitudes recognizably American. Moreover, the travelers express no doubt as to the existence of a distinctive national character. The native-born looking at their fellow countrymen readily identify them as New Englanders or Middle Westerners or Southerners, as products of old American stock or newcomers of immigrant origin; and they remember that at one period of their history the differences between Northerner and Southerner sharpened into a tragic war. But the detached observer from Europe has always been less impressed by these regional deviations than by the evidences of fundamental kinship, even in slavery times.

James Bryce, most perspicacious of the commentators, goes so far as to say, "Scotchmen and Irishmen are more unlike Englishmen, the native of Normandy more unlike the native of Provence, the Pomeranian more unlike the Wurtemberger, the Piedmontese more unlike the Neapolitan, the Basque more unlike the Andalusian, than the American from any part of the country is to the American from any other part." His conclusion is that "it is rather more difficult to take any assemblage of attributes in any of these European countries and call it the national type than it is to do the like in the United States." The preoccupation of American historians with local and sectional diversities has tended to obscure this underlying reality.

But the particular "assemblage of attributes" recorded by the travelers leaves much to be desired. Not only is the list incomplete, but it carelessly lumps the significant with the trivial. Since the typical European tried to cover as much ground as possible in a short time, his attention was caught by externals, with the result that annoying traits and ways assumed undue importance, much as dust in the eye of a wayfarer distorts the appearance of the landscape. The gospel of work, for example, hardly deserves to be equated with the addiction to spitting. Though the more thoughtful sought to correlate what they noticed with the avowed ideals of the people, they usually lacked sufficient knowledge of the deeper historical trends to grasp either the true import of the ideals or how they manifested themselves in action. Finally, the traveler gave little attention to the crucial problem of why the special combination of qualities and attitudes had become endemic within the borders of the United States.

Hence the judgment of these onlookers, though often clear-sighted and frequently valuable as a corrective, leaves ample room for the student of United States history to venture an answer to Crèvecœur's question. If the native-born historian be suspect as a party in interest, he may at least strive to observe that counsel of objectivity which his professional conscience reveres.

II

What then is the American from a historian's point of view? The answer, briefly expressed, is so simple as to be a platitude. This "new man" is the product of the interplay of Old World influences and New World conditions. But just what heritage did the colonists bring with them from Europe, and why and how was it changed? Predominantly it involved that part of Europe's social experience in which they themselves had shared. The great bulk of the settlers, like the immigrants of later times, belonged to the poorer classes. They and their ancestors, whether in England or on the Continent, had been artisans, small tradesmen, farmers, day laborers—the broad foundation which supported the fine superstructure of European civilization. Shut out from a life of wealth, leisure and aesthetic enjoyment, they had tended to regard the ways of their social superiors with misgiving, if not resentment, and by the same token they magnified their own qualities of sobriety, diligence and thrift. Even when many of them, as notably in England, improved their economic position in the seventeenth and eighteenth centuries as a result of the great growth of commerce and industry, they continued to exalt the ancient proprieties.

This attitude found its classic spiritual expression in Calvinism. As Professor Tawney has said, Calvinism was "perhaps the first systematic body of religious teaching which can be said to recognize and applaud the economic virtues." It neatly fitted the glove of divine sanction to the hand of prudential conduct, thereby giving a sense of personal rectitude to the business of getting ahead in the world. But whether in Britain or elsewhere, whether in the religious groups directly concerned or those more remotely affected, Calvinism merely intensified a pre-existing bent. It is similarly true that the stringent code of morals often attributed to Calvinism, and more particularly to the Puritans, represented a lower-middle-class mentality long antedating the Geneva teachings.

This, then, was the type of humanity upon which the untamed New World wielded its influence. It has often been observed that plants and animals undergo modification when removed to America. These mutations arise from differences in climate and geography. But other factors as well affected transplanted people. One was the temperament of the settler, the fact that he was more adventurous, more ambitious or more rebellious against conditions at home than his fellows. It is not necessary to believe with William Stoughton in 1670 that "God sifted a whole Nation that he might send Choice Grain over into this Wilderness," but undoubtedly the act of quitting a familiar existence for a strange and perilous one demanded uncommon attributes of hardihood, self-reliance and imagination. Once the ocean was crossed, sheer distance from the old country and the challenge of new experiences further weakened the bonds of custom, evoked latent capacities and awakened the settler to possibilities of improvement hitherto unsuspected.

The undeveloped continent prescribed the conditions of living the new life, the mold within which the American character took shape. Farming was the primary occupation. At first resorted to to keep from starvation, it quickly became the mainstay of existence. The Revolution was fought by a people of whom nineteen out of twenty tilled the soil. With good land obtainable for more than a century after Independence, agriculture continued, though with gradually diminishing effect, to provide the pervasive atmosphere of American life and thought. "The vast majority of the people of this country live by the land, and carry its quality in their manners and opinions," wrote Ralph Waldo Emerson in 1844. Even when the hosts from Continental Europe began to swell the population after the middle of the nineteenth century, the rural temper of the nation remained pretty much unaltered, for many of the immigrants also turned to farming. This long apprenticeship to the soil made an indelible impress on the developing American character, with results which the modern age of the city has not wholly effaced.

Agriculture in the New World, however, differed from agriculture in the Old. This was the initial lesson which the colonists were compelled to learn. Those who had been farmers in their homelands found many of the traditional methods unsuitable. Those who had worked at urban occupations suffered an even greater handicap. Densely forested land must be cleared; the wildness taken out of the soil; a knowledge gained of indigenous plants and of the best means of growing them. The settlers of Jamestown were barely able to struggle through the early years. "There were never Englishmen left in a forreigne Country in such miserie as wee," wrote one of them. "Unsufferable hunger" caused them to eat horses, dogs, rats and snakes, and instances even of cannibalism are recorded. As is well known, the Plymouth colonists experienced similar trials. Yet in both cases the woods abounded with native fruits, berries, roots and nuts, game was plentiful, and nearby waters teemed with fish.

Had these courageous men been more readily adaptable, they could have enjoyed a gastronomic abundance beyond the dreams of the wealthiest classes at home. But they had never faced such an experience before, and reversion to a stage of civilization which the white man had long since outgrown was not easy. At the very first, all the early settlements actually imported food supplies; the Swedish colony on the Delaware did so for twenty years. A knowledge of self-sufficient farming came slowly and painfully, with untold numbers of men, women and children perishing in the process. In the long run, however, the settlers learned how to master their environment. Utilizing native crops and Indian methods of tillage, they abandoned the intensive cultivation required by the limited land resources of the Old World. It was simpler to move on to new fields when the fertility of the old was exhausted. The typical farm was a small one, worked by the owner and his family. Even when the system of staple production developed in the South, the small independent farmers considerably outnumbered the great slaveholding planters.

Though the colonial agriculturalist owed much to the savage, he had no wish to live like one. Accustomed in the old country to simple comforts and mechanical devices in the home and about the farm, he duplicated them in the wilderness. Every husbandman became a manufacturer and every farmhouse a small factory, producing flour, soap and candles, tanning skins, preparing the winter's meat supply, making nails, harness, hats, shoes and rugs, contriving tools, churns, casks, beds, chairs and tables. Such activities he supplemented with trapping, hunting and fishing. As cold weather closed in, he used his spare time getting out rough timber products, such as shingles and planks, or spent the long evenings before the open fireplace carving gunstocks or making brooms while his womenfolk knitted, spun or wove.

Under pressure of circumstances the farmer thus became a Jack-of-all-trades. As Chancellor Livingston wrote, "being habituated from early life to rely upon himself he acquires a skill in every branch of his profession, which is unkown in countries where labour is more divided." Take the case of a typical New Englander, John Marshall of Braintree, early in the eighteenth century. Besides tending his farm, he bought and sold hogs, was a painter and a brickmaker, as well as a carpenter turning out as many as three hundred laths in a day, and, in addition, a precinct constable. The primitive state of society fostered a similar omnicompetence in other walks of life, as the career of Benjamin Franklin so well exemplifies. Lord Cornbury, the governor of New York, characterized Francis Makemie as "a Preacher, a Doctor of Physick, a Merchant, an Attorney, or Counsellor at Law, and," he ruefully added, "which is worse of all, a Disturber of Governments."

The pioneer farmer of later times was the colonial farmer reborn. Up and down the Mississippi Valley he faced the same difficulties and opportunities as his forefathers, and he dealt with them in much the same way. As time went on, to be sure, he managed to buy more and more of his tools and household conveniences. He also took advantage of new inventions like the metal plow and the reaper, while increasingly he raised crops for sale in a general market. Meanwhile along the Atlantic Seaboard similar changes occurred. But whether in the older or newer communities these innovations affected the surface rather than the substance of the traditional mode of life. Nor did the advent of cities at first do much to alter the situation. Mere islands in a sea of forests and farms, they long retained marked rural characteristics and depended for a large part of their growth on continued accessions from the countryside.

III

What elements of the national character are attributable to this long-time agrarian environment? First and foremost is the habit of work. For the colonial farmer ceaseless striving constituted the price of survival; every member of the community must be up and doing. When anyone failed to do his part, the authorities, whether Puritan, Anglican or otherwise, laid a heavy hand upon the culprit. The Virginia Assembly in 1619 ordered the slothful to be bound over to compulsory labor. A few years later the Massachusetts Bay Company instructed Governor John Endecott that "noe idle drone bee permitted to live amongst us," and the General Court followed this up in 1633 with a decree that "noe prson, howse houlder or othr, shall spend his time idlely or unproffitably, under paine of such punishmt as the Court shall thinke meete to inflicte." Such regulations had long existed in England, where it was hoped, vainly, they might combat the unemployment and vagrancy of a surplus laboring class; in America the object was to overcome a labor shortage—that exigent problem of every new country. Of course, most of the settlers, having been inured to toil in the homeland, needed no official prodding. They were the hardest-working people on earth, their only respite being afforded by strict observance of the Sabbath as demanded by both church and state.

The tradition of toil so begun found new sustenance as settlers opened up the boundless stretches of the interior. "In the free States," wrote Harriet Martineau in 1837, "labour is more really and heartily honoured than, perhaps, in any other part of the civilised world." Alonzo Potter voiced the general opinion of the American people when he asserted a few years later, "Without a definite pursuit, a man is an excrescence on society. . . . In isolating himself from the cares and employments of other men, he forfeits much of their sympathy, and can neither give nor receive great benefit." Even when the usual motives for work did not exist, the social compulsion remained. As William Ellery Channing put it, "The rich man has no more right to repose than the poor," for nobody should so live as to "throw all toil on another class of society."

One source of Northern antagonism to the system of human bondage was the fear that it was jeopardizing this basic tenet of the American creed. "Wherever labor is mainly performed by slaves," Daniel Webster told the United States Senate, "it is regarded as degrading to freemen"; and the Kentucky abolitionist David Rice pointed out that in the South "To labour, is to *slave;* to work, is *to work like a Negroe.*" After the Civil War, General W. T. Sherman found public occasion to thank God that now at long last Southern whites would have "to earn an honest living."

Probably no legacy from our farmer forebears has entered more deeply into the national psychology. If an American has no purposeful work on hand, the fever in his blood impels him nevertheless to some visible form of activity. When seated he keeps moving in a rocking chair. A European visitor in the

1890's saw more fact than fancy in a magazine caricature which pictured a foreigner as saying to his American hostess, "It's a defect in your country, that you have no leisured classes." "But we have them," she replied, "only we call them tramps." The traveler's own comment was: "America is the only country in the world, where one is ashamed of having nothing to do."

This worship of work has made it difficult for Americans to learn how to play. As Poor Richard saw it, "Leisure is the Time for doing something useful"; and James Russell Lowell confessed,

> Pleasure doos make us Yankees kind o'winch,
> Ez though 't wuz sunthin' paid for by the inch;
> But yit we du contrive to worry thru,
> Ef Dooty tells us thet the thing's to du.

The first mitigations of the daily grind took the form of hunting, fishing, barn-raisings and logrollings—activities that had no social stigma because they contributed to the basic needs of living. As the years went on, the great Southern planters, imitating the landed gentry in England, developed rural diversions of an elaborate sort; but their example, like that of the fashionable circles in the Northern cities, merely made the common man all the more self-conscious when he turned to recreation. Nor did the mid-nineteenth-century German and Irish immigrants, who indulged in spontaneous enjoyments when the day was over, have any other effect upon the native stock than to reinforce suspicions of the newcomers formed on other grounds. "The American," wrote the New Yorker Henry T. Tuckerman in 1857, "enters into festivity as if it were a serious business." And a serious business it has in considerable degree continued to be ever since.

Into it goes all the fierce energy that once felled the forests and broke the prairies. Americans play games not for fun but to win. They attend social gatherings grimly determined to have a "good time." Maxim Gorky said of Coney Island, "What an unhappy people it must be that turns for happiness here."

The "rich gift of extemporizing pleasures," of taking leisure leisurely, seems alien to the national temper. It is significant that the English *Who's Who* includes the recreations of the notables listed, while the American does not.

The importance attached to useful work had the further effect of helping to make "this new man" indifferent to aesthetic considerations. To the farmer a tree was not a thing of beauty and a joy forever, but an obstacle to be replaced as quickly as possible with a patch of corn. In the words of an eighteenth-century American, "The Plow-man that raiseth Grain is more serviceable to Mankind, than the Painter who draws only to please the Eye. The Carpenter who builds a good House to defend us from the Wind and Weather, is more serviceable than the curious Carver, who employs his Art to please the Fancy." The cult of beauty, in other words, had nothing to contribute to the stern business of living; it wasn't "practical." The bias thus given to the national mentality lasted well into America's urban age. One result has been the architectural monotony and ugliness which have invariably offended travelers used to the picturesque charm of Old World cities.

IV

On the other hand, the complicated nature of the farmer's job, especially during the first two and a half centuries, afforded an unexcelled training in mechanical ingenuity. These ex-Europeans and their descendants became a race of whittlers and tinkers, daily engaged in devising, improving and repairing tools and other utensils until, as Emerson said, they had "the power and habit of invention in their brain." "Would any one but an American," asked one of Emerson's contemporaries, "have ever invented a milking machine? or a machine to beat eggs? or machines to black boots, scour knives, pare apples, and do a hundred things that all other peoples have done with their ten fingers from time immemorial?"

As population increased and manufacturing developed on a

commercial scale, men merely turned to new purposes the skills and aptitudes that had become second nature to them. Thus Eli Whitney, who as a Massachusetts farm youth had made nails and hatpins for sale to his neighbors, later contrived the cotton gin and successfully applied the principle of interchangeable parts to the production of muskets; and Theodore T. Woodruff, a New York farm boy, won subsequent fame as the inventor of a sleeping car, a coffee-hulling machine and a steam plow. In this manner another trait became imbedded in the American character.

The farmer's success in coping with his multitudinous tasks aroused a pride of accomplishment that made him scorn the specialist or expert. As a Jack-of-all-trades he was content to be master of none, choosing to do many things well enough rather than anything supremely well. Accordingly, versatility became another outstanding American attribute. In public affairs the common man agreed with President Jackson that any intelligent citizen could discharge the duties of any governmental office. He had an abiding suspicion of the theorist or the "scholar in politics," preferring to trust his own quick perceptions and to deal from day to day with matters as they arose. In his breadwinning pursuits the American flitted freely from job to job in marked contrast to the European custom of following occupations which often descended from father to son.

The most casual scrutiny of the *Dictionary of American Biography* discloses countless instances reminiscent of John Marshall and Francis Makemie in colonial times. Thomas Buchanan Read, born on a Pennsylvania farm, was in turn a tailor's apprentice, grocer's assistant, cigar maker, tombstone carver, sign painter and actor before he became a portrait painter, novelist and poet. Another personage is listed as "ornithologist and wholesale druggist"; another as "preacher, railway president, author"; and still another as "physician, merchant, political leader, magazine editor, poet, and critic." The wonder is that, despite such a squandering of energies, they could yet gain sufficient distinction in any phase of their activities to be recalled by posterity.

Even in his principal occupation of growing food, the farmer encountered harsh criticism from foreign observers because of the way he wore out the land, neglected livestock and destroyed forest resources. But Old World agriculture rested on a ratio of man to land which in the New World was the reverse. It was as logical for the American farmer to "mine" the soil and move on to a virgin tract as it was for the European peasant to husband his few acres in the interest of generations unborn. Not till the opening years of the twentieth century, when the pressure of population dramatized the evils of past misuse, did the conservation of natural resources become a set national policy.

Meanwhile the tradition of wasteful living, bred by an environment of plenty, had fastened itself upon the American character, disposing men to condone extravagance in public as well as in private life. Even governmental corruption could be winked at on the ground that a wealthy country like the United States could afford it. In their daily living, Americans were improvident of riches that another people would have carefully preserved. One newcomer from England in the early nineteenth century wrote that the apples and peaches rotting in Ohio orchards were more "than would sink the British fleet." Another said of her neighbors that she wished "the poor people of England had the leavings of their tables, that goes to their dogs and hogs." A great national emergency like that of the Axis war revealed the extent to which the practice still prevails. People learned that by responding to the government's appeal to salvage kitchen fats, old iron and other materials usually discarded they could make a substantial contribution to the war effort.

Toward women the American male early acquired an attitude which sharply distinguished him from his brother in the Old World. As in every new country, women had a high scarcity value, both in the colonies and later in the pioneer West. They were in demand not only as sweethearts and wives, but also because of their economic importance, for they performed the endless work about the house and helped with the heavy farm labor. "The cry is everywhere for girls; girls, and more girls!" wrote a traveler in 1866. He noted that men outnumbered women in thirty-eight of the forty-five states and territories. In California the proportion was three to one; in Colorado, twenty to one. "Guess my husband's got to look after me, and make himself agreeable to me, if he can," a pretty Western girl remarked, "if he don't, there's plenty will." In the circumstances men paid women a deference and accorded them a status unknown in older societies. European observers attributed the high standard of sex morals largely to this fact, and it is significant that the most rapid strides toward equal suffrage took place in those commonwealths whose rural characteristics were strongest.

V

Since the agriculturalist regarded his farm as only a temporary abode—an investment rather than a home—he soon contracted the habit of being "permanently transitory." Distances that would have daunted the stoutest-hearted European deterred "this new man" not at all. Many an Atlantic Coast family migrated from place to place across the continent until the second or third generation reached the rim of the Pacific, then the next one began the journey back. "In no State of the Union," wrote James Bryce in 1888, "is the bulk of the population so fixed in its residence as everywhere in Europe; in many it is almost nomadic."

But for this constant mingling of people and ideas the spirit of sectionalism would have opened far deeper fissures in American society than it did, for the breadth of the land, the regional diversification of economic interests and the concentration of European immigrants in certain areas were all factors conducive to disaffection and disunity. Apart from the crisis of 1861, however, it has always been possible to adjust sectional differences peaceably. The war between North and South might itself have been avoided if the system of slave labor had not increasingly stopped the inflow of persons from other parts of the country as well as from Europe. Denied such infusions of new blood, the Southerners lived more and more to themselves, came to exalt their peculiarities over the traits they had in common with their fellow countrymen and, in the end, determined to establish an independent state.

As the nation grew older and its institutions took on a more settled aspect, the locomotive tendencies of the Americans showed no signs of abatement. On the principle of the man biting the dog, the *New York Times*, June 14, 1942, reported that a resident of Sebastapol, California, had lived in the same house for fifty years, though it admitted that his ten brothers and sisters had left the town. In the 1950's one out of five persons the country over changed his residence, a third of them removing to other states.

With the advent of the low-priced motorcar and the passion for long-distance touring, the rippling movement of humanity came to resemble the waves of the ocean. It seems as though the pursuit of happiness has become the happiness of pursuit. Foreigners had earlier expressed amazement at the spectacle of dwellings being hauled along the streets from one site to another, but in the last twenty years the American people have discovered in the automobile trailer a means of constantly living on wheels. In 1959 alone, sales of these vehicular homes amounted to almost $700,000,000.

Geographic or horizontal mobility, however, has been a less fundamental aspect of American life than social or vertical mobility, though the two are not unrelated. The European conception of a graded society, with each class everlastingly performing its allotted function, vanished quickly amidst primitive surroundings that invited the humblest to move upward as well as outward. Instead of everybody being nobody, they found that anybody might become somebody. In the language of James Russell Lowell, "Here, on the edge of the forest, where civilized man was brought face to face again with nature and taught mainly to rely on himself, mere manhood became a fact of prime importance." This emancipation from hoary custom was "no bantling of theory, no fruit of forethought," but "a gift of the sky and of the forest."

Accordingly, there arose the ingrained belief in equality of opportunity, the right of all men to a free and fair start—a view which in one of its most significant ramifications led to the establishment of free tax-supported schools. This was far from being a dogma of enforced equality. To benefit from equality of opportunity a man must be equal to his opportunities, with the government serving principally as an umpire to supervise the game with a minimum of rules. The upshot was a conception of democracy rigorously qualified by individualism.

This individualistic bias sometimes assumed forms that defied government. The colonists in their relations with the mother country evaded unwelcome regulations and, prompted by their theologians and lawyers, insisted that acts of Parliament contrary to their "unalienable rights" were void. Within the colonies those who dwelt remote from centers of law and order adopted a like attitude toward the provincial authorities. The Scotch-Irish who illegally occupied Pennsylvania soil in the early eighteenth century contended "it was against the laws of God and nature, that so much land should be idle while so many Christians wanted it to labor on and to raise their bread." As a substitute for constituted authority the settlers sometimes created their own unofficial tribunals, which adjudicated property titles and punished offenders against the public peace. In other instances they resorted to the swifter retribution of individual gunplay, or of mob action and lynch law, for from taking the law into one's hands when it could not function it was but a step to taking the law into one's hands when it did not function as one wanted it to.

The tendency to violence so generated has continued to condition the national mentality to the present time. Thoreau, the great philosopher of individualism, knew of no reason why a citizen should "ever for a moment, or in the least degree, resign his conscience to the legislator," declaring that "we should be men first, and subjects afterward." A similar conviction undoubtedly inspired William H. Seward's flaming declaration to the proslavery Senators in 1850 that "there is a higher law than the Constitution," just as it actuated the thousands of church-going Northerners who secretly banded together to violate the Fugitive Slave Act. But generally it has been self-interest or convenience, rather than conscience, that has provided the incentive to lawbreaking, as in the case of the businessman chafing against legislative restrictions or of the motorist disobeying traffic regulations. Sometimes the attitude has paraded under such high-sounding names as states' rights and nullification. This lawless streak in the American character has often been directed to wrong purposes, but it has also served as a check on the abuse of governmental powers and as a safeguard of minority rights.

In still another aspect, the individualism of the pioneer farmer does much to explain the intense cultivation of the acquisitive spirit. In the absence of hereditary distinctions of birth and rank the piling up of wealth constituted the most obvious badge of social superiority, and once the process was begun, the inbred urge to keep on working made it difficult to stop. "The poor struggle to be rich, the rich to be richer," remarked an onlooker in the mid-nineteenth century. Thanks to equality of opportunity with plenty for all, the class struggle in America has consisted in the struggle to climb out of one class into a higher one. The zest of competition frequently led to sharp trading, fraud and chicanery, but in the popular mind guilt attached less to the practices than to being caught at them. Financial success was accepted as the highest success, and not till the twentieth century did a religious leader venture to advance the un-American doctrine that ill-gotten wealth was "tainted money," even when devoted to benevolent uses.

VI

It would be a mistake, however, to think of the American simply as a mechanism set in motion by dropping a coin in the slot. When President Coolidge made his famous remark, "The business of America is business," he quite properly added, "The chief ideal of the American people is idealism. I cannot repeat too often that America is a nation of idealists." This ambivalence puzzled foreign commentators, who found it difficult, for example, to reconcile worship of the Almighty Dollar with the equally universal tendency to spend freely and give money away. In contrast to Europe, America has had practically no misers, and one consequence of the winning of Independence was the abolition of primogeniture and entail. Harriet Martineau was among those who concluded that "the eager pursuit of wealth does not necessarily indicate a love of wealth for its own sake."

The fact is that, for a people who recalled how hungry and oppressed their ancestors had been through long centuries in the Old World, the chance to make money was like the sunlight at the end of a tunnel. It was the means of living a life of human dignity. It was a symbol of idealism rather than materialism. Hence "this new man" had an instinctive sympathy for the underdog, and even persons of moderate substance freely shared it with the less fortunate, helping to endow charities, schools, hospitals and art galleries and to nourish humanitarian undertakings which might otherwise have died a-borning.

The energy that entered into many of these causes was heightened by another national attitude: optimism. It was this quality that sustained the European men and women who with heavy hearts left ancestral homes to try their fortunes in a wild and far-off continent. The same trait animated the pioneer farmers confronted by the hardships, loneliness and terrors of the primeval forest, and served also to spur their successors who, though facing less dire conditions, were constantly pitted against both the uncertainties of the weather and the unpredictable demands of the market. When Thomas Jefferson remarked, "I steer my bark with Hope in the head, leaving Fear astern," he spoke for his compatriots. To doubt the future was to confess oneself a failure since the life history of almost any American documented the opposite view. A belief in progress blossomed spontaneously in such a soil.

If this belief made some men tolerant of present abuses in the confident expectation that time would provide the cure, it fired others with an apostolic zeal to hasten the happy day. As a keen observer in the middle of the last century said of his countrymen, "Americans are sanguine enough to believe that no evil is without a remedy, if they could only find it, and they see no good reason why they should not try to find remedies for all the evils of life." Not even fatalism in religion could long withstand the bracing atmosphere of the New World. This quality of optimism sometimes soared to dizzy heights, impelling men to strive for earthly perfection in communistic societies or to prepare to greet the imminent return of Christ.

It attained its most blatant expression, however, in the national addiction to bragging. At bottom, this habit sprang from pride in a country of vast distances and huge elevations plus an illimitable faith in its possibilities of being great as well as big. The American glorified the future in much the same spirit as the European glorified the past, both tending to exalt what they had the most of. And by a simple transition the American went on to speak of expected events as though they had already happened, being prompted perhaps by an urge to compensate for an inner sense of inferiority. This frame of mind led statesmen to cultivate spread-eagle oratory—a style which the *North American Review* in 1858 defined as "a compound of exaggeration, effrontery, bombast, and extravagance, mixed metaphors, platitudes, defiant threats thrown at the world, and irreverent appeals flung at the Supreme Being."

For the same reason the ordinary citizen resorted to hyperbole. In the thinly settled sections this manner of speech went by the name of tall talk, causing the backwoods to be known as a "paradise of puffers." A Frenchman, however, referred to a national, not a regional, trait when he said Americans seemed loath to admit that Christopher Columbus himself had not been an American, and it was an Easterner writing in an Eastern magazine who soberly averred, "It is easier, say the midwives, to come into this world of America . . . than in any other world extant." In business life this indulgent attitude toward truth lent itself to deliberate attempts to defraud, and made the land speculator with his "lithographed mendacity" the natural forerunner of the dishonest stock promoter of later times. Boastfulness is an attribute of youth which greater national maturity has helped to temper. Still the War Department in its manual of behavior for Yankee soldiers in England during the Axis war thought it prudent to admonish them: "Don't show off or brag or bluster."

This facility for overstatement has lent a distinctive quality to American humor. In the United States humor has never been part of a general gaiety of spirit. It has had to break through a crust of life thick with serious purpose. Hence it has had to be boisterous and bold, delighting in exaggeration, incongruities and farcical effects and reaching a grand climax in the practical joke. Out of a comic mood so induced arose such folk heroes as Mike Fink, Paul Bunyan, Pecos Bill and the myth-embroidered Davy Crockett, whose fabulous exploits flourished in oral tradition long before they were reduced to print. In deference to the national sobriety of temperament the most successful professional humorists have been those who told their yarns while preserving a decorous gravity of expression.

VII

If this analysis of national characteristics is well founded, then certain modifications of the pattern were inevitable when the primacy of rural life gave way to the rise of urbanism. That change began to take place in the latter years of the nineteenth century. In 1860 only a sixth of the people lived in towns of eight thousand or more, but by 1900 a third dwelt in such communities and today well over half do. Along with urban concentration has gone a remarkable development of means of communication and transport—the telephone, rural free delivery, interurban electric transit, good roads, the automobile, the movie, the radio, television—that carried city ideas and ways to "the very finger-tips of the whole land." Though most of the historic traits continued to thrive in this new milieu, some were moderated and a few disappeared. The time is too short to gauge the full consequences, but several of the reversals of attitude are noteworthy.

One is the importance which Americans have come to attach to cultural achievement. The ancient prejudice against "useless" activities could not long withstand the compelling opportunities of the city. In the city were to be found the best schools and colleges, the best newspapers and magazines, and practically all the bookstores, libraries, publishing houses, concert halls, conservatories of music, art museums and theaters. There, too, America made closest contact with the vital thought of Europe. Stimulated by such an atmosphere the writer or artist could also command an appreciative audience and financial support. Who can ever know how dreadful a toll the two and a half centuries of agricultural life exacted in terms of creative advances of the mind and spirit, how many a mute inglorious Milton succumbed to the unremitting struggle with Nature? For persons like these the city meant a glad release, giving them a chance to mature their powers, consort with kindred spirits and enter the lists for fame and fortune. Even in earlier times cultural stirrings had centered in the towns and cities. Now as the urban influence became uppermost, Americans commenced to make contributions to scholarship, science, literature and the fine arts that challenged comparison with the best Europe could offer.

As a necessary consequence, much of the former aversion to specialization of talent vanished. In a civilization rapidly growing more complex, men began to place a higher value on thoroughly mastering a skill or conquering a particular intellectual domain. The business of making a living tended to fall into compartments, with the men best equipped by training or experience reaping the greatest rewards. This trend characterized not only industry and trade but also the arts and sciences. Even in public life expert knowledge steadily played a larger part, notably in the administrative services of city, state and nation. The derisive references to the New Deal's "Brain Trust" came from political opponents who, however, did not intend to forgo the same advantage when they returned to power.

A further result of the altered aspect of American society has been the great impetus given to voluntary associative activity. In a country environment the gregarious instinct was constantly balked by the dearth of neighbors. The hunger for companionship could discover only occasional outlet, as at the county fair or in the agitated throng gathered from far and near for a camp meeting. Now, to the rural birthright of liberty and equality the city added the boon of fraternity. In a crowded community, like could find like. The reformer, the businessman, the wage earner, the intellectual worker, the sports lover, the ancestor worshiper—all these and many others gravitated into special groups to further interests held in common, and these local societies seldom failed to expand into nation-wide federations. Soon the population became divided between the organized and those who organized them, until, if the late Will Rogers is to be believed, "Americans will join anything in town but their own family. Why, two Americans can't meet on the street without one banging a gavel and calling the other to order." Thus the passion for associative activity came to be a sovereign principle of life.

Quite as noteworthy has been another effect of city growth: the discrediting of individualism as the automatic cure of social and economic ills. As the nineteenth century advanced, the increasing domination of the national economy by urban magnates of business and finance caused the farmers to demand that the government intercede to protect their right to a decent livelihood. In the cities the cramped living quarters, the growing wretchedness of the poor and the rise of difficult social problems also created doubts as to the sufficiency of the laissez-faire brand of democracy. Only the rich and powerful seemed now to profit from a reign of unbridled individualism. Though the solid core of ancient habit yielded stubbornly, the average man came gradually to believe that under the changed conditions it was the duty of the government of all to safeguard the opportunities of all. After the American fashion it was a doctrineless conviction, the product of an adjustment to new times for the sake of preserving the traditional spirit of self-reliance and free competition.

Though the gospel of work continued as unquestioned as ever, willing workers could no longer be certain of regular employment, particularly in the towns and cities. Every sudden jar to the nation's business structure rendered large numbers idle. Through no fault of his own, the laborer was being denied an essential part of his heritage. As early as 1893 the American Federation of Labor resolved that "the right to work is the right to life," and declared that "when the private employer cannot or will not give work the municipality, state or nation must." But it was not till the Great Depression destroyed the livelihood of people in all walks of life that this novel view became an article of American faith. The New Deal assumed the obligation not merely of succoring the hungry, but of creating jobs for the idle and of guarding against such hazards in the future by means of unemployment insurance, retirement pay for aged wage earners and special provisions for farmers. Thus what had started originally because of the community's need that all should work became transformed, first into a doctrine of the right to work, and then into the duty of society to provide the means of work.

VIII

The national character, as we at present know it, is thus a mixture of long-persisting traits tempered by some newly acquired ones. Based upon the solid qualities of those Europeans who planted the colonies, it assumed distinctive form under pressure of adaptation to the radically different situation. "Our ancestors sought a new continent," said James Russell Lowell. "What they found was a new condition of mind." The protracted tutelage to the soil acted as the chief formative influence, dispelling ancient inhibitions, freeing dormant energies, revamping mental attitudes. The rise of the city confirmed or strengthened many of the earlier characteristics while reshaping others. Probably no one of the traits is peculiar to the American people; some occasion apology rather than pride; but the aggregate represents a way of life unlike that of any other nation.

Just as the American character has undergone modification in the past, so it will doubtless undergo modification in the future. Nevertheless, certain of its elements seem so deeply rooted as to withstand the erosion of time and circumstance. Of this order are the qualities that made possible the development of the continent, the building of a democratic society and the continuing concern for the welfare of the underprivileged. These are attributes better suited to peace than to war, yet every great crisis has found the people ready to die for their conception of life so that their children might live it. The American character, whatever its shortcomings, abounds in courage, creative energy and resourcefulness, and is bottomed upon the profound conviction that nothing in the world is beyond its power to accomplish.

15. HEYWOOD BROUN

*Heritage from a Father**

Heywood Campbell Broun was born in Brooklyn, New York, in 1888. His father was an English immigrant but well off enough to enter his son's name for membership in the Racquet and Tennis Club. Broun studied at the Horace Mann School and at Harvard where he was a member of the distinguished class in 1910, although he lost his degree because he could not meet the language requirement. Broun took a succession of newspaper jobs and briefly went overseas as a war correspondent. In 1919 he began the column which would make him famous, particularly after he shifted to the New York World *in 1921. The Sacco-Vanzetti case made a liberal of him, and the Depression completed the task. He ran for Congress on the Socialist ticket and helped form the Newspaper Guild before he died in 1939. The essay that follows touches on the ambiguity of his relationship to his father.*

I had not intended to write anything about the death of my father, but I must. If I include many other fathers in this brief column, it may be possible to escape the charge of bad taste. But this has always been, by intent and instinct, a personal record. There is such a thing as leaning over too far.

On the day my father died I sat down and marked time by writing a column about the sea and cats and preoccupations which may move men to achieve a literary style. It was warmed-over stuff from half and three-quarters remembered columns written years ago.

But in any such painful effort to gain detachment from the

* Heywood Broun, *It Seems to Me* (New York, 1935), pp. 109–12.

thing actually in your mind there must be a very palpable insincerity. That I came to realize. And the acuteness of the realization was accented by the paragraphs in the newspapers which marked the passing of a man of 80.

And at this point it is fair enough to generalize. Save in the case of the very great, and perhaps not even then, the news notes must inevitably be inadequate. The reporter ascertains when this man was born and where, with what business activities he was affiliated, the list of his clubs and the names of surviving relatives. Of this one it is said that for forty years he was engaged in the cotton market. Of another it may be related that he helped to found an athletic club or was a dignitary in some fraternal organization. And through any such wide-meshed set of facts the real man must slip through.

Every individual is more than his job, his social activities and his span of years. It is a pity that when each one of us dies the essence may not survive, whether the person be notable or not.

In the heart of everyone there is the desire to know what will be said about him in the papers. I remember a story of two years ago about a dying newspaperman who called his wife to his bedside when his end was near and with his remaining store of strength and voice dictated to her what he would like to have printed about himself. As he wrote it the paragraphs appeared humble and modest enough. But at least the dying man was assured that the facts were straight.

What I have in mind are things less tangible. Somebody called me on the telephone the afternoon of my father's death to ask for some little information about him. I failed, because there was much I forgot in the matter of mere material detail and even more I left out because it hardly fell within the tradition of what constitutes a conventional obituary.

Later it seemed to me unsatisfactory that a man of long life should have his existence summed up to some extent as "the father of the newspaper columnist." Such a report shifts the emphasis. It makes the wrong man seem the debtor.

And yet there are practical difficulties in presenting any true and live picture within the confines of limited newspaper space. Once there was written a complete portrait of my father, but by a man who never knew him. And this adequate portrait required the full generosity of a two-volume novel. If you play the game of identifying your friends with famous folk of fiction I can explain my father to you by saying that he was to the life Thackeray's Colonel Newcome with just a dash of Major Pendennis.

The reporter at the other end of the telephone would have been surprised if, instead of saying that Heywood Cox Broun was the founder of a printing business and a member of the Racquet and Tennis Club, I had said, "The most important thing to mention is that Mr. Broun was just about the most charming man anybody had ever known."

And yet this report would have been more accurate and vital.

I have always been interested in problems of heredity and the curious manner in which people are conditioned by ricochet rather than direct fire. For instance, there is the fact that my father was an ardent National Guardsman and at one time among the four or five crack rifle shots in the entire country. When I was a child the house was filled with gold and silver medals as tokens of this prowess. And I, his son, am a fanatical pacifist and have never so much as fired a gun in my life.

Yet there is consistency in this. We were always told, as children, never to point a gun at anybody—not even a cap pistol—and it is not altogether strange that I grew up with a feeling that there is something almost inherently evil in firearms.

When I went to tell him that I was running for Congress on the Socialist ticket he was a little surprised and yet not displeased, though I was turning on a road which ran almost at right angles from his highway. We kept close through many episodes in which I followed philosophies quite foreign to his own. We kept close because of his wisdom. All he ever wanted to know was whether I believed honestly and sincerely in the path which I had chosen. If I could convince him of that the thing I did was all right, whether or not he grasped the detail of my emotion or my reasoning.

And in some respects I have tried to follow more closely the tradition which he set. I take pride in the fact that my father was a gay man. That he liked to give and receive parties. For many years after he was well past 70 we kept, with all the ardor of a religious rite, a cocktail hour.

I have always felt that truly kindly people, like my father, must be men who have themselves a flair for fun. Only from the exuberant is it possible to get an enlivening return in the execution of the commandment "Love thy neighbor as thyself." Nor could his tombstone have a better inscription than this: "He took and gave much joy in life."

PART II

Industrial America

1890-1920

After 1890, the United States shed any remaining attributes of its once underdeveloped status. It moved to the forefront of industrial powers. The Spanish-American War and the First World War scarcely interrupted the dramatic growth of the economy. All the indices of production rose and the rate of population increase remained substantial as the nation continued along the course of industrialization and urbanization. The fact that the rewards of this process were inequitably distributed troubled not only the radicals, but also sensitive moderate men concerned about the direction of national development. But not until the panic of 1929 plunged the United States into a long depression were there questions about the fundamental soundness of its economic system. That downturn marked the end of a period that had generally been confident and optimistic.

Immigration reflected the expansive trends of these forty years. There was room for millions more. The flow of newcomers began to move with renewed force early in the 1890's and persisted well into the 1920's on a scale much larger than ever before. The movement was almost global. It drew along the discontented, the hopeful, the ambitious, and the rebellious from Western and Eastern Europe, from Northern and Southern Europe, and even from parts of Asia. This heterogeneous mass of newcomers supplied the energies to populate and build the country. Only toward the very close of the period did unrestricted immigration end; between 1917 and 1924, disillusionment with the world war and its results created a desire for isolation that finally shut the gates to outsiders.

The second generation born in these decades formed a far less coherent group than the earlier one, but one that was much more aware of its own identity. Its members were the children of parents of the most diverse antecedents—English, Germans, and Scandinavians, as before, but also French-Canadians, Armenians, Chinese, Italians, Dutch, and Eastern European Jews. Yet in important respects the writers who were the products of so many different heritages had more in common with one another than had their predecessors. Some of them were drawn together by the impact of Freudian ideas which, during their lifetime, stimulated self-consciousness about all questions of parentage. But a more general influence operated on these writers: the society in which they grew up made them conscious of their marginality and established their unique character as the second generation.

The sense of being adrift between the norms of two different cultures emerged most clearly in the descriptions of urban slum life. The men who lived through the great Depression of the 1930's, which exposed the deficiencies of the economy, were often harsh and critical observers of the world about them. But they were not cynics. The bitterness of their protests arose from a longing for what they lacked—the security of relationships that would safeguard human decencies in a hostile environment. Nelson Algren's brutish young man (No. 24) needed the redeeming strength of love, but was so enmired that he could not understand his own wants. Daniel Fuchs recognized a corruption so thoroughgoing that it besmirched both God and country.[1] Emile Gauvreau (No. 16) dealt, in a wider setting, with the mockery the mass media made of conventions. The protests were against a society that threatened the personality by abandoning man to face hostile forces too strong to be conquered alone.

Some people, like Walter Reuther (No. 22), took the plight of the workingman as a challenge to action, and sought to develop the organizations that could mediate between the isolated individual and the massive powers which he confronted. The labor movement was one of the constructive products of efforts that engaged many members of the second generation.

[1] See "Pioneers! O Pioneers!" Whit Burnett and Martha Foley, eds., *Story in America* (New York, 1934), pp. 224–235.

However, other aspects of isolation were not so susceptible to palliation. Peter De Vries (No. 26) probed the agony of a man deprived of traditional means for absorbing tragedy, who met blankly and alone the unanswerable questions raised by the death of a child. He was centuries removed from the absolute confidence in God's grace of earlier Americans. The quest for faith that led to the postwar revivals was already underway before 1939. In William Saroyan (No. 23) it produced a jolly acquiescence to differences, in Reinhold Niebuhr (No. 19), a searching inquiry into the religious meanings of American history.

But that quest could not be pursued in purely theological terms. The church in the United States had always borne an ethnic cast; and the desire for the emotional and spiritual comfort of faith raised for members of the second generation the problem of their relationship to their fathers whose God it was they sought.

The conflict between the American children and their uprooted parents often clearly expressed the separateness of their experience and of their views of the future. Rud (No. 20) arrayed a father and a son in open antagonism and implied that the second generation could find freedom only in escape from the domination of the first. In Rosenfeld's novel (No. 29) the conflict is more subtle but nevertheless still restricts the son's capacity for love.

This theme frequently recurred for it voiced the resentment of children against the limiting features of their heritage. But nostalgic memories of family warmth counter-balanced that sentiment. In the accounts of Lowe (No. 21) and Mangione (No. 25) the father was but one of a wider circle of relatives and friends, occupied in a round of ceremonial occasions that lent security and comfort to those enclosed. And the children knew that the same steps which removed them from parental control also removed them from family warmth. Hence the ambiguity in Fante's recollection of the pride and shame of being a Wop (No. 27). Perhaps as Hansen (No. 18) suggested, only the third generation would be able to take itself for granted.

Concern with their own identity and with the successive crises through which the United States passed in their lifetime turned the thoughts of the second generation to the meaning of America. Some, like Archibald MacLeish (No. 17), wrote in global terms and emphasized the country's democratic mission. More typical was the association of the experience of the individual with that of the nation. The land of opportunity enabled each man to make of himself what he could and spurred each on in the pursuit of success. The words that celebrated that idea emerged with acerbic irony from the mouth of Fuchs' protagonist. Delmore Schwartz's evocative story (No. 28) was probably more representative than either the optimism of MacLeish or the pessimism of Fuchs; the striving toward American success was painful and costly but also elicited from those engaged in it the qualities of dignity and grandeur.

16. EMILE GAUVREAU

*Tabloid Editor**

Emile H. Gauvreau was born in Centerville near New Haven in 1891, the son of French-Canadian immigrants. As a boy he lived for a while in Canada but returned to Connecticut and early adopted the career of a journalist. After working on various newspapers, he became the managing editor of the Hartford Courant *at the age of twenty-six. In 1924 he helped Bernarr Macfadden launch the New York* Graphic, *the most spectacular of the tabloids. Five years later, he transferred his services to Hearst's* Daily Mirror. *For more than a decade he cultivated the art of sensational appeal to a mass audience. In 1935 he resigned and after holding several government positions devoted himself to writing. See also Emile Gauvreau,* My Last Million Readers *(New York, 1941).*

"Something is wrong with you, Peters."

I looked up questioningly at the blond young man who was pronouncing this rather general diagnosis. We were lunching at the Fish Pond Inn, a thriving speakeasy frequented by judges, lawyers, police officials and newspapermen who enjoyed its convenience in the shadow of the City Hall and the Criminal Courts Building. The bar of this speakeasy attracted me, not only because of the quality of its liquor, but for the reason that the bar itself was a huge glass tank in which swam an amazing variety of fish. After three drinks of Bourbon I liked to lean against this bar in melancholy contemplation and watch the aimless performance in the tank. Hundreds of fish of all sizes and colors usually followed the largest fish, who would

* Emile Gauvreau, *Hot News* (New York, 1931), pp. 56–69, 75–86.

come to the side and glare at me. When he opened and closed his mouth he seemed to take on the appearance of Bunnyweather in anger. Suddenly he would dart off, with hundreds of the little fish in his wake after him. Like *The Comet* and its readers, I would think cynically as I ordered another drink. Poor fish!

"I said something is wrong with you, Peters," repeated the blond young man, arousing me from a reverie. A sneer distorted his thick negroid lips, and his half closed little eyes, peering over huge horn-rimmed spectacles, gave him the appearance of a vampire bat.

"Well, what's wrong? Tell me the worst," I replied, somewhat startled, because the young man, for the time being, spoke with the voice of Richard Bunnyweather II.

Having surrounded himself with a Board of Ministers to register respectability, R.B. now and then attached some young highbrow to his staff to impress the intelligentsia. Odd fish of this type never survived very long in the whirlpool of Bunnyweather Publications, but while they were there they put on great airs and posed as evangels from R.B.'s sanctum. Their functions were never clearly defined and their authority was nil. They were usually attached to the office of the Public Relations Counsel, a gentleman whose problem it was to give Bunnyweather a background. They were privileged to address memos to Bunnyweather, which passed only through the hands of three intermediaries before reaching the waste basket.

Gerald Warwick, the blond young man, was one of those unhappy intellectuals, charged with the function of advising *The Comet*. He belonged to a generation that took nothing seriously except its cocktails and its psycho-analysis.

"I'll tell you what's wrong with you, Peters," he said. "You've still got a conscience, a sort of atavistic survival of your early childhood. As I analyze it, you'll have to extirpate that conscience if you want to make a real success of *The Comet*."

Perhaps his words were spoken more or less in jest. He uttered them and forgot them a minute later, but for some reason or other they rankled in my mind. I determined to strangle within myself the voices of my Puritan ancestors. I would free myself deliberately from all moral scruples.

"You're right," I said, tossing off a third beaker. "Hereafter, in the editorial conduct of *The Comet*, we shall disregard every copybook maxim. To hell with all the accepted forms of journalism!"

"Put on a Maxim silencer," Warwick jeered.

"So be it," I said. " 'they ain't seen nothin' yet,' as the farm-hand said. Watch *The Comet* from now on."

"Don't take me too seriously," Warwick lisped, a bit apprehensively. . . .

I would live up to my own dictum with a vengeance. "Make the news if there is no news." I would give the post-War generation that couldn't take a drink except for the kick that was in it, that couldn't read a story except for the thrill, the stimulation its polluted palate craved! . . .

I was on the hunt for new laurels. Something had to be done. When Smatterblow's visits to my office became increasingly frequent I knew that circulation was at a standstill. With us, merely to hold what circulation we had was to confess failure. We had to keep going up. Up! Up! Those were the orders.

An isolated sensation, now and then, was not sufficient in the battle for readers. Why not create a character or a number of characters whom I could drag through a series of exciting experiences, like Punch and Judy, for the benefit of *The Comet's* circulation? It had got so that it was not sufficient to be an editor in this racket. It was not enough to record the fate of others. I must play the part of fate myself.

One Sunday, looking over the illustrated sections of the Sunday papers, I came upon the picture of Raymond Rodgers, a millionaire chocolate manufacturer who seemed to be getting more than his share of publicity over nothing at all lately. I had noticed that he was almost invariably featured in the company of young girls. Frequently, he was to be seen distributing five pound packages of chocolates in orphan asylums or entertaining parties of orphans at his palatial home. City editors would receive little notes advising them of the event in advance with the two words which always warm the heart of a tabloid editor: "Photographers Welcome."

There was a rumor that it was the manufacturer's intention to adopt legally an entire asylum of one hundred and fifty girls. Jennings went off on the scent.

The stories he brought back read like the tales collected by the Brothers Grimm. Rodgers enjoyed playing the part of the fairy godmother. He was generally regarded as a good-natured eccentric, but stray gossip, reaching my ears, aroused the sleeping sleuth in my bosom.

I detached one of my "detective reporters" to trail Rodgers. The detective reporter is a new species, sired by yellow journalism and damed by the tabloids. News hound and sleuth in one, he has developed a nose for scandal exceeding the hog's unfailing instinct for truffles.

Jennings, aided by clews turned up by my hounds, soon unearthed a delightful morsel. He found that Rodgers once even intended to make one of the hundred and fifty orphans his bride, after adopting, if possible, the entire orphanage.

When I sprang the story, the authorities of the asylum prohibited further visits from the millionaire. A week later new pictures of Rodgers appeared, distributing his sweets in a camp of girl scouts.

"I think the old bird went into the manufacture of chocolate chiefly to attract young girls with his sweets. It looks like it, anyhow," said Jennings, as he looked the pictures over.

Our photographers were soon prevailing upon Rodgers to pose for them while bestowing paternal kisses upon little girls in the street. I began to scent rich copy in this middle-aged gentleman. Here was my Punch and Judy man! God's gift to *The Comet!* I sought his acquaintance.

One talk made clear that, while Rodgers functioned normally along most lines, his mind was thrown out of compass by every skirt uplifted in the wind. I discovered that his penchant for young femininity had induced his wife, after vainly trying to restrain him, to give him his freedom for one million dollars.

Since his divorce, Rodgers had surrounded himself with an ever changing bevy of young protégées. He loved to be photographed with pretty girls. The publicity flattered his inordinate vanity and attracted new devotees into his pleasant web.

For weeks nothing startling happened in Rodgers' little world. Then, thanks to the untiring sleuthing of my reporters, a story which we called "big" finally broke. Rodgers had showered gifts upon a young Irish maidservant. The girl appreciated his generosity, but did not reciprocate his affection. One night, according to report, when his endearments had become more than fatherly, she escaped from his country estate and was found in a state of hysteria on a lonely road in the rain. This was the condiment I needed to season my paper. *The Comet* made a sensation of the incident, depicting the girl's pitiful plight in a series of composographs calculated to draw tears from the eyes of a stone crocodile.

The circulation leaped again.

Newspaper circulation, like the stock market, does not go up all the time, even in periods where plus signs predominate. Our circulation continued to mount. But every now and then, there were periodic reactions and spells of depression. While my tendency was to keep track of the plus signs, Mr. Moorehead, the treasurer, kept his eagle eye fixed on the minuses. Whenever there was a decided drop in the circulation, red, pink, green and blue slips would flutter to me from the main office, some initialed by R.B., some by Moorehead. A period of depression of this type had accounted for Warwick's visit on the historic occasion when he adjured me to get rid of my conscience.

While the newsboys were selling my pink extras about the flight of the Irish maidservant, Rodgers called on me. I expected a frightful exhibition of rage. Much to my surprise, he was exceedingly affable. He pretended to enjoy the joke on himself. A moral exhibitionist, he relished his notoriety. It gave him a thrill to see himself lampooned in the press. Publicity went to his head like synthetic gin. I saw at once that Rodgers was my man. I became his adviser, playing the Mephistopheles to his Faust.

Soon, he became my most ardent collaborator in exploiting his own foibles. If I had not slain my conscience on orders from headquarters, communicated to me by my blond young highbrow with horn-rimmed spectacles, the situation would have revolted me. Abandoning all thought of my soul, I concentrated my attention on the circulation. The pathological weakness of Raymond Rodgers was to prove to be my greatest builder of readers since the Mid-Continent Township Pulchritude Carnival.

I met Rodgers occasionally at the Ginger Pot, a fashionable night club of dubious reputation. His inflammable heart by now was burning bright for Marjorie McGinnis, a popular hostess. Marjorie, plump and a widow, had tried to enrope the rich manufacturer, but his flames proved to be straw fire only. Even when he was dancing with Marjorie, he winked discreetly at Susan, Marjorie's younger sister, who sold cigarettes in the costume of a Bohemian peasant. He explained his interest in the girl by insinuating that he would adopt Susan after marrying Marjorie. His promises of marriage, like his offers of adoption, were never in writing. He had learned how to escape the meshes of matrimony without becoming involved in the pitfalls of breach of promise or damaged heart suits.

Marjorie was prettier than Susan. But Marjorie was twenty-five and Susan was seventeen. Marjorie relied upon the chemist for her complexion. Susan combined the natural bloom of early girlhood with the mellowness of a plum.

"She is the sweetest girl I have ever met," the middle-aged manufacturer sighed. "She is——" Rodgers himself gave me the word with a palpitating heart—"a sugar plum!"

"Sugar Plum" suggested itself to me as an attractive name for the girl. It had great headline possibilities. I was soon to make that name re-echo throughout the nation.

Marjorie's suspicions, already aroused by the old man's antics, were confirmed when she saw Rodgers implant a surreptitious kiss on the dainty pink lobe of her sister's ear. In vain Rodgers attempted to assuage her indignation. Without definitely committing himself, he suggested the possibility of reversing his original program by marrying Susan and adopting Marjorie. This idea, demolishing her hope of sharing the wealth derived from his world-famous cocoa beans, enraged the hostess.

"I am not going to be the daughter of my kid sister," she said.

Swept into hysterics, she seized the cigarettes and cigars on her sister Susan's tray and threw them, one after another, into Rodgers' face. Not unaccustomed to such emergencies, he ducked. Next, Marjorie seized the plates on the table, the glasses, forks and knives, and threw them at the elderly Don Juan, who sought refuge under a table. Sister Susan fled to the coat room. The manager, hurrying to the scene, received a salvo of gin mixed with ginger ale on his white shirt bosom. The place was in an uproar, but even before the police arrived my photographer, who hovered near the scene on a hunch that something was bound to happen, had taken a series of shots of the enraged girl and of Rodgers peering from his hiding place like a playful bear cub. We even got a flashlight of Susan trying to conceal herself behind a barrage of fur coats. I sprang the story of the entanglement with two full pages of illustrations, appearing exclusively in *The Comet*.

It is true that I played the part of fate in the life of Raymond Rodgers, then and thereafter, but it is not true that I instigated the duel between the sisters, and the scene at the night club. That was merely a lucky break. The story had every appeal of melodrama. With its publication our sales leaped over night by thirty-five thousand. I made the most of the jealousy between the two sisters, which gave a new twist to the triangle.

Raymond Rodgers, Sugar Plum and Sister Maggie were by far my greatest tabloid characters and I treasure their memory as I write. I resolved to develop them and to make them undergo every thrill their constitutions could stand, with the same slapstick methods and the same disregard for the feelings of my victims with which a cartoonist determines the fate of the little people that inhabit his comic strip and animated movies.

I instructed my editors to refer to Rodgers hereafter as "Uncle Cocoa" a name by which he had become known among the habitués of the Ginger Pot, and to Susan as "Sugar Plum." Marjorie became "Sister Maggie." These designations appealed to the popular imagination. The trio became very precious to me. They were the figures in a game of chess in which I hoped to checkmate Anthony Wayne and *The Lantern.* I seriously thought of insuring them in case their escapades should bring them to an untimely end. I have created many other characters who have played a part in Tabloidia, but Sugar Plum, Uncle Cocoa, and Sister Maggie were my most magnificent inspirations. They were the raw material out of which I evolved a new journalistic technique. . . .

I decided that the next step to titillate my readers must be a romantic reconciliation between the sisters, followed by the marriage of Uncle Cocoa and Sugar Plum. This denouement appealed to Bunnyweather's high moral sense. Matrimony was the cloak that covered every transgression.

At my suggestion, Uncle Cocoa provided a heart balm for Sister Maggie and I published a picture of the three under the caption "Uncle Cocoa mends a broken heart." Then began the courtship of Uncle Cocoa and Sugar Plum under my stage direction. No competitor had a look-in. I cast a thousand spotlights upon every kiss bestowed upon Sugar Plum's cheeks by her elderly lover. Warwick, at Bunnyweather's request, wrote for *The Comet* a full page editorial pointing out that a difference in years should never check the course of true love!

Day after day, while the preparations for the wedding were going on, I kept up the story full blast. Rodgers was as happy as a schoolboy. He bought 10,000 copies of *The Comet* for distribution among his employees, and shipped 50,000 more to his customers.

Stretching out the period of his engagement as long as possible, I employed my most proficient ghost writers to write the story of Sugar Plum's courtship under Sugar Plum's name. That story was eaten up like a strawberry sundae every day by every little flapper who hoped to marry a millionaire. When, at last, the marriage ceremony took place, it was staged and played up by *The Comet* with the precision of a movie set. I printed a picture of the Hispano-Suiza with its uniformed chauffeur, which conveyed the bridal couple to the church, and of the sumptuous bridal chamber with its four poster bed.

The street was lined with thousands of curious spectators as if it were a wedding of royalty. Mothers, with their little girls, tried to stand under the canopy of the church while Uncle Cocoa and Sugar Plum emerged though a storm of confetti. It became necessary to call the police to make room for my Punch and Judy show.

After the wedding, the circulation, which had hovered for some weeks at 300,000 when every breathless minute was filled with the doings of Uncle Cocoa and Sugar Plum, began to recede. "For Christ's sake," Smatterlow, the circulation manager cried, "bring back Sugar Plum at once." . . .

I sought out Uncle Cocoa, appealed to his vanity, and succeeded in obtaining his permission to let me print Sugar Plum's honeymoon diary. My best ghost writer haunted Sugar Plum every morning for half an hour to draw from her inspiration for a daily chapter of four thousand words, revealing the intimate thoughts and experiences of the millionaire bride. The diary was illustrated with posed photographs of Sugar Plum, buxom, blooming, rosy-cheeked, surrounded by every imaginable luxury. A few months before, she had been only a cigarette girl in a night club. Now, she feasted every day in Uncle Cocoa's palace and with her, living on Uncle Cocoa's bounty, hovering grimly on the darkening horizon, was her sister Maggie.

The publication of Sugar Plum's nuptial confessions in *The Comet* soon trickled from Mammoth City into the country at large. Uncle Cocoa and Sugar Plum and Sister Maggie became living realities on the stage and in the press. In Chicago, Philadelphia, Baltimore, New York and San Francisco, no vaudeville act was complete without some reference to Uncle Cocoa's honeymoon. Even the conservative papers could not banish Uncle Cocoa and Sugar Plum from the front page.

Uncle Cocoa, being a subscriber to all clipping bureaus, was deluged with press cuttings. He waddled in them with the enjoyment of a hippopotamus in a mud bath. Not satisfied with the returns of the clipping bureaus, the chocolate manufacturer installed a special office force to extract from the newspapers every sweet morsel of publicity. He built special bookcases to hold the huge scrapbooks wherein his fame was enshrined. Newspaper photographs of Uncle Cocoa and Sugar Plum leered at the visitor from every wall. Uncle Cocoa feasted his eyes on them, smacking his lips and rubbing his smooth palms. In daily communications with me, he suggested what to emphasize and what to soft-pedal in the stories of Sugar Plum's marital ecstasies. . . .

It was impossible to satisfy Uncle Cocoa's greed for publicity. "I want the papers to talk about me all the time. It doesn't hurt anybody," he confided to me whiningly. "I want the crowds to rush after me. I want them to know who I am. Before I made my money I was kicked around on a farm. Even when I became a successful manufacturer I was nobody! Every word uttered by Rockefeller, Ford and Morgan was news. I was submerged in an ocean of anonymity. Now the whole country knows who I am, don't they? It knows my name and it knows why the girls like me. And, incidentally, it eats my chocolate. My new confection, 'Sugar Plum,' is a wow!" . . .

The Comet was now being published without stopping for editions; we kept on printing for twenty-four hours. Nations might go to war, presidents come and go; nothing mattered to *The Comet* except Sugar Plum's honeymoon! Nothing was more important. Avoiding home, with its harassing memories of the baby and Claire's silent and vocal remonstrances as much as possible, I threw myself with morbid energy into my work. I was married to the paper. It was my wife and family and my mistress. Tarrying in the press room, I gloated over the indicators, as the figures of our output mounted hour by hour. *The Comet* was the talk of the town.

I wondered what I would do after my readers grew tired of reading the story of Sugar Plum's honeymoon. Somehow, in the back of my mind, there seemed to be pressing forward into my consciousness the figure of Sugar Plum's sister.

The last instalment of the honeymoon daybook, bolstered up day after day by the office ghost, had reached its mushy conclusion. For several days the circulation remained stationary at half a million. Then it began to drop precipitately, in spite of various devices to reinflate it. Our competitors began to breathe more easily. Anthony Wayne picked up a sensation which, while juicy, did not hold the popular appeal of Sugar Plum and Uncle Cocoa. Nevertheless, for the time being, it pushed the circulation of *The Lantern* over mine.

One rainy night, while I was still at the office, Sugar Plum's sister, dressed in the height of fashion, insinuated herself into my cubbyhole. She had come to me for advice, whipped by the scorpions of envy, disguised as sisterly solicitude. She painted Sugar Plum's life in ghastly colors.

"Rodgers," she confided in me, "is a half-demented old creature who almost drives her to distraction. Sugar Plum is his prisoner. Frantic with jealousy, the old man spies on her every minute. She has no peace at home and she has no peace when she goes out.

"Sugar Plum can no longer appear in public without being mobbed. On several occasions, when she went out for tea to a hotel, it was necessary to call out the police reserves.

"Wherever she goes," her sister grumbled, "great crowds gather. Ruffians stand outside of the gate of the estate yelling, 'Hurrah for Uncle Cocoa and Sugar Plum!' "

The arrow of notoriety had overshot its mark.

Uncle Cocoa, Maggie admitted, tried to cheer up his bride. He treated her like a child and romped for her in the bed chamber on all fours like a dog. Almost hourly messenger boys arrived bearing ardent love notes and gifts, including a collection of expensive French dolls.

Sugar Plum's sister indicated by tapping her head that all was not well in the upper story of Mr. Rodgers.

"But," I interjected, "Sugar Plum seemed to be perfectly happy——"

Sugar Plum's sister, squinting at me poisonously, shook her marcelled head. "No," she screamed, "her life with Rodgers will drive her to the madhouse. Though she tries to conceal her grief, she is in hysterics most of the time. I would not be surprised if Rodgers——" she made a motion as if someone was cutting Sugar Plum's throat.

I saw another leap in my circulation. While the enraged woman enlarged upon her grievance, I was already planning a new series of revelations, "Why I Left Uncle Cocoa," illustrated with startling composographs of Sugar Plum's marital troubles.

Poor Rodgers with his chocolate millions! I would rear the edifice of my circulation upon a mountain of cocoa beans! Before I was thirty-five, I would hold the world's record as the greatest circulation builder, the liveliest editor, the most ingenious news maker in the land. I would build up a solid million circulation but then—ah, then! Then, after reaching a million circulation, I would begin to tone down *The Comet* and trick a docile audience, accustomed to eat out of my hand, into accepting respectability. Respectability meant advertising —the weakest spot in our armor. In spite of our immense circulation we were still in the red figures in our counting room.

The Comet was losing nearly $25,000 a week. It had already eaten up more than three million dollars of Bunnyweather's surplus. But R.B.'s purse was as fat as its master. He was rather proud of being able to lose so much money. He mentioned it now and then in an offhand way, with a smile.

"Publishing a daily paper," he added, "is a disease, not a business."

On twenty-seven different occasions he told me, each time

with a new wrinkle, the story of a wager between a young profligate and the Devil. The Devil held that the young man would be unable to spend, without actually throwing the money out of the window, the inexhaustible funds placed at his disposal by the Exchequer of Hell. The young man lightly accepted. He bought the cats and dogs of the Stock Exchange at the rate of a million shares a day, but instead of losing his money he became richer and richer. He purchased country estates, yachts, race horses. His estates increased fabulously in value. His yachts and his horses won race after race. He played angel to half a dozen musical comedy stars on Mammoth Boulevard and every one of his shows drew crowded houses. He was unable to spend even one half of his income. Where he least expected it, success dogged his footsteps.

One day, he had the bright idea of buying a newspaper; Satan supplied the capital. After publishing the sheet for less than a year, he was notified by the bank that he had overdrawn his account. The same thing happened week after week. He was constantly compelled to ask for more money. Every new circulation stunt required a new outlay until finally the Devil's Exchequer was nearly exhausted. For the first time, since the memorable occasion when Satan was flung headlong to bottomless perdition, there was talk of a revolution in the Infernal Regions.

Gloomy-looking groups of devils met in mass meetings denouncing the extravagance of the Government. "If this goes on," they protested, "we shall soon be broke." Finally a committee of head devils called on the young publisher.

"What?" the young man cried furiously, "you want to welch on your promise?"

The Infernal delegation replied: "Hell has never repudiated an agreement. In fact, His Infernal Majesty is a stickler for observing with proud punctilio the letter of every engagement. However, you have placed us in a terrible predicament. We don't look upon treaties as scraps of paper, but we appeal to your generosity to release us from our contract."

"Why should I release you?" the young publisher asked.

"Because," the chief of the delegates replied, "there are not enough funds in all Hell to pay for a newspaper that is losing money."

Bunnyweather's enormous belly shook like a mountain convulsed by an earthquake, when he related this story.

In spite of the philosophical calm with which he took his losses on *The Comet*, Bunnyweather hoped to accomplish the miracle of turning red into black. He wanted to demonstrate that he could run a newspaper as successfully as a magazine. Gazing into the future, he envisaged a chain of tabloids encircling the country from the Pacific to the Atlantic.

Every large city had one or more tabloids. There were three in New York, one in Philadelphia, one in Chicago and one in Boston. Others sprang up in Washington and in Detroit. In Los Angeles and San Francisco tabloids established by a young millionaire were going through a financial crisis. Bunnyweather watched the mushroom growth and the tribulations of the tabloids in various cities like a hawk. Sooner or later, opportunity would throw them into his lap, he figured. Enshrined in the depth of his overworked heart, he cherished the vision of ascending first to the Governorship, then to the White House, on a ladder of tabloids. He loved power even more than riches. Beginning with abject poverty, he had made so large a fortune that he had lost all sense of the value of money. Where the gratification of his own whims was concerned, no price was too high. When it came to paying another man for his labor, R.B. vividly remembered that he had started as a poor boy, struggling for every penny.

In *The Comet* and in his magazines, Bunnyweather saw another expression of his inflated ego. He looked upon *The Comet* as part of himself. His interest had assumed such proportions that I could venture to wake him up in the middle of the night, to obtain his O.K. He liked to be disturbed. It gave him a sense of importance. He felt as if the fate of empires hung on his decisions. It would flatter him immensely if I asked him now to decide the fate of Sugar Plum. It was one o'clock in the morning. Sugar Plum's sister Maggie was still with me, fretting and fuming.

I had convinced her that she must induce her sister to leave Uncle Cocoa's love nest. After hiding the two sisters in the country, I would startle the world by announcing their disappearance. With the sisters practically my prisoners, I would assign my most gifted ghost writer, a half consumptive old newspaperman who preserved himself only by pickling his insides with alcohol, to prepare the story of Sugar Plum's marital woes.

Old Bunnyweather was elated.

"This will give us a million, Peters, sure as Hell! Spare no expense. I'll give you one of my own limousines to facilitate the escape of the unfortunate girl from her gilded cage."

The "escape" of Sugar Plum from the Rodgers estate took place under my own stage direction. Uncle Cocoa was not at home, I learned, as I conferred with my aides in the moonlight. No one barred Sugar Plum's get-away. She could have walked out of the front door with all her baggage unchallenged. But that would not have been in accordance with *The Comet* tradition. I insisted that she must climb down a long ladder from the window of her boudoir.

While Sugar Plum in pajamas descended from the second story of her husband's house, my flashlight cameras, booming from the lawn beneath, illuminated the surrounding grounds. Their duty done, my photographers jumped into one of Bunnyweather's limousines with the plates.

Standing there on a little knoll like Napoleon overlooking a battle, I controlled my excitement.

"Get back with those plates, boys!" I shouted. "Tell Otto Schubart to rush the ladder picture through and to put it on the front page. If anything happens to those plates on the way, I'll make you look like an architect's working drawing of a hamburger steak. A raise for every man who makes good on this story!"

I took Sugar Plum and her aunt to the home of a friend, a retired civil engineer, who lived in a Swiss châlet with a Japanese servant, one hundred miles from Mammoth City. Here she would find the seclusion she sought and the opportunity to devote herself to her literary endeavors.

Sugar Plum consumed large quantities of my friend's choice liquor, under the strain of her literary work. Reporting ghost writers, in daily conference with her, wrested from her mind every intimate detail of her fantastic marital life with Uncle Cocoa.

Uncle Cocoa's affairs had once more reached a point where they engaged the breathless attention of Mammoth City. The Rodgers case overshadowed every other item in the news of the sensational press. The excitement was spreading from the tabloids to their nervous competitors. Each outdid the other in devising new stunts involving Raymond Rodgers and his reluctant bride. Our circulation rose so precipitately that Wayne of *The Lantern* smashed his office furniture in a blind rage and kicked his hat out of the window. I had stolen a march on him because both sisters were completely under my tutelage. Uncle Cocoa, chuckling over this new wave of publicity, gave the preference to me in all proclamations issued from his headquarters to the expectant multitudes.

Unwilling to concede defeat, Wayne now took a desperate chance, determined to steal my thunder; he printed a two column article announcing that Sugar Plum Rodgers was hiding in a suburban town known exclusively to *The Lantern.* I have never fully understood the motive of this announcement. Possibly some sleuth had promised to produce the girl in time for the next edition. Once he could lay hands on the girl he trusted in the power of his persuasion and the ample pocketbook of his employer. Wayne would not have hesitated to kidnap Sugar Plum. Abduction in the interest of a story was no crime in Tabloidia.

The announcement by *The Lantern* threw *The Comet* into a great commotion. It was a bombshell. I tore my hair at the idea of Sugar Plum's betrayal. If she had deserted me, I would castigate her until she would no longer dare to show her face wherever the English language was spoken. She could not be reached by telephone. I cursed myself for having instructed her to talk to no one over the wire. After vainly trying to hire an airplane, I borrowed one of Bunnyweather's high-powered cars for a mad dash to Sugar Plum's retreat. Francis Scott Key could not have been more enraptured when he saw the Star Spangled Banner still waving over the land of the free than I was when I found that Sugar Plum had remained faithful to me, and *The Comet*.

In a scathing editorial covering the entire back page of my newspaper, I denounced Wayne as a liar. He countered by a libel suit. That, of course, was a bluff. Before the threatened suit materialized, Wayne and I met dramatically at the Fish Pond Inn in front of the glass bar and its colored fish. Perhaps thirty-three then, he was a little dynamo panting with energy. But for all his enterprise, I had him baffled this time. The numerous highballs he had consumed could not conceal his worried look. His myopic eyes constantly roved in search of some lost inspiration. His unpressed trousers conveyed the impression that he was too much preoccupied with his work to consider his personal appearance. A mop of black hair tumbled down over his forehead.

We looked at each other like two fighting cocks. A hush fell over the bar flies. No one would have been surprised if we had come to blows. Somebody got us together. An electric spark seemed to leap from one to the other. He had a human smile and twinkling eye. Talking things over, we found that we had much in common.

Wayne and I became fast friends, although professional enemies. In time our friendship grew. We began to commiserate with each other. At midnight cocktail parties we would retire to a quiet corner, exchange confidences and discuss circulation. Wayne would say:

"How much have you got now? I've got 495,000."

"Well, to-day we sold 504,000 net."

"What the hell difference would it make if you had a million!"

But difference or no, we both worked feverishly in an effort to reach that million. We were both helpless in the toils of jazz journalism. Living in a hectic world, governed by fantastic rules, we could not escape. We could no more liberate ourselves from the gravitational force of Tabloidia than any creature walking on the face of the earth can disengage himself from the earth's pull.

Competition became so hot that Bunnyweather appropriated a substantial sum for the employment of spies on other papers to steal their exclusive stories. "Everything is fair in love and war, and newspaper work," was his motto. The other newspapers met our challenge. While one of my spies worked in the City room of *The Lantern,* the smartest lady reporter of *The Lantern* disguised herself as a telephone operator to listen in on my plans. Every now and then, after a sensational leak, we discovered the enemy emissaries in our midst and dismissed them after violent scenes. Episodes of this type, while at times irritating, in no way affected my relations with Wayne. We accepted them as part of the game and laughed privately over them.

The killing I made of Sugar Plum's diary had driven Wayne to desperation. The climax of my recital was furnished by the scene in which poor old Uncle Cocoa, in the vain attempt to please his girlish bride, pranced on all fours on the rug in their bedroom pretending to be a chow dog. I showed Uncle Cocoa in a startling composograph, romping on all fours while Sugar Plum sat up in her Louis Quatorze bed with terror in every line of her jejune face.

"Wow, wow, I'm a chow," was the balloon caption, streaming from Uncle Cocoa's mouth. The picture reminded those familiar with such literature of an episode in Zola's *Nana.* It amused our readers at large, who had no such memories.

17. ARCHIBALD MACLEISH

*Democracy in Action**

Archibald MacLeish was born in 1892, the son of a Glasgow Scot who was a partner in a well-known Chicago department store. Hotchkiss, Yale, and Harvard Law School gave him an education. After service in World War I, he tried teaching and legal practice, then lived in France for five years while he wrote poetry. In the 1930's he shifted careers, serving as staff writer for Fortune, *Librarian of Congress, and official in various government agencies before he became Boylston Professor of Rhetoric at Harvard. Meanwhile, he won three Pulitzer Prizes for writing that looked beyond the immediate problems of politics to the larger issues of moral order in society.*

The issue before the American people is not a political issue nor an issue to be decided by a public act. It is an issue between the American people and themselves: an issue which involves the vitality and the resources of the American soul.

These, I am well aware, are large and ornate words. They are words which a man would have used at the risk of his reputation for sincerity a dozen months ago. But they are words which none of us can help but use today. History, not rhetoric, has put them in our mouths. History has shown us at late last that the issue which divides our time is far more than an issue between armed forces. History has shown us that it is an issue between worlds: an issue which depends more surely on our souls than on our weapons: an issue which no nation can avoid. Specifically and precisely, history has made plain to

* Archibald MacLeish, *The American Cause* (New York, 1941), pp. 11–28.

us a fact we had refused before to see—the fact that the enemy which attacks us attacks us not with planes alone or tanks alone or arms, but with violence of belief. And the issue which the people of this country face, the issue which lies between this people and itself, is the issue whether or not those who believe in democracy—those specifically who believe in democracy in the United States—can bring against the violence and fanatical obsession of that invading faith a stronger faith, a more resisting ardor of their own.

Before the Battle of France—a battle which may prove to have been more decisive in our own history than in the history of Europe—fascism had seemed to us a force of weapons driven onward by the fear of force behind. But in the Battle of France we learned, in the words of a manifesto issued by a group of the most distinguished scholars in this country, that the enemy "were stronger in arms because they were stronger in heart. It was their fanatical faith that gave them wings and fire. It was the singleness of their purpose that quickened the spearhead of their march."* In France also we learned that the weakness of the democracies—the weakness at least of the democracy which there fell—was not, as we had wished to believe, a weakness only in arms, only in mechanical contrivances. We learned, in the words of the same manifesto, that the blindness of democratic diplomacy and the helplessness of democratic strategy "were the external symptoms of a decay of the men. . . . This they called appeasement. It implied that no conviction is worth fighting for and that the boundaries between good and evil had fallen. Military defeat was the embodiment of moral abdication."

It was the Battle of France which posed the issue we now face. Before that battle we had thought ourselves spectators of a war in Europe. After it, we knew the war was not in Europe but nearer—in the darker and more vulnerable countries of men's hearts. And after it we were not certain it was we who were spectators.

* *The City of Man, a Declaration on World Democracy* (The Viking Press, 1940).

But the Battle of France did more than pose this issue. It weighted it—and weighted it against us. Before the Battle of France we had not understood—as a nation we had not understood—that the vitality of our democratic faith was put in issue. After the Battle of France we feared the issue was already lost. We saw then that the war was not, as we had wished to believe, a war between European powers which wanted conflicting things but a war between human beings who believed conflicting things. We saw that the differences of belief were differences as to the kind of society in which men should live. We saw that those who believed in the kind of society in which we also believe had been opposed not only by weapons, not only by machines, but by other men who believed, and believed fanatically, in the total destruction of that society. We saw that in the fighting which followed it had been those who believed fanatically in destruction who had been stronger and those who believed in the society in which we believe who had been less strong—less strong not only in their weapons but in their devotion to their cause. And we had wondered. We wondered whether the sickness of democracy in France would prove to be the sickness of democracy in every country. We wondered whether democracy, which had been unable to match conviction with conviction and certainty with certainty in France, would be able to match conviction with conviction elsewhere. We still are wondering. We are wondering whether democracy in the United States has other spiritual weapons than the doubts and misgivings which ten years of depression and twenty years of skepticism provided for the men of France to fight with.

It is of this fear I wish to speak. And to speak as candidly and earnestly as I am capable of speaking. It is a fear which exists—and which exists in the minds not of foolish or of frightened people, but of responsible men who love this country as well as any of its people love it. It is also an understandable fear, for events which all of us have witnessed make it understandable. It is not a fear therefore which scornful men can put aside, or which demagogues can shout down, or which the patriotic societies can suppress with resolutions. It is a fear of which we must take account. But it is nevertheless—or so at least it seems to me—a fear both needless and mistaken. For it rests upon a total misconception of the democratic cause. It rests, to be precise, upon the misconception of democracy which those who most despise democracy have done their best to propagate and broadcast through the world. It is the fear of those who, being democrats themselves, accept the definition of democracy their enemies have written.

The enemies of liberty are not saboteurs in material things alone. They are saboteurs also in the things of the mind. And it is in the things of the mind that their sabotage is most dangerous. To destroy a machine or a manufacturing plant is one thing. The loss is great but the plant or the machine is replaceable. To destroy the integrity of words and to destroy the credibility of the users of words is another: neither can be replaced. The enemies of liberty, here as in other countries, practice the destruction of the integrity of words and the destruction of the credibility of the users of words. Indeed, it is this practice which principally characterizes the enemies of freedom in our time. They are the first men—the first men in the five hundred years since Johannes Gutenberg Zum Jungen, Knight of Mainz, invented the art of printing—the first men to use the printing press, deliberately and systematically, as an instrument of confusion and deceit. They are the first men in the five centuries of printing to turn the printing presses, like machine guns, on the people.

And nowhere have they used these Kulturwaffen to destroy a word more skillfully than with the word democracy—the word essential to our cause—the word which *is* our cause—the word we must defend whatever else we lose, or fail to fight for, or do not defend. What the enemies of liberty would have us take the word democracy to mean is not what Adams thought it meant, or Jefferson, or those who took it westward through the Shenandoah, or those who came to find it here by shipload after shipload through a hundred years. What the enemies of liberty would have us take the word to mean is something men and money and machines created in the nineteenth century and *called* democracy—a way of owning property, a scheme of doing business, an opportunity for comfort or for power or for certain forms of gain or entertainment.

It is this the enemies of liberty would have us take the word to mean. And it is with this meaning in our minds that they would have us make the choice before us—a choice, they say, between the new oncoming order of their fascist world and an old corrupted system full of fat and death—a choice between the new and iron cause for which a people can forget itself and sacrifice itself and go without and suffer and if need be die, and, on the other side, a world of goods and things and comforts and amusements with nothing to believe in but more goods, more things.

This was the choice which their confusions and their defamations and deceits presented to the citizens of France—and which the citizens of France, duped by confusions and deceits, accepted. It is the choice which many in this country, duped or themselves the dupers, would accept as well. The diplomat who tells us that democracy is dead in England, meaning by democracy a way of trading stocks, a chance to make ten millions in the market, accepts the choice the citizens of France accepted. The famous woman who assures us in a beautiful and cadenced prose that democracy is old in every country, and that the future like a wave will drown it down, accepts the same alternatives of terror and despair.

But the fears and desperations and defeats which these and others like them breed and scatter are unreal fears. The democracy of which this writer and this statesman speak is not democracy but a distorted lie which both, but for their different reasons, take for true. Democracy itself has never been and is not now and never can become a way of trade, a world of goods, a heap of products, whether those products are of gold or steel or corn or silk or what-not: whether the trade is large or small or free or planned or neither. And only a very foolish man—only a man who had no understanding of the word democracy, or what it had been once, or what it can be—would take the issue in these terms and let his enemies compel him to defend, not the dream of freedom in the mind, not the way of freedom toward the future, but things already made, systems established, ways of trading, heaps of goods piled up.

If democracy is what the fascists say it is—if democracy is nothing but the world of innumerable automobiles and the best telephone system on earth and a new gadget just around the corner and the radios driveling on in the hotel lobbies eighteen hours out of twenty-four and the simpering legs in the magazine advertisements and the simpering voices on the movie screen and the hundreds of thousands of miles of roadside billboards with the billboard faces and the ten millions of unemployed waiting for the next boom—if democracy is only this, then democracy cannot survive attack, for democracy is not a cause that men will fight for.

But the true issue is not this issue; democracy is not the world that men and money and machines built in the nineteenth century and called democracy. The real issue is an issue to be fought in the hard and stony passes of the human spirit—the strict Thermopylaes of time where even if a man is killed he cannot die. And democracy itself is neither things nor goods nor fatness and indifference and an empty heart, but winter on the Massachusetts Bay and cold at Trenton and the gunfire in Kentucky and the hungry ground. The real issue is an issue between the frenzy on the one side of a herded, whipped-up, crowd-begotton "cause," and on the other side the single man's belief in liberty of mind and spirit; his willingness to sacrifice his goods and comforts and his earnings for its sake.

The democratic faith which swept the world—the democratic faith which men believed in and men fought for, the faith which men believe in and will fight for still, is not a faith in things or goods or fortunes. John Milton knew the democratic faith that men will fight for. He spoke of it not once but often:

"And as for you, citizens, it is of no small concern, what manner of men ye are, whether to acquire, or to keep possession of your liberty. Unless your liberty be of that kind which can neither be gotten nor taken away by arms (and that alone is such which springing from piety, justice, temperance, in fine from real virtue, shall take deep and intimate root in your minds) you may be assured that there will not be wanting one, who, even without arms, will speedily deprive you of what it is your boast to have gained by force of arms. . . . For know (that you may not feel resentment, or be able to blame anybody but yourselves), that as to be free is precisely the same thing as to be pious, wise, just and temperate, careful of one's own, abstinent from what is another's, and thence in fine, magnanimous and brave—so to be the opposite of these, is the same thing as to be a slave; and by the wonted judgment and as it were by the just retribution of God, it comes to pass, that the nation, which has been incapable of governing and ordering itself, and has delivered itself up to the slavery of its own lusts, is itself delivered over against its will to other masters—and whether it will or no is compelled to serve."

John Milton's democracy was a democracy in which men believed. It was a democracy for which a band of sober and unmilitary men fought as armies had not fought before them. It was a faith more powerful than any faith or cause which could be brought against it. It has been a faith more powerful than any other for three centuries of time and on two continents. It is still a faith more powerful than any other. All our history has made this plain. Whenever in the history of this nation we have given ourselves to the labor of creating upon this continent a life in which every man might have the freedom of his mind, we have been confident and certain of our future and assured and asked no questions either of ourselves or anyone. Whenever we have given ourselves to other labors, we have lost the meaning of our lives and lost our certainty and questioned everyone and most of all ourselves.

Three generations back in the thirties and the forties of the last century when the four-hundred-foot side-wheelers with the crystal chandeliers and the mahogany bars and the eight course dinners and the filigree funnels with their sparks like crazy stars went hooting and slapping up the Ohio and the

Hudson and the Mississippi, the Americans had no questions about democracy. They had a job to do. They had the toughest job a people ever undertook—the job of clearing and settling and tying together with ships and roads and rails and words and names the largest area lived on as a single social unit by any nation, at any time. They had the job of creating on an undiscovered continent a country where a hundred million men could live in freedom from the rest and from each other. They had the actual and present job of clearing on this continent the quarter sections where a man could build his freedom out of logs and nails.

And while they had that job to do they asked no questions. They knew what democracy was. They knew what they were too. They were the smartest, toughest, luckiest, leanest, all-around knowingest nation on God's green earth. Their way of living was the handsomest way of living human beings had ever hit on. Their institutions were the institutions history had been waiting for. If you had told them anyone else had a harder hold on the earth than they had, or anyone else believed in himself more than they believed in themselves, they would have laughed in your face. And gone on with their working.

Who they were, what they were, never bothered the Americans. Virginia gentlemen and Boston philosophers and Long Island poets and visiting British lecturers might write and talk and wonder about American manners and American origins and American politics and the American soul. Americans didn't wonder. They knew all about them. They knew about origins. They had all the origins of Europe in their veins before the century was over—all the races a man ever heard of and a lot more beside. Races didn't bother the Americans. They were something a lot better than any race. They were a People. They were the first self-constituted, self-declared, self-created People in the history of the world. And their manners were their own business. And so were their politics. And so, but ten times so, were their souls.

Who an American was and what democracy was, was nothing to talk about. You could see for yourself. An American was a man who had the luck to be born on this continent where the heat was hotter and the cold was colder and the sun was brighter and the nights were blacker and the distances were farther and the faces were nearer and the rain was more like rain and the mornings were more like mornings than anywhere else on earth—sooner and sweeter and lovelier over unused hills.

An American was a man who knew which way to take to reach tomorrow. An American was a man who could let himself in and let himself out and nobody asking him "please" not even the President. An American was a man who never asked anyone anything—who he was or where he came from or what he did—because it was answer enough to be a man. At least in America.

That was the way it used to be in this country. That was the way it was while the people of this country were clearing the quarter sections for a free man's field. That is the way it has been whenever we have remembered clearly and understood with reality what democracy is.

For democracy is never a thing done. Democracy is always something that a nation must be doing. The quarter sections which were freedom a hundred years ago are now not freedom. Freedom will be somewhere else. But the labor of creating freedom is the same. And the consequences.

What is necessary now is one thing and one thing only—that the issue of democracy be made precise and clear—that democracy become again democracy in action, not democracy accomplished and piled up in goods and gold.

Democracy in action is a cause for which the stones themselves will fight.

18. MARCUS LEE HANSEN

*The Third Generation**

Marcus Lee Hansen was born in rural Wisconsin in 1892, the son of immigrants, his father from Denmark and his mother from Norway. Educated in the Middle West, Hansen came to Harvard to do graduate work in history under Frederick Jackson Turner from whom he acquired an appreciation of the necessity for viewing immigration as an aspect of the great movements of population in modern times. From his own home, Hansen drew valuable insights into the processes of cultural transplantation. He never lost sight of the fact that his research dealt with human beings as well as with impersonal forces. He taught at Smith College and the University of Illinois until a tragic death cut his career short at the age of forty-five. His pioneering works on American immigration were not published until after his death. See also his Atlantic Migration *(New York, 1961).*

By long established custom whoever speaks of immigration must refer to it as a "problem." It was a problem to the first English pioneers in the New World scattered up and down the Atlantic coast. Whenever a vessel anchored in the James River and a few score weary and emaciated gentlemen, worn out by three months upon the Atlantic, stumbled up the bank, the veterans who had survived Nature's rigorous "seasoning" looked at one another in despair and asked: "Who is to feed them? Who is to teach them to fight the Indians, or grow tobacco, or clear the marshy lands and build a home in the

* "The Problem of the Third Generation Immigrant," *Augustana Historical Society Publications* (Rock Island, 1938).

malaria-infested swamps? These immigrants certainly are a problem." And three hundred years later when in the course of a summer more than a million Europeans walked down the gangplanks of the ocean greyhounds into the large reception halls built to receive them, government officials, social workers, journalists said: "How are these people from the peasant farms of the Mediterranean going to adjust themselves to the routine of mines and industries, and how are they going to live in a country where the language is strange, and how are they, former subjects of monarchs and lords, going to partake in the business of governing themselves? These immigrants certainly are a problem."

They certainly were. The adventurers (call them colonists or immigrants) who transferred civilization across the Atlantic numbered more than forty million souls. Every one of them was a problem to his family and himself, to the officials and landlords from whom he parted, to the officials and landlords whom he joined. On every mile of the journey, on land and on sea, they caused concern to someone. The public authorities at the ports of embarkation sighed the traditional sigh of relief when the emigrant vessel was warped away from the dock and stood out to the open sea carrying the bewildered persons who for a week or more had wandered about the streets; the captain of that vessel was happy when the last of his passengers who had complained of everything from food to weather said goodbye—often with a clenched fist; and the officers of New York and Baltimore were no less happy when the newly-arrived American set out for the West. How much of a problem the forty million actually were will not be known until their history is written with realism as well as sympathy.

The problem of the immigrant was not solved; it disappeared. Foreign-born to the number of almost fifteen million are still part of the American population, but they are no longer immigrants. By one adjustment after the other they have accommodated themselves and reconciled themselves to the surrounding world of society, and when they became what the natives called "Americanized" (which was often nothing but a treaty of peace with society) they ceased to be a problem. This was the normal evolution of an individual, but as long as the group classified as immigrants was being constantly recruited by the continual influx of Europeans the problem remained. The quota law of 1924 erected the first dam against the current and the depression of 1929 cut off the stream entirely. Statistics reveal what has happened. During the year ending June 30, 1936, there were admitted as immigrants only 36,329 aliens. During the same period 35,817 aliens left the United States for permanent residence abroad—a net gain of only 512. But this was the first year since 1931 that there had been any gain at all. The great historic westward tide of Europeans has come to an end and there is no indication in American conditions or sentiment that it will ever be revived.

Thus there has been removed from the pages of magazines, from the debates in Congress, and from the thoughts of social workers the well-known expression: the problem of the immigrant. Its going has foreshadowed the disappearance of a related matter of concern which was almost as troublesome as the first, a rather uncertain worry which was called "the problem of the second generation."

The sons and the daughters of the immigrants were really in a most uncomfortable position. They were subjected to the criticism and taunts of the native Americans and to the criticism and taunts of their elders as well. All who exercised any authority over them found fault with the response. Too often in the schoolroom the Yankee schoolmistress regarded them as mere dullards hardly worthy of her valuable attention. Thus neglected they strayed about the streets where the truant officer picked them up and reported them as incorrigible. The delinquency of the second generation was talked about so incessantly that finally little Fritz and little Hans became convinced that they were not like the children from the other side of the tracks. They were not slow in comprehending the source of all their woes: it lay in the strange dualism into which they had been born.

Life at home was hardly more pleasant. Whereas in the

schoolroom they were too foreign, at home they were too American. Even the immigrant father who compromised most willingly in adjusting his outside affairs to the realities that surrounded him insisted that family life, at least, should retain the pattern that he had known as a boy. Language, religion, customs and parental authority were not to be modified simply because the home had been moved four or five thousand miles to the westward. When the son and the daughter refused to conform, their action was considered a rebellion of ungrateful children for whom so many advantages had been provided. The gap between the two generations was widened and family spirit embittered by repeated misunderstanding. How to inhabit two worlds at the same time was the problem of the second generation.

That problem was solved by escape. As soon as he was free economically, an independence that usually came several years before he was free legally, the son struck out for himself. He wanted to forget everything: the foreign language that left an unmistakable trace in his English speech, the religion that continually recalled childhood struggles, the family customs that should have been the happiest of all memories. He wanted to be away from all physical reminders of early days, in an environment so different, so American, that all associates naturally assumed that he was as American as they. This picture has been deliberately overdrawn, but who will deny that the second generation wanted to forget, and even when the ties of family affection were strong, wanted to lose as many of the evidences of foreign origin as they could shuffle off?

Most easy to lose was that which, if retained, might have meant the most to the civilization of the American republic. The immigrant brought with him European culture. This does not mean that the man who wielded the pickaxe was really a Michael Angelo or that the one who took to house painting was in fact an unrecognized Rembrandt. They brought a popular though uncritical appreciation of art and music; they felt at home in an environment where such aspects of culture were taken for granted and (what is not to be overlooked in any consideration of the development of American life) they did not subscribe to the prevailing American sentiment that it was not quite moral for a strong, able-bodied man to earn his living by playing a fiddle. If they did not come in loaded down with culture, at least they were plentifully supplied with the seeds of culture that, scattered in a fertile soil, could flourish mightily.

The soil was not fertile. Americans of the nineteenth century were not entirely unfriendly to a little art now and then if it were limited to the front parlor and restricted to the women. . . . The second generation was entirely aware of the contempt in which such artistic activities were held and they hastened to prove that they knew nothing about casts, symphonies or canvas. Nothing was more Yankee than a Yankeeized person of foreign descent.

The leaders among the natives proclaimed loudly: It is wonderful how these young people catch the spirit of American institutions. The leaders among the foreign-born sighed and said to themselves: This apostasy means nothing good. It is not good for the sons and daughters who give up a heritage richer than farm acres and city lots; it is not good for this uncouth pioneer nation which has spent its time chopping down trees and rolling stones and has never learned how the genius of one might brighten the life of many and satisfy some human longings that corn bread and apple pie can never appease. Blind, stupid America, they said, the one nation of the globe which has had offered to it the rich gifts that every people of Europe brought and laid at its feet and it spurned them all. The immigrants, perhaps, may be excused. Their thoughts and efforts were taken up with material cares and they were naturally under some suspicion. But nothing can absolve the traitors of the second generation who deliberately threw away what had been preserved in the home. When they are gone all the hope will be lost and the immigration of the nineteenth century will have contributed nothing to the development of America but what came out of the strong muscles of a few million patient plodders.

These pessimists were wrong. All has not been lost. After the second generation comes the third and with the third appears a new force and a new opportunity which, if recognized in time, can not only do a good job of salvaging but probably can accomplish more than either the first or the second could ever have achieved.

Anyone who has the courage to codify the laws of history must include what can be designated "the principle of third-generation interest." The principle is applicable in all fields of historical study. It explains the recurrence of movements that seemingly are dead; it is a factor that should be kept in mind particularly in literary or cultural history; it makes it possible for the present to know something about the future.

The theory is derived from the almost universal phenomenon that what the son wishes to forget the grandson wishes to remember. The tendency might be illustrated by a hundred examples. The case of the Civil War may be cited. The Southerners who survived the four years of that struggle never forgot. In politics and in conversation the "lost cause" was an endless theme. Those who listened became weary and the sons of the Confederate veterans were among them. *That* second generation made little effort to justify the action of their fathers. Their expressed opinion was that, after all, the result was inevitable and undoubtedly for the best. These sons went North and won success in every field of business and in every branch of learning. But now the grandsons of the Confederates rule in the place of the sons and there is no apologizing for the events of 1861; instead there is a belligerency that asserts the moral and constitutional justice of their grandfathers' policy. The South has been revived. Its history is taught with a fervid patriotism in the universities and schools. Recently there has been formed the Southern Historical Association as an evidence of the growing interest. The great novel of the Civil War and reconstruction era was not written by one who had participated in the events or witnessed the scenes. It did not come from the pen of one who had listened to a father's reminiscences. *Gone with the Wind* was written by a granddaughter of the Confederacy, in the year 1936, approximately sixty years after the period with which it dealt had come to an end.

Immigration not only has its history, it has its historiography. The writing of descriptions of that great epic movement began almost as early as the movement itself. Every immigrant letter written from new shores was history, very personal and very uncritical. Every sheaf of reminiscences written by one of the participants in his later years was also history, a little more uncritical. There was much to be recounted and since sons would not listen the grayheaded participants got together and, organized as pioneer societies, they told one another of the glorious deeds that they had seen and sometimes performed and listened to the reading of the obituaries of the giants that had fallen. When the last of them had joined his ancestors the pioneer society automatically disbanded leaving behind as the first chapter of immigrant historiography a conglomerate mass of literature, much and often most of it useless. All of it seemed useless to the son who cleared out his father's desk and he resolved not to waste any of his time on such pointless pursuits.

As a broad generalization it may be said that the second generation is not interested in and does not write any history. That is just another aspect of their policy of forgetting. Then, however, appears the "third generation." They have no reason to feel any inferiority when they look about them. They are American-born. Their speech is the same as that of those with whom they associate. Their material wealth is the average possession of the typical citizen. When anyone speaks to him about immigrants, he always makes it clear that he has in mind the more recent hordes that have been pouring through the gates and any suggestion that the onrush should be stemmed is usually prefaced with the remark that recent immigrants are not so desirable as the pioneers that arrived in earlier times. It is in an attitude of pride that the substantial land owner or merchant looks about him and says: "This prosperity is our achievement, that of myself and of my fathers; it is a sign of the hardy stock from which we have sprung; who were they and why did they come?" And so their curiosity is projected back into the family beginnings. Those who are acquainted with the universities of the Middle West, where a large proportion of the students are grandchildren and great-grandchildren of the 19th-century immigrants can sense this attitude of inquiry and cannot escape the feeling of pride in which they study the history and culture of the nations from which their ancestors came.

To show how universal this spirit has been we can retrace some periodic resurgences of national spirit and relate them to the time of immigration. There were Irishmen in America before the Revolution but there is no reason to question the generalization that until 1840 two-thirds of the emigrants from Ireland were the so-called Scotch-Irish. In the 1830's their influx was particularly large; in fact, the great proportion of Ulstermen who came to America arrived in the course of the decade. Sixty years later (at the time of the third generation) a renaissance of Scotch-Irish sentiment in the United States was strikingly apparent. Local societies were formed that met in monthly or quarterly conclave to sing the praises of their forebears and to glory in the achievements of the Presbyterian Church. Beginning in 1889 and continuing for more than a decade representatives of these societies met in an annual national meeting called a "Scotch-Irish Congress." Then the movement lost its impetus. Leaders died or took up other activities; members refrained from paying dues; attendance at sessions dwindled. After 1903 no more Scotch-Irish congresses were held.

We can pass to another example. The large German immigration reached its crest in the late 1840's and early 1850's. A little over half a century later, in the first decade of the twentieth century, a breeze of historical interest stirred the German-American community. One of the number was moved to offer a prize for the best historical discussion of the contribution of the German element to American life. Not only the prize-winning work (the well-known volume by A. B. Faust) but many of the manuscripts that had been submitted in the competition were published, forming a library of German-American activity in many fields. Several local and state historical societies were formed and the study of German literature in universities and schools enjoyed an amazing popularity that later observers could ascribe only to the propaganda of an intriguing nation. The Theodore Roosevelt Professorship established at the University of Berlin in 1907 was an expression of the same revival. The war naturally put an end to this activity and obscured much of the valuable work that the investigators had performed.

The auspices under which we have met this evening suggest the next example to be cited. The large Scandinavian immigration began in the 1850's and after the interruption of the Civil War reached its culmination in the 1880's. True to expectations we find that at present the most lively interest in history of this nature is exhibited in Scandinavian circles in America. Among Scandinavians, Norwegians were pioneers and in historical research they are also a step in advance. The Swedes came a little later and an intelligent prophet of that period looking forward to the cultural development of the nationality in their new home would have said: "About 1930 a historical society will be formed." It was. In June, 1930, the Augustana Historical Society was organized among the members of the Augustana Synod which so faithfully represents the more than a million people of Swedish descent who are citizens of the American republic. And now . . . I come to the topic of the evening, a subject which will be interpreted in the light of the foregoing remarks. It reads: The problem of the third generation immigrant.

As problems go it is not one to cause worry or to be shunned. It has none of the bitterness or heart-breaking features of its predecessors. It is welcome. In summary form it may be stated as follows: Whenever any immigrant group reaches the third-generation stage in its development a spontaneous and almost irresistible impulse arises which forces the thoughts of many people of different professions, different positions in life and different points of view to interest themselves in that one factor which they have in common: heritage —the heritage of blood. The problem: how can this impulse be organized and directed so that the results growing therefrom will be worthy of the high instincts from which it has sprung and a dignified tribute to the pioneers and at the same time be a contribution to the history of the United States which has received all Europeans on a basis of equality and which should record their achievements in the same spirit of impartiality?

It is hardly necessary for me to remind this gathering that the Swedish stock in America is fast approaching the third generation stage. During the decade of the eighties their coming reached its height in numbers. The census of 1930 records that of the persons born in Sweden giving the date of their arrival in the country fifty-two per cent landed before 1900—and this in spite of the great mortality that the newcomers of that period have suffered. The children that crowd the Sunday school rooms of the churches of this Synod it is well known are the grandsons and granddaughters of the pioneers that built the churches; grandsons and granddaughters, I am also sure, are present in increasing numbers in the student body of this college which those same pioneers at the cost of many sacrifices, built for the sake of those who were to come after them. Among the leaders of this society are men of the first generation and of the second generation but they are the proverbial exception, or it may be better to say they are third generation in spirit. No matter how active they are in leadership the organization can succeed only if the grandchildren of the pioneers will follow.

We will assume that this will be the case; that the membership of the Augustana Historical Society will continue to increase in numbers, that the members will continue to pay their dues, that a few patrons will arise to sponsor special enterprises in research and publication. It is not my object to enlighten you on how to bring about this happy condition. We will assume that many members will carry on their own investigations, that now and then an expert can be subsidized to probe deeply into some vital aspects of Swedish-American history and that the publications will continue to be of the high standard that has already been established. My suggestions will be of a different nature and will center about another set of questions: What fields shall be investigated? Where shall the emphasis be put in research and publication? What should be the attitude in which the past, which belongs not only to the Swedes but also to the Americans, should be approached? In attempting an answer I speak with no authority except that which comes from several years of delving into the records of most of the pioneer and historical societies in America.

Everyone accepts the premise that self-laudation is not the end in view. Nevertheless it will be hard to keep out because of the human characteristic of speaking nothing but good of the men who labored hard and have now disappeared from the earthly stage. At the first meeting of the Scotch-Irish Congress the speakers presented one paper after the other which dealt with the achievements of the Ulsterman at home and abroad, during all ages and in all spheres of human effort. Finally one of the delegates arose and made a cutting remark that only a Scotch-Irishman would dare to make. While listening to the programs, he said, he had been asking himself the question: "What on earth have the rest of creation been doing for the last eighteen hundred years?" That question should be in the mind of every writer who is tempted to generalize on the contribution of ethnic groups to the development of American life.

If not to the laudation of great men, to what activities should the efforts of the society be directed? Let that question first be approached by a calm realization of the fact that the society will not live forever. The time will come when membership will dwindle, when promising subjects for research will be few in number and of little popular interest. That has been the life-course of every organization of this nature. The constituency becomes gradually thinned out as the third generation merges into the fourth and the fourth shades off into the fifth. Even societies with substantial endowments have in their later years found it difficult to continue to produce work of high scholarly quality. The final judgment rendered regarding the success or failure of this society as of others will rest upon the answer given to two pertinent inquiries: Did they, when the time was appropriate, write the history of the special group with whom they were concerned on broad impartial lines, and did they make a permanent contribution to the meaning of American history at large? A few proposals by the following of which a satisfactory reply can be given to both of those questions are now in order.

First of all let it be remembered that the history of any immigrant stock in America is far broader than the history of the particular religious organization that was predominant in the number of communicants that it could claim. The neglect of that fact was the first error made by historical writers in America. When they set out to write the story of the settlement of Englishmen in New England they centered it all about the migration of the Puritan church and neglected a hundred other factors that surrounded the coming and establishment of the colonies on that coast. In recent years some correction has been made but the traditional emphasis has been so great that in spite of the labors of many scholars and the resources of a dozen secular institutions, the history of New England is still less satisfactory than that of any other section of the older part of the country. From such a false start may the Augustana Historical Society be preserved!

Religion must certainly be a leading theme in the program. The church was the first, the most important and the most significant institution that the immigrants established. Its policies reacted upon every other phase of their existence but in turn and, in fact, first those other phases of their existence established the conditions under which the church was planted and grew. If one should study the agriculture, the system of land purchase, the distribution of population, the state of the roads, the circulation of books and newspapers, the development of amusements, he would be in a better position to appraise the situation that the church did occupy in the life of every community. In Mr. Rölvaag's stirring novel *Giants in the*

Earth no episode is presented with more effect than that which recounts the coming of the clergyman, and the effect is produced not by the description of the man and his mission. It is the background of dull, material routine that has preceded that gives to the brief chapter its epic quality. History had been made before the clergyman and the church appeared and to be understood they must be placed in their proper order in the sequence of events.

Moreover, for an understanding of religious development to the formation of those churches that broke with the faith of the old country relatively more attention should be given than the number of their communicants would warrant. In no other experience was the psychology of the immigrant more clearly reflected. When they said that they passed from the old world to the new many of them meant that the world should be new in all respects. When they gave up allegiance to a government it was easy to give up allegiance to a church. The secessions from the Lutheran faith can be dealt with conveniently, quickly and without embarrassment by ascribing them to the successful methods of proselyting that the well-financed American home missionary societies employed. But the immigrant met the proselyter halfway—perhaps more than halfway—and when one knows what was going on in the mind of the person who did break away from his mother church it will be easier to understand the actions of some of those who did not break away but certainly caused frictions within the church to which they remained true and created situations that could not have arisen in the old Swedish parish from which they had recently come.

Even the study of politics is not entirely foreign to an organization which has chosen as its mission the history of the Augustana Synod. The clergymen of that Synod like the clergymen of any other religious body in the republic had no intention of destroying the fundamental separation of Church and State which the Fathers of the constitution had ordained, but how they itched to go into politics! How they lived to find in every Sunday's text some idea that could be applied to the decision of that burning political issue that the men in the audience had been discussing before the services had begun and which they would surely begin to discuss again as soon as the benediction had been pronounced. There is much evidence to suggest that the immigrant church had a great influence in determining the way in which the naturalized citizen would cast his vote. But not a single study has been made of church influence in any election and the results of such a study would throw as much light upon the status of the church as it would upon the political history of that election.

The church had some competitors in the matter of interest, affection, and usefulness. Whatever the difficulties that attended the founding of the pioneer congregation, that of inducing the immigrant to join was hardly existent. The immigrant was an inveterate joiner—a habit which was, without question, the result of his feeling of lonesomeness. In Europe the individual was born into many groups that he had to join in America and he entered into them rather light-heartedly hoping that from all he would derive the satisfaction that no single one could yield. When some energetic spirit said to him: come and join this fraternal organization, he went; when the suggestion of a singing society was broached he fell in with the plan; when some one undertook to line up a shooting corps he took down his gun and practiced marksmanship. All of these pursuits weakened somewhat the hold of the church and the minister was led to adopt an uncompromising attitude toward amusements that otherwise would have been held both innocent and useful. Therefore, it can be said that without a knowledge of the social environment the policy of the church cannot be understood.

If these suggestions should be followed, the product would be a history of the Swedes in America that no one could accuse of being tainted with partiality. Perhaps not all the passages would be read with a glow of pride but there would be no humiliation and the pride in the achievement of what no other ethnic group in America has been willing to do would soon overcome regrets that arose out of what truth made it necessary to say. In such an accomplishment the Augustana Historical Society would achieve all that its founders had hoped for it in the field of religious history, and the incidental products would give to the world a true and inspiring picture of what the Swedish pioneers had done in the task of subduing the primitive American wilderness.

Although a historical society has justified its existence when it has faithfully recorded the experiences and achievements of the particular element in the population or the particular region in the country that it was created to serve, still unless the story that is written from these records can be made to fit in as one chapter in the larger volume that is called American history, the charge of antiquarianism can hardly be escaped. Men of insight who understand that it is the ultimate fate of any national group to be amalgamated into the composite American race will be reconciled to the thought that their historical activities will in time be merged with the activities of other societies of the same nature and finally with the main line of American historiography itself. How such a merging may profoundly influence the course of all national historical writing is illustrated by reference to that one group which is the most mature among the population minorities.

The Scotch-Irish Congress during the fourteen years of its existence published ten volumes of *Proceedings.* A study of the contents of these volumes reveals the widening nature of the interests growing out of the researches. The laudatory character of the contributions to the first publication has been mentioned. Such papers are not entirely absent from the last volume but there also appear titles such as these: "Paths and Roads of our Forefathers," "The Colonial Defenses of Franklin County," "German Life and Thought in a Scotch-Irish Settlement"—substantial contributions to the pioneer history of the environment in which the group developed. It is well known that during the decade of the 1890's the character of American historical writing changed. A new emphasis appeared. Scholars looked beyond the older settlements ranged along the seaboard into the communities in the back country.

A word that every schoolboy can now explain crept into the textbooks. This word and this theory now almost dominate every page in the volume. The word is "frontier" and the theory is the "frontier interpretation of American history." . . .

This new emphasis is universally credited to Professor Frederick J. Turner. However, Turner or no Turner the frontier hypothesis was bound to come and to appear in the very decade during which he wrote his famous essay. In fact, the hypothesis may be distilled from the conglomerate mass of information and theory jumbled together in the ten volumes of Scotch-Irish proceedings. It is doubtful whether the pronouncement of one man, no matter how brilliant, could have turned the course of historical writing unless it were already veering in that direction. It is quite possible that Turner who wrote in 1893 drew upon the frontier interest that the Scotch-Irish were arousing by their studies of the part that the Ulstermen took in the movement of settlement into the West. The interest that they awakened united with the scholars that Professor Turner trained to give to American history its new and significant social interpretation.

The frontier doctrine in its original narrow statement has been overdone. We are beginning to see that the Mississippi Valley was for fifty years the frontier of Europe as well as of the eastern states and that it reacted upon England, Germany and Scandinavia with a force comparable to that which it exerted upon Atlantic America. Some historians with the orthodox professional training have recognized this fact and they are attempting, in a rather clumsy way, to analyze the operation of these influences. There is, however, one omission in their training. They know nothing about the hundreds of immigrant communities in America that formed the human connecting link between the old world and the new, nothing about the millions of personal contacts that brought humble public opinion on both sides of the Atlantic so close together.

The next stage in American historical writing will concern itself with this widened outlook. Herein lies not only the great opportunity but also the great obligation of the third generation historical activity. It alone can provide the atmosphere; it alone can uncover the sources; it alone can interpret the mentality of the millions of persons who had not entirely ceased to be Europeans and had not yet become accepted Americans. The problem of the third generation immigrant is to undertake the job that has been assigned and to perform it well.

The close of this discourse may very properly be a warning. It can be assumed too readily that the history of migration cannot be anything but a desirable influence. That is not necessarily the case. Prejudice and super-nationalism may be the product. Societies organized with the laudable intention of commemorating the deeds of which any people should be proud may fall into the hands of those who will use them for instruments of propaganda. Instead of a world covered with a network of associations which will foster an appreciation of the best that each nation has produced, we may find international societies for the promotion of hatred and intolerance. Historians must recognize an obligation to guide the national curiosity to know the past along those lines which will serve the good of all.

If told as it transpired, the epic of migration can add an ideal to take the place of one of the many that recent decades have shattered. For it is a simple story of how troubled men, by courage and action, overcame their difficulties, and how people of different tongues and varied culture have managed to live together in peace.

19. REINHOLD NIEBUHR

*Religion in American Experience**

Reinhold Niebuhr was born in Wright City, Missouri, in 1892, the son of German Lutheran immigrants. After brief periods of study at Elmhurst College (Illinois) and at the Eden Theological Seminary in St. Louis, he took his Bachelor of Divinity degree at Yale University in 1914. A year later he was ordained to the ministry of the Evangelical Synod of North America. For fourteen years he was a pastor in Detroit where he had some opportunity to observe the social effects of industrialization. After 1928 he taught at the Union Theological Seminary. Niebuhr's thinking was all along informed by an awareness of the human problems of modern society; but the Depression and the war undermined his "youthful optimism" and directed him toward a painful quest for "fuller knowledge of the 'unsearchable riches of Christ.'" See also Jules Bingham, Courage to Change. An Introduction to the Life and Thought of Reinhold Niebuhr *(New York, 1961); Charles W. Kegley and Robert W. Bretall,* Reinhold Niebuhr *(New York, 1956).*

The coexistence of the "godly" and the "godless" of traditional piety and modern secularism has been a characteristic of Western civilization since the seventeenth and eighteenth centuries. The rise of modern science created a rift in a traditionally Christian civilization and generated a "secular" spirit, which was denounced by the pious as heresy and which was welcomed by the "enlightened" as the harbinger of a promising future for mankind, as the guarantor of every private

* Reinhold Niebuhr, *Pious and Secular America* (New York, 1958), pp. 1–13.

virtue and public justice. Neither party was able to annihilate the other as simply as it had hoped. Western civilization, thereupon, became the realm of very interesting forms of interpenetration and cooperation, some advertent and some inadvertent, between piety and secularism. But in no nation has this coexistence brought more remarkable results than in our own. For here we are in the twentieth century, at once the most religious and the most secular of Western nations. How shall we explain this paradox? Could it be that we are most religious partly in consequence of being the most secular culture? That would add a special depth to the paradox.

Let us begin by defining our terms. We are "religious" in the sense that religious communities enjoy the devotion and engage the active loyalty of more laymen than in any nation of the Western world. We are "secular" in the sense that we pursue the immediate goals of life, without asking too many ultimate questions about the meaning of life and without being too disturbed by the tragedies and antimonies of life. Our secularism is of two varieties. There is a theoretic secularism which dismisses ultimate questions about the meaning of existence, partly because it believes that science has answered these questions and partly because it regards the questions as unanswerable or uninteresting. There is a practical secularism, which expresses itself in the pursuit of the immediate goals of life. Our detractors in Europe and Asia think that our practical secularism expresses itself in "materialism" that is in the pursuit, not of happiness, but of comfort and physical security against all the hazards of nature and of history. If there should be a measure of truth in this charge, it would add a peculiarly ironic note to our contest with communism. For we profess to be "Godly" and the communists are philosophical materialists, who think that piety deflects men from seeking the obvious goods of life successfully. But our "Godly materialism" has been immeasurably more successful than their "godless" variety. One must hasten to add that not our piety, but our secular and scientific proficiencies, have greatly contributed to our superiority over the communist pursuit of happiness.

Actually, our detractors are not quite right in accusing us of "materialism." Our passion has been technical efficiency. We have been able to give ourselves to technics with greater abandon than any other nation. We are uninhibited by the traditional restraints upon the technical enterprise which obtained in European nations, including the first industrial nation of Europe, Britain. This passion for technical efficiency, together with the natural resources of a richly endowed continent and the advantages of a single continental economic unit, has given us a cornucopia. We are not displeased with the fruits of this cornucopia. They were not, however, the first concern of our enterprise. That was efficiency. We are somewhat embarrassed by the fact that we are the first culture which is in danger of being subordinated to its economy. We have to live as luxuriously as possible in order to keep our productive enterprise from stalling.

If religion has not only survived, but gained a new relevance in this secular environment, this curious development must be partly attributed to the limitations of both a theoretic and practical secularism. A theoretic secularism is inclined to hold the pursuit of happiness as the final meaning of life. This pursuit of happiness easily degenerates into the pursuit of comfort and security. But a culture which gives itself wholeheartedly to these ends is bound to discover the limits of this frame of meaning for the life of man.

Not all, but many, forms of secularism try to comprehend human life in a too simple frame of meaning. They may not equate happiness with comfort and security; but they usually do not appreciate those dimensions of human striving in which joy and sorrow are curiously blended and achieve, not happiness, but fulfillment. American secularism, following the French Enlightenment, makes much of the "dignity of man." But it is usually oblivious to the "misery of man," which is equally, with his dignity, the undoubted fruit of the unique freedom, which distinguishes him from the brutes. For the same freedom which makes man historically creative also gives him the capacity to be destructive and lifts him above natural vicissitudes to contemplate the vanity and brevity of life with melancholy. This glorious human creature undoubtedly dies as the animals do; but he is anxious about his life and his death. All the advances in medical science offer no cure for senility, or materially alter the brevity of human existence.

To the misery of human frailty and brevity one must add the perplexities of a guilty conscience. They cannot be eliminated simply by living a "blameless" life; for our responsibilities involve us in guilt. No one anticipated in the nineteenth century that the responsibility of saving our civilization would involve us in the guilt of risking an atomic war. We do much evil in order to do good. Furthermore, there are forms of guilt which cannot be reduced to the proportions of neurotic guilt, subject to psychiatric ministrations. There are of course forms of neurotic guilt feelings which require psychiatric attention.

It is because a philosophy of the enlightened mind and a civilization of great technical power cannot solve these ultimate problems of human existence that the frame of meaning, established by the traditionally historic religions, has become much more relevant to the modern man than seemed possible a century ago. There is in these religions a sense of mystery and meaning, which outrages the canons of pure rationality but which makes "sense" out of life. Our national culture was not only more completely devoted to the promises of nineteenth-century culture (the so-called "century of hope"), but it was more efficient in fulfilling the prescriptions for happiness than any other nation. The reaction to unfulfilled hopes is correspondingly more obvious. This is particularly true because we are subject not only to the perennial antinomies and tragedies of life which our enlightenment and our technical efficiency have not been able to overcome; but we are, as a nation, subject to frustrations in the days of our seeming omnipotence which we did not foresee in the days of our national weakness and innocence. We are less the masters of our fate in this day of American power than when we were still rocked in the cradle of continental security. The whole drama of history is evidently more mysterious and meaningful, even as individual existence, more filled with beauty and terror than the secular philosophies anticipated.

The non-technical cultures of Asia and Africa will naturally regret the premature religious resignation which contributed to their technical backwardness and will try to achieve a more rational understanding of the complexities of life and a more adequate technical conquest of nature. But we have travelled that path of progress almost to its limit. The religious quest of ultimate meanings was, therefore, bound to gain new relevance among us.

These facts do not, of course, preclude the possibility that the religious revival in our day may contain elements of rather frantic pursuits of the secular ends of "success" or "power" and represent religious versions of "secularism." In the current debate between piety and secularism it is always well to bear in mind that neither piety nor enlightenment are as simply the guarantors of either private goodness or public virtue as the proponents of each side contend. The cooperation between secularism and piety has been fruitful on the whole because each side possessed more common virtue than the opponent was willing to admit. Partly, each side had a unique virtue which prevented the other side from pursuing its characteristic virtues so consistently that they degenerated into vices. The democracy of the whole of Western civilization, including our own, is obviously the fruit of such cooperation.

Genuine piety sets up an authority for the individual conscience which prevents the state or the community from becoming an idolatrous end of human existence. Religious faith makes a rigorous affirmation, "We must obey God, rather than men," in opposition to all tyranny. But, unfortunately, piety develops its own idolatries by claiming a too simple alliance between the divine will and human ends. The soberness of a secular pursuit of immediate ends and a tolerant appreciation of the fragmentariness of all human viewpoints is necessary for the "limited warfare" of parliamentary democracy. This spirit of tolerance and the contrasting spirit of fanaticism may each be the fruits of either religious piety or rational enlightenment, contrary to the assumption of each side that the evil fruit is the product of the other side and the good fruit the characteristic consequence of our own world view. It is as rare an achievement for the pious man to be charitable as for the rational man to be "reasonable." Both achievements depend upon the recognition of the limited character of each one's vision of the truth.

Another religious reaction to a secular civilization has been developed in an unusual degree in America. Technical civilizations create great urban centers in which the individual is in danger of losing his identity in the crowd, gathered together by technics, but lacking the virtues of genuine community. Some of the current popularity of religion in our nation is undoubtedly due to the fact that religious congregations have been able to establish integral communities in the impersonal and technical togetherness of our urban centers. In these communities, the individual comes to his own as a person and lives in an environment of faith in which the vicissitudes of his existence are understood. It is interesting that Americans are a more urban people than Europeans. They do not require roots in the country as do most Englishmen. It is also interesting that this urbanness has increased, rather than diminished, loyalty to the religious communities, though it was previously assumed that religious faith flourished in the countryside and withered in the sophisticated city. This did not prove to be so in America. The reason was probably that religious faith was, in more ways than one, used as an antidote to the simple meanings and fulfillments of a technical culture.

Two very different types of religious congregations, both uniquely American, contributed to the vitality of religious loyalty in our nation. And both also contributed to the uniquely American religiosity, which was at once more vital and more "secular" than European religion. The one was the sectarian church and the other the immigrant church. The sect-church represented an exclusive religious community in Europe, emphasizing voluntary membership, lay responsibility, and a critical attitude toward all the traditional "means of grace" in the church, the sacraments, liturgies and theologies, and professional ministers, and an emphasis upon religious immediacy and personal religious "experience." The radical sect, whether individualistic or socially radical, always remained a minority group in Europe as compared with the churches of inclusive membership, and frequently lived under direct state auspices. In America, this sect conquered the frontier. Its religious immediacy and the mobility of its quasi-lay leadership (the Methodist circuit rider, for instance) was suited to the frontier. On the frontier, the sect became the dominant church in America. The traditional churches remained in their urban settings. But in less than a century, the sect-churches colored the religious climate of the whole of America. In a sense, every church became a sect, at least in terms of emphasis upon lay responsibility and integral religious fellowship. The Methodist and Baptist churches are numerically the dominant churches in America. Most of them have grown respectable and only show vestigial remnants of the charismatic power by which they conquered the frontier.

But the same sect which revitalized religious life in America also "secularized" religious faith and prompted the criticism of European Christians, even to this day, that American faith is "secularized." What validity did this charge have? Over a century ago, De Toqueville, that perceptive French observer of the American scene, affirmed that the evangelical preachers of the American frontier were highly pragmatic in their exposition of their religion. They did not envisage "eternal felicity" as the end of the religious quest, he said, but rather commended religion as an aid in the pursuit of worldly ends such as "prosperity" and "civic peace and righteousness."

This disavowal of "otherworldliness" will seem very natural to American observers even today; but it was, unfortunately, accompanied by the frontier's rather sentimental "thisworldliness," that is by the hope that the frustrations of life, as known in the old world would disappear on the frontier where "liberty and equality" seemed for the first time realizable ideals.

Thus, the Enlightenment and evangelical Christianity were merged on the American frontier and the result was that note of sentimentality which has characterized both political and religious thought in our nation ever since. "If one compliments an American," declared De Toqueville, "on the virtues of American life, he will take the compliment for granted and enlarge upon the vices and corruptions of European nations." The heaven of evangelical Christianity and the utopia of the Enlightenment were, thus, blended on the frontier. But utopia was uppermost in the imagination of the frontier. And it was an achieved utopia, not a future one. America was a kind of Kingdom of God. The final spiritual fruit of this frontier religious sentimentality came a century later when the "social gospel" thought the problems of life, including those of a technical civilization, would be solved if only people could be persuaded to love one another. The recalcitrance of human nature, expressed in St. Paul's well-known confession, "the good that I would do, I do not do; and the evil that I would not, that I do," is obscured in this sentimentality and all the hard problems of achieving justice in a community of self-seeking men are made easy by these hopes. Thus, a great thinker of the social gospel could say at the beginning of this century: "The impulse to give justice is evangelical; but the impulse to get justice is not. There is an ominous desire to get justice which reveals that we have lost confidence in spiritual forces."

Thus, a dissipated evangelicalism relied on "love," while the Enlightenment relied on "reason" to achieve utopia on earth. But both the secular and the religious version of utopianism denied the real problems of human existence and expected dreams to turn into reality cheaply. That is why the religious revival in America is only partly a reaction to disappointed secular hopes and is partly a religious expression of those same hopes. Nothing could illustrate the bewildering confusion of secularism and religiosity in our nation more vividly. Perhaps we are so religious because religion has two forms among us. One challenges the gospel of prosperity, success, and achievement of heaven on earth. The other claims to furnish religious instruments for the attainment of these objectives.

The other unique American religious force which made a community for the individual in the anonymity of the urban center was the church of the immigrant. America was refashioned by the hordes of immigrants which came to our shores in the latter part of the nineteenth and the early part of the twentieth centuries. They brought their churches along with them. These churches, Catholic, Protestant, and for the Jews the synagogue, were anchored in a culture in the land of the immigrants' birth. But in the American environment, they became exclusive, and without organic relation to the American culture. They generated much more lay activity than in Europe and became fellowships which performed the function of guarding the immigrant against the anonymity of an urban and strange culture and of preserving something of the old world culture, including the language of the immigrant.

According to the thesis of Will Herberg's sociological analysis *Protestant, Catholic, Jew,* the immigrant church proved a very ready instrument both for preserving and for adapting the culture of the immigrant to America. For the church became the means of his self-identification without a too-obvious connotation of foreignness. The church was recognized as part of the "American way of life" and yet it was reminiscent of the culture of the home country. The immigrant church was, thus, popular for other than purely religious reasons. In a different way than the sectarian church, it pursued religious interest for essentially secular reasons and thereby became another instrument for the curious mingling of secularism and piety in America.

It must be added that the members of these immigrant churches were attracted to America, partly by its free institutions but mostly by its economic opportunities. These immigrants were first employed as poorly paid workers in our expanding economy. But in time, many of them rose into the managerial and owning class. Their religious faith did not inhibit them from pursuing the goals of economic well-being with absolute devotion. It may have actually supplied the discipline by which the economic activity could be more successfully engaged in. Thus, the immigrant church together with the sectarian church was at one and the same time a refuge from a secular culture, and a resource for the uninhibited pursuits of essentially secular ends of life.

Thus, the religion of the immigrant achieved the same relation to secular ends in a few generations, which required a century of development in New England, where the original Puritanism was transmuted into "Yankeeism" of the New England business man.

If this analysis of the unique relation of piety to secularism in our own nation is at all correct, it becomes apparent that we are more religious and more secular than any other nation, not by accident, but by the effect of definitely ascertainable historic causes peculiar to the American experience. If the results are extravagant, it is always possible to console ourselves that the interpenetration of piety and secularism in our culture has been more creative in the political sphere than in the economic realm. In that sphere the secular devotion to immediate ends and the religious apprehension of ultimate authority, beyond the realm of the political order, have saved us from both authoritarian politics of traditional piety and from the totalitarian politics of a consistent secularism, as developed historically from the French Revolution to the Russian Revolution.

In our economic life, we may have extravagantly pursued the immediate ends of life with such consistency that religion tended to become both a refuge against the anonymous social togetherness of an urban society, a balm for the inevitable disillusionments in which the rational and the technical "pursuit of happiness" is bound to end and (occasionally) a pious version of the secular pursuit.

The striking contrast between the relatively creative interpenetration of secularism and piety in our political life and the comparatively uncreative relation between the two in our economic life deserves a closing word.

We have seen that political democracy depended upon both piety and secularism, each contributing its characteristic insights to the organization of a free society. Secularism furnished the immediate and proximate goals of justice and prevented religion from confusing immediate with final goals of life, and, thus, developing its own idolatries. Piety, on the other hand, gave the individual a final divine authority, which enabled him to defy tyrannical political authority.

In the realm of economics, on the other hand, an efficient economy was the product of a secularism, which began by regarding happiness as the final end of life, continued by substituting comfort and security for happiness and ended by regarding efficiency as an end in itself. The idolatry which substituted a means to an end as the final end of existence has tended to vulgarize our culture. Piety has not essentially challenged this vulgarity or futility. Sometimes it has provided asylums of fellowship for the victims of the cult of efficiency; sometimes it has been a resource for further efficiency; and only occasionally it has challenged the inadequacy of these immediate goals as containing the final goals of life and a fulfillment of the meaning of human existence.

Our gadget-filled paradise suspended in a hell of international insecurity certainly does not offer us even the happiness of which the former century dreamed. Only when we finally realize the cause of these disappointed hopes can we have a truly religious culture. It will probably disappoint the traditionally pious as much as the present paradise disappoints the children of the Enlightenment.

In that event piety will have recaptured some of the characteristic accents of the historic religions, which, in their traditional form, may have regarded historic existence too much as a "vale of sorrows" but which had the virtue of knowing that there could be no complete happiness in human life because a creative life could never arrive at the neat harmonies which are the prerequisite of happiness. They knew that all human virtue remains fragmentary and all human achievements remain tentative. They knew that the meanings of life were surrounded by a penumbra of mystery and that life's joys and sorrows are curiously mingled. The great historic religions, in short, were rooted in the experiences of the ages so that they could not be deluded by the illusions of a technical age.

20. ANTHONY M. RUD

*The Second Generation**

Anthony M. Rud was born in 1893, the son of a Chicago doctor who had come to America from Kongsberg, Norway, at the age of twelve. His mother was of Canadian descent. He was educated at St. John's Military Academy, Delafield, Wisconsin, at Dartmouth College, and at Rush Medical School. He is author of several novels of western life. See also A. O. Barton, "Two Norwegian-American Novelists," Norwegian-American Historical Association, Studies and Records, *Vol. VI* (1931).

"Not yet, Hulda. At least not yet. The father is unreasonable and will not have it; I am penniless."

A dozen times before Einar had made this reply, always to Hulda's questions in which lay no suspicion, no impatience, only that untiring persistence which the forest instills. The hours he could spend with her at the *saeter* were few in the course of a month. Chris Merssen watched his sons with the vigilance of a wood-hawk near its nest. A love affair was his greatest worry; it meant the possible loss of one of his chief assets. Because Einar was forced to steal out after nine o'clock, when the Merssen home became quiet for the night, robbing himself of rest which eased the next day's labours, or had to invent errand or pretext long enough in advance so that Hulda might leave her herd in the care of Ida or Thorvald Broderson to meet him, her questions and his answers often briefed themselves to single sentences. Always they were curt.

The moment of her last, inevitable query was dreaded by

* Anthony M. Rud, *The Second Generation* (Garden City, 1923), pp. 1–10, 217–21, 315–18.

Einar. Immediately it passed he tossed aside his smothered feeling of depression with a shrug of his shoulders just as he had shed physical weariness. Hulda gave no sign that she disliked his answer. She nodded, seating herself crosswise on his knees, encircling his neck with her bare arm, and relaxing until her cheek touched his.

Einar preferred her to Ida and the other herd girls about Mount Gausta. At first he had been attracted to her by a chastity that seemed to him outrageous and strange in a herd girl—particularly one who had come of age and who had not lacked attention.

His long courting finished, the reason for his first interest was forgotten speedily. Chiefly now he sought her out because she possessed the sacred instinct of cleanliness. Einar was of the soil. He doused himself in tepid suds once each fortnight on the same day the Merssen clothes were washed. His brothers and sisters followed with him the example of their elders, who had inherited the tradition of farms. He knew nothing of Hulda's more frequent ablutions, nor of the essence stewed from pine cones to scent the goose fat she applied to keep her skin smooth and free from nettle rash and other vegetable irritations. Had he suspected he would have laughed. Dirt was of no consequence to him, yet he revelled in the sweetness of Hulda's body.

Ida, who had entertained him once at her hut when her brother's visit to Skien had coincided with an absence of Chris Merssen, reeked always of the cows she tended. Though pleasing to Einar because of more fulsome bodily development and sprier wit—Hulda said little, seldom attempting a head of froth to her goblet of conversational spirit—he never repeated the visit. Ida coaxed, but always there was excuse ready to hand. The father had become suspicious. The distance around Mount Gausta was so great he could not negotiate it and return before the early morning. But Einar managed his occasional speedy trip to Hulda's *saeter*. There with her was intoxication of mind and body greater than that caused by Chris Merssen's mead, though not as long enduring.

Einar achieved his nearest approach to content with Hulda in his arms. He forgot his aches, his disappointments, and almost all of his ambition. The last, fed on secret hope and extra work of which he spoke not even to Hulda, never quite left him. Even in most sublime moments something deep in his mind took for granted that Hulda was but a palliative. Each night at his departure, and on the swift run homeward, Hulda was replaced by the subject thought, which grew and took on definite shape as the months sped by. Sated passion opened the gate to unsated ambition.

"Some time, some day . . . is it when the father dies, Einar?" pursued Hulda unexpectedly.

"I know not. Why do you keep nagging so much?" he answered with a brusqueness she rarely heard from him. He lifted her to her feet, and arose, stretching in exaggerated fashion.

She stared past him into the hearth, where browned pine branches, twigs, and heavier sticks of wood were arranged for a fire she had not lighted. A shadow more sombre than usual clouded the blue of her eyes, but Einar was not trained in detecting flare and shadow of the spirit. He knew only that the sole stirring of his conscience that caused him discomfort was aroused by the herd girl, who by rights should have welcomed his attentions, asking no more than his week-long or year-long constancy. Marriage or lack of that state was unimportant. Hulda wished to marry him, yet he might have refused her outright except that he felt dully that she might see no difference between him and Thorvald. In fact, Thorvald had brought her a rhinestone brooch from Trondhjem the time he had been down to witness the coronation. Hulda had accepted the gift though she disregarded the man's obvious attempts to capture her affection. Up in the forest near her the herd man would have a double advantage were Einar to tell her bluntly the thought which lay behind his caresses. He was willing that some day Thorvald should step in, but not until Einar's own way cleared before him. He wished Hulda to be happy, yet at this moment the full savagery of a relation that must be broken sometime came near finding expression. He opened his mouth slowly, then closed it, biting the long blond hairs which straggled from his upper lip.

"It may be . . . years, dear one . . . a long time, anyway," he said in weak compromise, impatient but careful. "The father says that when I am twenty-five he will give me a hundred kronen and some stock. Then if I can find a small place to lease hereabouts . . ." He waved his hand toward the fjeld to the north with a vagueness betokening the evasion in his mind.

"And you now are twenty-three?"

"Almost. A few months."

"The day of your birth falls in November," she continued with more positiveness. "Two years and seven months from now you will get the money and the cattle. During the winter you should be able to rent some farm. Old Gram, for instance, has no sons and is in his dotage. He——"

"Oh, no doubt," interrupted Einar uncomfortably. "Let us not trouble the future. I must be getting back now or brother Axel may waken and start a hullabaloo because of my absence. He hates me and is jealous because Chris, the father, allows me now a keg of the tobacco stalks for my own using. Even when I gave to Axel for his pipe, he hated me, so now I keep all for myself."

"The next spring, then, two years hence, we shall be married," went on Hulda as if she had not heard him. "That will be March or April in 1865. I shall help you fix up the house and plant the crops. We will have no children that year. The first baby then will be old enough to walk about with us and keep out of trouble."

"The first *baby!*" cried Einar, startled out of his sullen composure. "We shall have no children!"

"Aye! It is no longer in our hands," responded Hulda with a certain imperturbable spirit. She seized his rough and blackened hand. "Next July or August, I think!" she told him. "I have felt him kick now for a week."

Overcome by affrighted thrill, Einar sank back on the couch from which he had risen, eyeing Hulda who stood upright and smiling before him. "I–I——" he gasped, but he could get no further. A baby meant ten kronen to a midwife, and as much more for clothes and blankets, at the very least. He had not counted on this expense, and it would mean a delay of many months in the execution of his plan.

Hulda nodded. "It had been agreed that we should marry, so wherein is the wrong? That the banns follow instead of coming first will make them only more holy to me. I am yours always, Einar!"

Resting roughened hands upon his hairy forearm she dropped to her knees. Mist sparkled in her eyes, the first tears of emotion Einar had seen on those placid pools.

"Wrong?" he repeated in a strangled tone. "*Wrong?*" As yet he had not comprehended that the creed of this girl would allow any transgression of social law that her love dictated save the one unpardonable offense of unfathered children. He saw only ruin of his plan, wastage of the little store of coins he had saved against the day of his departure, and years of struggle with the barren soil for a livelihood. That Hulda would bear him many sons who could help when they grew older scarcely mitigated the appalling prospect of that first decade. In his heart Einar knew that Chris Merssen would find some pretext to avoid giving him the promised stake at the age of twenty-five. His brother Svend had been turned out the winter after he became twenty-four because of attending a circus at which one of the features advertised had been the first and original black Negro from America ever brought to Norway. That had been the excuse. Einar knew that his own many fractures of parental law would ease the break for his father, who would mortgage the futures of all his offspring for a few hundred kronen.

A way out of his difficulty did not manifest itself at first to his benumbed brain; for now, if he turned Hulda off, the story might be noised about his neighbourhood. No longer would he get odd jobs from neighbours who sympathized with him because they hated Chris, his father. Norwegian opinion is not harsh on the subject of illegitimacy, yet Skien was a straitlaced community. When the Lutheran pastor denounced him in service, he would be marked for years as a man who had evaded his obligations. The preacher would do it, too. Lars Dahl had been censured publicly for just this thing, and still—after two years—he was shunned by good farmers and their daughters, as a pariah.

"No, it is not wrong, Einar. It is beautiful," Hulda contradicted. "Only—for the sake of a name for our child we must not delay longer than is necessary. Right now, if you wished to come up here, we might live together as man and wife. A place like Thorvald holds is yours for the asking. We could be happy——"

"A place at fifty öre a day!" retorted Einar, voicing deep contempt. "Luxury! A fortune indeed!"

"No, not much, it is true. Still, love——"

"Won't make us rich!" he finished roughly. "No, Hulda, we must wait. I am taken aback by what you have told me, but presently I shall be able to think and plan again. I shall come soon to see you and talk this out at length. It was not in my calculations that we should have children right away."

"The sooner they are born the sooner they will help us, and the better able they will be to support us in our old age," she answered quietly, leaning over to stroke his yellow hair.

Einar looked at her in sudden doubt. This was not the way *she* talked. She was borrowing his words, or rather the sentiments of Chris, which he had approved bitterly as money-wise. It was part and parcel of the execution of her plan to make it seem to emanate from him. Dull enough on most points calling for fine perception, Einar's home training had developed in him a raw streak of nature which was sensitized to suspicion. As a patient with an open sore recoils from a caustic dressing, he shrank from agreement with statements that might commit him with his own conscience.

"Yah!" he snarled. "Chattels! I would not believe you regarded a family thus, Hulda!" He bent down, tugging savagely at the straps which tightened his boots, buckling them at the last notches though he knew this would make his ankles uncomfortable."

She sighed. "How is it given us to choose?" she asked, and tiredness of body seemed all at once to lapse into her tone. "You will work out happiness with me and our children. Must we concern ourselves with the next lives that are to be lived when we are old—or dead?"

Einar rose abruptly. "It is too late now for questions," he growled. "Let us both think. I must return." The kiss he gave her in parting was a hollow smack which sought to conceal its emptiness by volume of noise. Hulda supplemented this by a second embrace into which she put the full strength of her arms, and a silent, determined kiss upon his reddened cheek. If she knew that she had made a mistake, Einar caught no sign.

Outside, on the border of the fjeld, was darkness as yet unrelieved by the pallor of dawn. To the north slim traceries like breaths of chalk-dust driven by a celestial cyclone fled toward the zenith; there were the ever-present advance guards of the borealis which in winter dominated the night with chromatic splendour.

Einar's path lay out past the cattle pens and sheds, where all verdure had been chewed and trampled to extinction, and where the smells of dirty beasts and spilled milk souring on the ground contaminated and overwhelmed the fragrance of dampened pine and the lush grass of the fjeld.

One hundred paces on his way he stopped abruptly. The hut of the *saeter* still was in sight behind him, its ungainly conglomerate of half-trimmed logs, with sod banking to the level of the single window, personifying to Einar the wretchedness of such impecunious existence. He would not herd cattle! Such might be well enough for Thorvald who had no schooling and no ambition, but for one who could read of the glorious life in America, and dared bestir himself, it was worse than oblivion. It was dismal failure! The dollar-a-day-and-keep paid to farm helpers across the ocean could be his if he desired it. Let's see: a dollar amounted to four kronen or four hundred öre. With this wage, if he wished, he could hire at least eight Thorvalds to work for *him!*

There was magic in the thought. He would go. Nothing could restrain him. He would work for this princely wage a few years and then come back and live as a jarl. The people of Skien would elect him to the *Forligelseskommission,* perhaps later even to the *Höiesteret!* He would be rich, marry well, and have many sons to work for him when old age came. He swung around, striding fast across the open fjeld.

Impatience once aroused to the pitch of passion, Einar found no further difficulties with Hulda in his mind. She did not count. She would be angry for a time in her silent, terrible fashion. She might even expose him, yet what could she do and what would it all matter? The jesters of the village soon would see a ludicrous side to the situation in which a pregnant herd girl expected marriage with a man above her class. When he finally did come back, rich, all would have become a mouldy jape, long forgotten.

His walk increased to a jog, the jog to a run, keeping pace with the leaping flames of his imagination. Only when the dim bulk of the Merssen sheds and farmhouse rose before him did he slacken, breathless.

Now he was exultant, but cautious. He dug up his cache of coins from beneath the corner of the curing shed, and wrapped the accumulation—a mere ninety kronen—carefully in his handkerchief. Then he opened the sliding door of the stable by inches, brought out two of the best ponies, and hitched them to the family's Sunday cart. He led the animals and rig carefully out past the well and the windmill into the soft dirt of the road. Then he leaped to the seat, flicked the reins, and was off, driving madly across the divide of mountains, and into the reddening dawn toward Christiansand and the coast.

[Years later, Leif, son of Einar and Hulda, follows his father to America and, in his turn, wishes to escape parental restraint in order to pursue his own ambitions.]

Now he had learned the meaning of ambition, the urge of it was in his bowels. Why should any father wish to be allowed to hold his sons in slavery?

Lief knew that once he departed the Merssen roof every cent he spent for living or education first would have to be earned by his own sweat; yet of this he had no fear. He would work summers and save. He was a competent hand now, and would earn good money, sufficient to pay for tuition and books, at least. Odd jobs at mowing lawns, shovelling snow, tending furnaces and the like would provide food and shelter while in school. If only he had not consented to the adoption!

He walked fast along the dark homeward road, sometimes breaking into a jog. He had forgotten the two books Rand had lent, yet what did they matter now anyway? No one could start to make a living at twenty-eight years of age, and still hope for great success. It was cruel. Then and there Lief resolved that if ever *he* had sons and daughters they would be treated in a different manner!

"Before God!" he exclaimed aloud, lifting his face toward the scudding clouds which played like pennons before the face of a quarter-moon. "They'll get their chance *given* to them!"

Next evening Lief returned for the "Anatomy" and the dictionary. He obtained them from the housekeeper, for Rand himself was out making calls.

Returning, the boy mulled over a new idea which had come to him. Why not run away? He owed Einar nothing, and little to any of the others. Louise alone had given him affection, and even with her this had proved to be little more than an undiscriminating flair based upon Lief's resemblance to a man he had learned to hate. Yes, he would run away, but first he would give Einar one chance to do the decent thing. Immediately upon reaching the house he went to his father's bedside.

Frieda snored, but Einar himself was still awake.

"What d'you want?" he growled, his tones heavy with fatigue.

Without answering Lief struck a match and lit the lamp. Then he turned. "I have come to ask you something, Father," he stated dully. "As you know it is my wish to study medicine and dentistry, becoming an oral surgeon."

"What of it? *Huh?*" Einar shook with repressed savagery. As long as he did not awaken Frieda he could get back at the boy for some of the humiliation Einar conceived that Lief had caused him. "You better get that notion out of your head or some day I'll whale it out! You're my son now, and you're going to work for me. The law says so. What's more, you better send back those fool medical books or one of these times I'll chuck them in the stove!"

"I came to ask you," continued Lief in the same tone, neither respectful nor insolent, "if you would let me go to school here this coming winter, work for you through harvest the next year, and then go away to preparatory."

"Huh?" Einar was startled and exceedingly angry now. "Leave? Go away before you're twenty-five? I should *say* not!" He hunched up, throwing one heavy leg out from under the covers as if about to launch himself at the boy. Frieda awakened, but now Einar was too aroused to care. "Go to bed now, you!" he yelled. "Worthless, lazy good-for-nothing . . ."

"That is not true!" retorted Lief, shoulders squaring before the unjust accusation. "Also, when I reach twenty-*one* I am free. I wished to know only if you would not treat me as Hulda, the mother, might have asked. All I want is to be allowed to earn my own living and pay for my education."

"Well, you won't!"

Suddenly Einar leaped from bed, unheeding the clutch of Frieda who sought to detain him. Raising his heavy fist he launched a smashing blow full at Lief. The boy raised an arm for guard, but too late. The fist slammed straight against the side of his jaw with stunning impact.

Lief dropped without a sound save gasping exhalation. From a corner of his mouth a trickle of blood ran to the pine floor.

"Now you've done it," remarked Frieda grimly, hurling Einar back to the bed as she went to the boy. "Killed him, I guess. And I'll see that you hang if he don't come to. A fine father, you are!"

"Oh, he ain't dead. Don't worry," growled Einar, quieting a little as he observed the pale face of Lief and the queer contortion the blow had given to the boy's jaw. "A loafer like him is tough. When he wakes up I'll paste him some more. Damn his hide!"

The last was rumble, empty threat. Frieda knew it. She merely glanced upward contemptuously. "Better hitch up and get Doctor Rand," she advised. "Broke his jaw, looks like."

"Broke hell! Here, let me see it."

He moved to lift Lief, but Frieda interfered. "You've done about enough for one night," she snapped. "Get out of this room. Quick! I don't blame him for wanting to get away from you."

Frieda drove her husband away, and lifted Lief to the bed. Bringing the lamp close she satisfied herself that he was breathing, and merely stunned. His jaw, however, looked queer. It was canted at an angle to the right, and seemed to be pulled outward. Following the ridge line of mandible with her heavy, sure fingers, Frieda determined that nothing was broken. Then she seized firm hold, and with a strong wrench threw back the dislocation. Lief groaned, yet Frieda saw with satisfaction that her Spartan treatment looked satisfactory. She measured out a tablespoonful of brandy and poured it between his lips; when he roused, sitting up dizzily, she helped him to his own room and left, saying nothing. Tenderness was impossible to Frieda.

Lief, still dazed and nauseated, partly undressed before full memory of what had occurred returned. Then, with the taste of blood and brandy in his mouth, and torn ligaments swelling beneath his left ear, he stopped, sitting dizzily upon the edge of his bed. In the double bed next to him Axel and Ole slept noisily. They had heard nothing.

Dull anger, blending indistinguishably with the revulsion at the pit of his stomach, possessed the boy. Not since the age of seven had any one struck him as punishment. He had been in only a few fights, and these were different. The fact that this man possessed the right to knock him down, without suffering retaliation, brought burning humiliation. Lief gazed dry-eyed at the knob of the closed door. Then slowly, noiselessly, he put on his shoes and shirt again, gathered up a single change of clothing, and bound it in a bandanna handkerchief, took the two heavy volumes secured from Doctor Rand, and opened the door.

No sound except the heavy breathing from his two half-brothers came to his ears. He reached the stairs, tip-toeing. The fifth step from the bottom creaked loudly. He froze. From the direction of the room to which Einar had been banished came a heavy thump as of bare feet striking the floor. Lief went quicker. The bottom stair also rasped out a noise of case-hardened plank.

"Who's that?" his father's voice rumbled hoarsely. Einar had not been certain just how badly Lief had been injured, and was listening. Now he scratched a match across a sandpaper pad, and his bulk showed in the doorway, swollen grotesquely in the flicker.

Lief ran. Behind him he heard an oath, and the jar of pursuit. The screen door was hooked. He did not wait to seek the catch but threw his shoulder against the frame and burst through. A second later he was sprinting out across the gravel, making for the main highway, unheeding the bellow of rage and threat that rose behind.

While lights blinked up in the farmhouse, Lief deserted the road, circling out across the cow pasture toward the wooded swamp and creek to the northward . . . Two hours later he curled up behind the jutting of a snake fence on Ham Lytell's property, his head pillowed upon two heavy technical volumes; he alternated between sleep and shivering till dawn. . . .

Lief drove with Patricia in a hired brougham. They came to Lincoln Park. Lief dismissed the carriage, suggesting a walk through the wooded pleasance. He was queer in manner, almost stiff. This was love—and the acute agony of his apprehension came near to submerging hope. This girl meant more to him now than all his striving, all the partial success—more even than his first research experiments even now being published in the *American Medical Journal*. And for these latterly he had given heart's blood!

By the lake they found an unoccupied bench. Patricia, straight—almost frigid in bearing—acquiesced in all his careful manœuvring. She knew what was to come, and a tremor crept into her limbs. What would she say? She persisted in clinging to doubt, though inevitability whispered. No matter if the worst she suspected of him was true, what could she do? Love came more than once in the life of a man. Perhaps she could forget . . .

Lief laid two papers in her lap. One was an official notice of divorce decree; the second was a note, smoothed out after being crumpled in anger, telling why Sarah had left him.

"Read them both. I once loved her. She was my wife one week, I wanted you to know," he said jerkily, carefully looking away. His hands were clenched about the edge of the bench. During the ensuing minute he suffered the tortures of one damned. Life here would cease—or begin.

"This—that is to explain what I once said to you," he offered huskily, when no sound came from her. "I thought I—hated women."

Breath left her sibilantly. "And—why do you give me this?" she demanded. Turmoil of revolt, of fierce anger toward a man who dared ask her love by sign and deed after such an experience, struggled with very real emotion of another sort.

"Because I love you, Pat," he answered. "I want you! Will you be my wife? I thought that much was your due—seeing that, I mean. The woman is worse than dead now. Long since I have ceased to care for her. I never loved as I love you! Cannot you give me a chance? I—I never loved this way."

Impulse stronger than calculation gripped the woman. He was honest, clean, no matter what had gone before. After all, what did a week of mistaken love mean in a lifetime? She turned. Her arms went about his shoulders.

"Lief, I love you!" she answered. Then, incomprehensibly, she buried her face upon his shoulder and cried. It was surrender.

The fourth of June they were married. Only Leon and his wife attended. The brother gave as a present a chest of silver, the finest obtainable at Peacock's. Dorrit, a happy little woman who smiled often from sparkling brown eyes, gave Patricia four low-cut nightgowns of rose silk hand-embroidered in pale blue, and a Japanese silk kimono with garish figures. At first Patricia shuddered at the kimono; later she came to like it especially.

The following March, Patricia went to the Presbyterian Hospital. There she presented Lief with an eight-pound son—who was born with black hair already sprouted from his infant scalp.

"We'll call him Lief!" stated Patricia listlessly, smiling then in spite of her great weariness, first at her husband and then at the energetic, twelve-hour-old baby.

Lief, on one knee beside the high bed, smiled strangely. He had cherished another name for the baby in case it proved to be a boy, yet what matter? The youngster was here, he was sound in wind and limb, and he bore an absurd resemblance to Pat's brother Leon—but after all, what matter? The child would have all that Lief could provide, advantages such as Lief himself had dreamed of giving. He would be a true American, a man started on to who could guess what accomplishment? Love...

An inarticulate sound came from the man's throat, a sound of happiness and rejoicing beyond words. Right index finger, trembling as it never did when it guided keen steel, caressed a quarter-inch lock of the baby's hair. His boy!

Then of a sudden Lief bent his lips, pressing them against the back of her hand in overwhelming love and reverence.

21. PARDEE LOWE

*The Ties of the Clan**

Pardee Lowe was born in California in September, 1904. He received his bachelor's degree from Stanford, then studied at the Harvard School of Business Administration, and secured his doctorate from the University of California. He grew up in the Chinese household which was the subject of his book, was a research associate in sociology at Stanford, and worked for the Institute of Pacific Relations. When war broke out in 1941, he enlisted in the United States Army and after the peace entered the foreign service.

Until Father informally introduced me and Sister Mabel to Chinatown's harlots in the luxurious Banquet Hall of the Blossoming Almond, I did not fully appreciate the unadorned wickedness I found littering the Barbary Coast.

Each of the four seasons was always formally ushered in by huge banquets given by either the district organizations, the family groups, or the fighting tongs. Such a feast was known as *Hoy Teng*, or "Opening a Reception." Father was a fixture at most of these celebrations, since he occupied the same special position in both the Masculine Concord Consolidated Districts Benevolent Association, and the Four Brothers, our clan society. He was their Secretary of Foreign Affairs.

These receptions, I was told by kinsmen who also attended, served a definite social purpose. They reproduced exactly the same social atmosphere as found in Canton and Hong Kong, but never in the smaller provincial villages. It was explained to

* Pardee Lowe, *Father and Glorious Descendant* (Boston, 1943), pp. 43–57, 66–80.

me also that the organizations in San Francisco's Chinatown, for lack of social entertainment and feminine companionship, had developed the institution of Opening a Reception. It took the place of the periodical ancestral gatherings and it made it possible for the young men to enjoy the companionship of their friends, male and female. Under the protective covering of good food and drink at a *Hoy Teng* gambling was permitted, assignations with daughters of joy were made, nefarious tong plots were hatched, and straightforward business deals consummated. I could well understand their importance to Father and why he, as one of the community leaders, found it necessary to attend. Here, lying fully exposed, were the cogs and wheels which made Chinatown's world go around.

What pleased me about these gatherings was the immense amount and costly variety of sumptuous food that was set before us. The dishes served were equaled only by those served in the City of the Rams. Some said that they were unsurpassed. Portly waiters walked back and forth in flowing white aprons carrying giant pewter dishes filled with duck, eels, squabs, chicken, snakes, frogs, sharks and turtles and snails. It was much more than could ever be found at family banquets honoring the birth of a baby or the marriage of a kinsman. These affairs were tame and shabby by contrast.

Opening a Reception, I found, represented one of the wonders of pre-Revolutionary Chinatown. These affairs were always held in the largest and best-known restaurants, with their carved gilt walls, expensive mirrors and tiled floors, and there were never fewer than three or four hundred guests, all of them men, lolling at moon-shaped tables of ten.

A group of seven Chinese musicians, five of whom were women, sat in one corner, flanked by two luxurious bamboo couches reserved for those who were overcome by too much food or drink. These creatures were dressed in ravishing, dainty garments, the like of which I saw on no other women of the quarter. To the accompaniment of the *Law,* a brass gong; the *Yuet Kum,* the moon guitar, the Tartar fiddle; wooden and skin drums, and clashing cymbals, they sang in shrill falsetto endless operatic ballads, mostly celebrating the past glories of the Three Kingdoms. The entire performance struck me as being totally alien. Fed up, I informed Father: "I like 'Yankee Doodle Dandy' much better!"

At least four of these singsong girls sat at every table of ten. They did not sit side by side with the diners, but just behind them. They were adept conversationalists. When the talk lagged they raised small thimblefuls of *Ng Ka Pay,* blood-red brandy, and toasted their guests. Their language was florid. It fluttered with high-flown terms of respect and was devoid of terms of endearment. "Worthy Master," "Respected Elder," "Honored Scholar," and "First-Born," they called Father and his friends.

When my Chinese playmates at these banquets (and there were a number of them) told me that these were *Loh Kur* I refused to believe them. "It can't be," I replied. These women did not resemble those I had seen half-naked on the Barbary Coast. In contrast they were overdressed and excessively modest! "True," I admitted, "they do paint and perfume themselves." And they did resemble puppet figures much more than did the girls of the Barbary Coast. "Beyond that," I pointed out, "they don't look or act alike."

My friend, a worldly-wise youngster of twelve, nicknamed "Pickled Pear," snickered, "Well, maybe not, but I know they are just the same!"

I questioned Father about these facts of life. He told me that what my playmate said was true, but that there were sharp distinctions, implying again in his matter-of-fact manner that I should find out for myself.

I tried my best.

A sense of refined gentility, I observed, hung over these gatherings. No word of obscenity passed the lips of these pleasure girls; they were painfully dignified and correct. Yet I recalled that we could hardly take a step on the Barbary Coast without hearing foul epithets uttered by men and girls alike. At a Reception, no one became debauched, rowdy, or intoxicated. Under the flaring gas lamps which drenched the banquet hall, no girls were manhandled, ungraceful gestures were conspicuously absent, and the only expressions used by the girls were those of respect. However, the institution, I was told by Pickled Pear (who proved most illuminating), did represent professional sin. Direct solicitation was never permitted at any of the banquets. These painted girls were there to entertain and to amuse. Any intimacy would depend upon arrangements made between the prospective pleasure seeker and their chaperones, who were eager to give to anyone the addresses of their charming "daughters" on Bartlett and Sullivan Alleys.

I concentrated my attention on these elderly women companions. Resembling Spanish duennas, they usually gathered in a corner by themselves and cackled boisterously over their latest gossip. "Turtle women," Pickled Pear called them. Not knowing what a "turtle woman" was, I became confused, saying, "I see nothing turtlish about them." Later I found out that these soberly clad procuresses did have reptilian attributes. Tough and hard as the shell of a turtle, they could, when opposed, bite with equally deadly ferocity. Even the bloodthirstiest highbinders would exclaim, "*Lay Hoy!*" (Dangerous!) and avoid them.

With the coming of the Chinese Republic, these receptions became more rare. To begin with, they were considered old-fashioned, hence monarchial. The Kuomintang, the Chinese-American Society, and the Americanized young men's organizations bitterly opposed them. Besides, churches began to interest more and more Chinese with the Barbarian ideas of sin. Mission societies, with their rescue homes, were making life miserable, I understood, for the owners of these singsong girls. When information reached the missions that the inmates were too young they raided these brothels. They encouraged the girls to desert their keepers, accept a Christian life, and marry a Chinese Christian to become entirely respectable housewives. These rescues were not, however, without endless complications. Some singsong girls, told that their rescuers were devils who would carve out their brains and swallow them, refused to be saved. The masters of those who did marry never considered that any girl was free until she had redeemed her personal contract in hard cash. Their hired thugs threatened the husband with shotguns. Such marriages, on many occasions, I was told, led to bitter disputes, ending in bloody tong wars.

Nevertheless, each time we attended these gorgeous affairs, Sister Mabel and I enjoyed ourselves. Evidently there was nothing wrong in bringing little children to such banquets. Father apparently did not think so because we were always invited. When my sister was seven, however, she stopped going with us. I did not know the reason why. Mother began to frown, I noticed, whenever Father mentioned that he wanted me to join him in Opening another Reception. She offered no verbal protest, but I could see a glint of disapproval in her eye.

When we two pleasure seekers returned home on the early morning East Belleville ferry after a night of very beguiling entertainment, Mother would welcome us with a worried look. She was more concerned about decorous Chinese harlots than the flamboyant bawds of the Barbary Coast. She would look at me hard to see if all was well. All was. The *Loh Kur* never bothered us children, except to offer some sweetmeats. We had played Blindman's Buff, Hide and Seek, and Shuttlecock on the spacious restaurant balcony to our hearts' content. I was filled with good food. My pockets were loaded down with silver quarters given me by doting kinsmen. Father felt mellow too with good wine, good conversation, and good food. Having shared excitement and pleasure together both of us failed to notice that Mother's odd expression had not disappeared. She, for one, certainly had no use for such traditions of glittering elegance and sociability.

Shortly following my ninth birthday, Mother took Father to task one morning after our return from such a banquet. I heard heated conversation behind my parents' bedroom door. Mother was chanting over and over again an ancient Chinese proverb: "Keep away from the wicked so that their misery may be avoided." She kept declaring that it wasn't right to take me, at my tender age, to such disreputable affairs. "Glorious Descendant is too impressionable," she insisted.

Father did not believe so. It never dawned upon him that I might be contaminated by such deep-dyed iniquity. "After all," he defended himself, "other fathers take their sons there. Besides, what harm is there for tiny boys to meet and play with companions of their own age, partake of a very sumptuous repast, and receive money gifts?"

It was not a disagreement over sex. That I now know. Father and Mother possessed earthly understanding. Both respected the demands which nature made upon healthy young men and women. It could not be denied, they said to their friends repeatedly. When it was, tragedy followed. Traditionally a boy or a girl was expected to marry young. Where marriage was not possible recourse to singsong girls was not frowned upon. Sex was sex. It wasn't sin, but natural. And that was exactly the way in which the Chinatown of Father's and Mother's generation treated it.

But Mother was adamant only because she was afraid I might become a hatchet man, not a wild-oats sower. She instinctively disliked this questionable environment which Father unintentionally provided for me at the Restaurant of the Blossoming Almond. She was firm with Father. If I should grow up and turn into a highbinder, she said, it wouldn't be her fault but, nevertheless, she would get the blame. Chinatown's gossips would sniff, "*Moh Kah Gau!*" (No family breeding!)

In the end, Father admitted the strength of her charge. He too believed in shaping my life properly. He took his fatherhood seriously. There was no possible doubt whatsoever. Having accepted Mother's viewpoint, he agreed to cease and desist. He stopped altogether bringing me to these attractive affairs, although he continued to go himself. When I asked him why, Father pointed to Mother:—

"She says, '*Hoh Jung!*' " (It's hatefully carnal!)

With the odds always so much against us, our home life was far from placid. It could not be otherwise. The loss of Father's fortune, the ruining of his business, had made it necessary for him to seek a home where Mother could work as well as bring up the family. Finding East Belleville most congenial, he bought the dry-goods business from Cousin Ming. In nostalgic memory of his first enterprise, Kwong Hop, he renamed it Kwong Chong.

It was agreed that Mother, since she had acquired a smattering of English, would run the East Belleville shop as well as her home, while Father would work as a partner in Sun Loy—a combination immigrant remittance bank and dry-goods store located in San Francisco's Chinatown. In this manner, he hoped eventually to repay the huge debt he owed his two brothers for purchasing Kwong Hop, the family dry-goods business.

This was a sore point. Father felt definitely obligated to pay this debt, even though the earthquake had deprived him of the full enjoyment of ownership. On the other hand, Mother was equally determined. The old store no longer existed, she pointed out. "There's no sense in working so hard to maintain both store and home merely to enrich one's brothers-in-law."

Matters were made more difficult when in 1911 Paternal Uncles Number One and Number Two brought their eldest sons to this country for education, and to escape trouble. Kwangtung Province, they told Mother, was seething with rebellion. Seventy-two revolutionists had died at Canton in an unsuccessful attack upon the Manchus and Dr. Sun's right-hand man, General Huang Hsing, was recruiting an army. Civil war was inevitable. Clan loyalty required that Father take care of his two nephews. Our home was theirs. Father was doubly obligated since he was indebted to their parents. But already the family was overburdened with *Chun-chick* (relatives by marriage). Mother had her younger brother and sister with her (Uncle Jack and Aunt Lillian)—her own mother having died several years before.

Our family finances were so limited it was difficult for my parents to decide whether *Hing-tay*, Father's kinsmen, or his relatives (that is, his wife's kinsmen) should be maintained. Tradition demanded that loyalty to one's kinsmen come first, but Father's love for Mother was so great he wanted to support both. Obviously this was impossible.

When our kinsmen and relatives realized the awkward situation, the problem soon solved itself. For board, shelter, and the chance of obtaining a Western education, Cousin Chang, renamed Robert, became a house boy in an American household in East Belleville. Cousin Mook, renamed Lawrence, joined his father, Uncle Number One, in the sun-drenched grape belt of Fresno, drying raisins. I was only too glad to see them go. Both cousins were older than I and we never seemed to get along together. They called me *"Kum-sahn Ting"* (an American ignoramus), while I could only retaliate *"Heong Ha Jay!"* (Village bumpkin!) Fighting was continuous.

Aunt Lillian, having become an eligible lady, was asked for by a middle-aged businessman, who had made a tidy fortune growing potatoes along the sluggish San Joaquin River. Mother had a tremendous responsibility, she realized. She owed it to her ancestors. It was her duty to select the best mate available and to marry off her younger sister in the very best manner possible. But not hurriedly and giving the impression that because of our family's limited resources it was necessary to marry her off in haste. Hearing Mother's explanation of the situation Aunt Lillian finally agreed that marriage was the best possible solution. Mother promised her a wedding every bit as perfect as her own. *"T'ing Hoh!"* (None better!) she told everybody.

This called for an old-fashioned Chinese marriage. Having entered school by this time, I was becoming aware of some of the thousand and one details which make up a perfect Chinese wedding celebration. Weeks ahead of the Day Mother began tidying up the house, refurbishing it even more elegantly than during the Chinese New Year.

During this period, Madame Wang became a constant visitor to our home. She was the middle woman, I was told, like Emily Post, and knew every minute wedding detail. Middle woman or not, it didn't make much difference to me. I remember her only as a fat, gray-haired woman with an enormous, jolly laugh which revealed gold-filled teeth. Everyone addressed her behind her back as "*Fay Paw*" (The Fat Woman). Her reputation was fabulous. Besides being the most successful matchmaker in the community she was also an infallible midwife. Whenever summoned she blessed a Chinese home in a number of ways. The infant would always be a boy. Nor would she attend any but healthy mothers. And whenever she attended a confinement the mother would always regain her normal health. She was especially adept at preparing bouillons made of chicken stewed with Chinese gin, or toddies compounded of pigs' knuckles soaked for hours in boiling vinegar. Her extremely reliable tonics were considered indispensable to a woman's speedy recovery.

Following a fortnight's preparations, the Fat Lady finally called at our home with a wagonload of dull-gold and bright-red lacquer boxes stacked with Chinese wedding cakes, confections, and other wedding delicacies. The bridegroom, she explained, was offering these paltry gifts to our family as a token of his humble respect and had, with the aid of necromancy, settled on the "Lucky Day."

The night before the wedding Fat Lady kept Aunt Lillian in her chamber and permitted only Mother's women friends and relatives to enter. Gathered together, they began to wail. At first it frightened me. I did not quite understand who had suddenly died to arouse such a storm of grief.

I climbed the stairs and peered into the bedroom. There was no corpse. Only Aunt Lillian crying as though her heart were breaking. Everybody was consoling her. I wondered whether her feet might not be causing her anguish. She was stumbling around in wedding slippers with four-inch stilts.

"What are they all crying for?" I asked the Fat Lady, whom I had been carefully instructed always to address as "Paternal Aunt" even though she was not related to us.

"Sad or not, one must weep. It is the custom," she answered, "to indicate our sorrow at the bride's departure." She patted me on the head. "These tears are deceptive. On such an occasion there can be no sorrow—only joy."

"And why does Aunt Lillian have to totter on those funny slippers?"

"Because," the Fat Lady laughed, "Maternal Grandmother did not bind your aunt's feet into natural golden lilies."

During this wailing Mother's friends plucked Aunt Lillian's eyebrows, cut her bangs and braided her hair, doing it up in bridal fashion. Then they dressed Aunt Lillian in deep-red wedding garments and covered her head with a gorgeous headdress dangling with beads, jewelry, and tassels. Meanwhile, in the store below Father and our invited kinsmen were having a hilarious time celebrating over the banquet tables.

Suddenly there came a knock at the front door. Cousin Robert opened it and there stood a liveried Irish coachman with black frock coat and stovepipe hat. He inquired, very red of face, whether this was the home of Mr. Lowe, explaining that he had come all the way from San Francisco to pick up the "Chinee bride."

Fat Lady rushed upstairs. Breathless, she shouted: "It's come! It's come!" Mother hugged Aunt Lillian and dabbed some rice powder and rouge on her cheeks, and rouged her lips. Suddenly, to my amazement, Aunt Lillian, giggling and weeping by turns, mounted a chair and climbed pickaback upon the go-between's shoulders. To the shouts and cries of the assembled guests she was carried downstairs, across the pavement, and into the waiting brougham. Two giant lanterns, painted with Chinese good-luck characters, had taken the place of the brougham's tiny side lamps. They bobbed and twisted like grotesque Halloween jack-o'-lanterns when the Fat Lady and Aunt Lillian plumped themselves down.

The moment the bridal coachman flicked his whip Father signaled our kinsmen to toss lighted packages of firecrackers into the street. We were saluting Aunt Lillian's departure. But this series of midnight explosions had a galvanizing effect upon our sleeping American neighbors. Suspecting a tong war, they telephoned for the riot squad. The neighborhood, while realizing that our family was celebrating more elaborately than usual, were unaware that Aunt Lillian was being married.

The damage had been done. When the police remonstrated, Father apologized for the disturbance and explained that while there were no deaths, we were nevertheless missing one aunt. The police shuffled off completely mollified when Father offered them brandy and cigars. The Sergeant, at parting, good-naturedly warned Father: "Lowe, next time be more American. Throw rice, not firecrackers."

We did not hear from Aunt Lillian until *Fahn Sahm Jiu.* Three days later, obeying the precise rules of etiquette, she arrived punctiliously at noon to pay Mother her first visit as a matron—dressed not as we had seen her last in a flaming red-silk bridal ensemble and beaded headdress, but in a gray suit and ostrich-plumed hat. She came laden with gifts. The tiniest ones she pulled out of a bushy black muff. They were a pair of applejade earrings for Sister Mabel, and for me a pure-gold necktie pin consisting of crossed flags—the Stars and Stripes, and the red-white-blue banner of the new Chinese Republic.

Aunt Lillian was quite pleased with her new status in life. Everybody could see it in her smiling face. She had a home of her own, she proudly reported to Father, and a husband both kind and generous. . . .

According to Father's ideas, we children were to have an American education but were to follow at home the ancestral ways of Kwangtung, where his grandparents had lived, on the banks of the Pearl River. And in this Mother abetted him. She had been born in the New World, but she had been brought up under the strict Cantonese family discipline characteristic of the Chinatown of the eighteen-nineties. She knew only too well how to wield the wrong end of a pliant Chinese bamboo duster. With this Rod of Purification she directed our lives, and we became, as our Chinese friends put it, "model children who had partaken generously of paternal instruction."

In the family circle, at least, we gave no cause for complaint. For us this was no mean mark of distinction since the circle was good-sized. Besides Father, Mother, three sisters, and my little twin brothers, our home now took in at times, particularly on feast days, every available member of our clan and district to be found in the city—about two hundred all told. Of these only a score were women, and they seldom came. The mile of dirt road between Belleville's Chinatown and our house was too much for their "lily feet." The men, who addressed Father as Senior Elder, came often to consult him about the probable economic effects of some particularly disastrous tong war, the high price of remittances to Hong Kong, or the lack of employment. Father never withheld advice nor Mother hospitality. Many a kinsman coming for a talk stayed not only overnight but for weeks—even in some cases years. Our neighborhood dry-goods store was a perpetual Chinese work-relief project. It was to these relatives mainly that we were "children of virtue."

At dawn, throughout the day, and before going to bed, we respectfully hailed our male elders with their proper titles. *Ah Bahk* (Senior Uncle), we called the graybeards, while the younger men were greeted as *Ah Sook*, Junior Uncle. When their womenfolk came visiting, we poured tea. We were duly silent in their presence. We ate decorously, never allowing our chopsticks to stray surreptitiously past the center of the serving dishes for some choice morsel of food. Indeed, no ecclesiastic ever observed daily rituals with more assiduity than we. At home our lives were a round of polite Oriental salutations and formal bowings and scrapings.

For the most part, all this bored us, and we longed to escape from it and do as our American school friends did. But that was not so during our great New Year's feast. This was one thing on the Chinese side of our existence that appealed to us children. Mother always began thinking of *Neen Chaw Yut* (literally, the Year's Original Day) immediately after what she called in her Cantonese idiom "The Festival of the Barbecued Turkey"—Thanksgiving. Coached by a past master, Sixth Paternal Junior Uncle, she celebrated Thanksgiving for us in the traditional American way, though it meant a good deal of trouble. "We share the holiday of our American neighbors," she explained to us, "because we wish to live in peace and harmony with them and because I do not wish you children to grow wicked with envy of others."

However, our New Year's was for her, as for us, the day of days. It was her firm belief that no matter how hard her lot in life might be, it would always grow happier if this Chinese feast was properly observed. In preparation for it, she would labor long and zealously. In the early weeks of January, she would scrub the house from cellar to attic and decorate the rooms with fragrant water lilies, apple, peach, and apricot blossoms, and with oranges, pomelos, and tangerines. Then, she would steam batch upon batch of Chinese pudding cakes, usually nine layers high, made of either rice flour and brown sugar or taro flour and sesame seeds. In her spare moments, she fried doughnuts and turnovers stuffed with crushed almond, black soybeans, peanuts, or shredded coconuts.

While Mother worked, we children became daily more eager with anticipation. Americanized as we were, we still appreciated the fact that only *Neen Chaw Yut* could offer us a fortnight's existence in which there were only joys and no sorrows. As I look back upon it, there was no other holiday season which could even begin to compare with it. There were more firecrackers than on the Fourth of July, more cymbals, bells, and roaring drums than on the Western New Year's Eve, more entertainment than in a Mardi Gras celebration—for whenever the firecrackers spluttered the Lion cavorted and pranced, scattering good fortune, or the sinuous Dragon writhed in block-long ecstasy through the narrow alleys of Chinatown, propelled by a hundred frenzied men carrying giant halberds, staves, and flaming lanterns. There were also more gifts than at Christmas, for besides the usual presents we received from Santa Claus, there were "ceremonial cash gifts," wrapped in telltale red envelopes. We reaped a silver harvest. It was not at all unusual for each of us children to deposit better than $100 in our savings account after the Day of Man. Uncles, elderly friends, and business associates found this the only way to express their appreciation for Father's beneficial advice and for Mother's delicious Chinese dinners.

Instead of a one-day feast as at Thanksgiving, we had then fourteen consecutive days of feasting, each dedicated to some special dish. On New Year's Day itself, there was invariably "nun's and monk's food," which contained no meat but all sorts of dried vegetables soaked in water, cooked in peanut oil, and garnished with lettuce leaves. This vegetarian fare was prepared, Mother said, "to thank our parents for human existence, to revere the memory of the ancestors, and to kowtow humbly in the sight of heaven." The next day was wholly devoted to the consumption of all manner of flesh and fowl. Mother called it Opening the Year, signifying that we no longer needed to fast. The boiled chicken, roast ducks, and barbecued squabs we could now eat to our stomach's content. Each of the succeeding days saw some new and toothsome delicacy added to our diet. On the seventh day, known as the Day of Man, we ate the Chinese prototype of *Sukiyaki*. It was a fabulous dish in which sea food, diced meats, and vegetables were cooked in front of us on a giant single gasplate. We dipped the tidbits we desired in the swirling, scalding chicken broth, and when they were cooked fished them out with our chopsticks.

Mother always followed the custom of paying ceremonial New Year's visits to the wives of all our friends and relatives. During these visits, we saw what seemed to our "American" eyes some very odd things. The most peculiar, I remember, were the religious offerings of food which our kinswomen placed before their family altars.

As our home had never possessed such an altar, Mother made no effort during our early years to observe these rites. But one year, shortly after we moved to Belleville, an old friend persuaded her that there was no harm in them and that their observance might even change her luck. Since times were difficult, Mother yielded, and we acquired a Chinese New Year's altar. After that, Mother's friend came regularly, in her old-style Chinese gown, to act as informal priestess on our behalf. The routine never varied. She would set out the food and drink offerings, arrange the candles, incense, and ghost money, pour the libations, and whisper the prayers to the ancestors, beseeching them to join the festivities and to grant us righteous, upright lives, households overflowing with children, prosperity, and good health.

I always eyed our priestess, whom we called Elder Paternal Aunt Jo, with open contempt because I considered her so hopelessly old-fashioned. Whenever I protested that this was all "old junk" and a positive disgrace to our Americanism, Father would chuckle tolerantly. "There is no harm in it, Glorious Descendant," he would say. "Women are always superstitious. If it makes your Mother and Aunt Jo happy, who are we to object? We are men, and worshiping is not our affair. Let them pray for good fortune and we will try to make it."

Long before the advent of President Franklin Delano Roosevelt and the New Deal, Father was an outstanding exponent of the Good Neighbor Policy. This was because Father's mind was always clear about fundamentals. He believed in human beings as individuals. "*Kow Ming Kow Lay,*" he always taught me. (Seek name, then gain.) Because he desired a good name above great riches, he yearned for the friendship of all men, Chinese or Barbarian. Nothing, I observed, made him happier than to hear people greet him smilingly. "Here comes Mr. Lowe Fat Yuen!"

Father's frank and friendly attitude made him a universal favorite. Chinatown respected him for his deep knowledge of American ways of civic and economic thinking. The Americans, on the other hand, liked Father for the very un-Chinese quality of his business and social dealings.

Father's associates in Chinatown were mostly drawn from the Fragrant Mountain District and the Four Families: Lowe, Kwan, Chung, and Jiu. Not that he didn't have friends from other districts or clans, but it was the common thing to consort and do business with those whom one could implicitly trust. No person could be depended upon better, according to Father, than those whose antecedents were fully known. His business partners at Sun Loy, for instance, were all from the same village of the same district, Sahn Kay Gawk. Although they bore different surnames, all twenty were related by kinship or marriage.

When no disagreements intervened, this arrangement, Father explained, produced unity, economy, profits, and social effectiveness. Kinsmen were like hands and feet: they helped each other. However, when they got in each other's way or when difficulties arose, such associations were extremely nasty. A man's hatred was all the greater when he believed that a kinsman had failed to understand or to co-operate, or had been disloyal.

However, Father seldom lost the confidence of his Chinese friends and kinsmen. He was above all an excellent compromiser and conciliator. He was never a person for fighting if the controversy could be settled by peaceful methods. "Better be a dog in peace," he warned our hot-headed cousins, "than a man in anarchy!" In fact, his compromising activities were notorious.

Intelligence, Father said, was the only way to solve a problem. Fighting as a principle was bad. "No good man ever fights," he added. But when one was assaulted or challenged to mortal combat, he agreed there was no other recourse. Then Father emphasized the old Chinese proverb: "*Seen Hah Suah Way Kurng.*" (He who delivers the first blow wins.) Father knew that offense, and offense alone, could win a war.

Whenever members of our district or clan could not settle their problems they could always be persuaded to come to our home. As Father grew older his wisdom increased and so did his social influence and effectiveness. He could win friends easily by his sympathetic humanism, and influence people by his hard-headed common sense. It was a byword among our kinsmen that whenever Father took it upon himself to conciliate affairs the decision was always fair and just.

Father's conciliation and arbitration services were so expert that before his thirtieth birthday he was already accepted as one of Chinatown's leaders. By his fortieth birthday, he had held every important post which his district, clan and trade-guild organizations had to offer except one: the chief eldership of Chinatown's supreme organization, the Chinese Consolidated Districts Benevolent Association. At this point, the graybeards of our clan began to address Father respectfully as

"The Venerable Greater Uncle." This meritorious title, I discovered, was not bestowed without good reason.

Father was the Nestor of our district. He never lost touch with the realities of human existence. A good listener, he could follow a man's troubles for hours with a cocked head and sympathetic ear. He was an easy man to talk to. Kinsmen responded to him without undue strain. Father made it easy for them. Politely, deferentially, and tranquilly, he heard out each kinsman's tale of woe, no matter how late into the night. When they finished Father always had the right answer.

But Mother had a better one. She always had food to beguile the weary and worried visitor. Tea to soothe his nerves, fried noodles or boiled ravioli or steamed salt fish and pork to strengthen the inner man, sometimes even a black infusion of bitter herbs to heal his temporary ailments. When the kinsman left our home, he was a new man. But these long conferences took a terrific toll of both my parents' energies. They did not complain. For them there was only one rule of living for the clan: To nourish it and keep it alive in glowing health. Remember, they told me, "*Kah Sahn Yun Mawng.*" (When the family goes to pieces the individual vanishes.)

Where Father's attitude towards his Chinese associates was based upon his kinship, his relationships with Americans were predicated upon business. The average American meeting Father for the first time accorded him respect because he was so different. In the first place, he was much taller than and did not dress like the average Oriental. In the second, he spoke passable English in a day when most Chinese could not speak English at all. Furthermore, his appearance was commanding, particularly his mustache. It lent him a certain natural dignity for it did not droop like a mandarin's or point upwards like the Kaiser's. It honored the Roosevelt I tradition. It was bushy. And when people came to know him more intimately, I noticed that they respected him also for his mental and spiritual qualities.

My daily trips with Father included visits to the wholesale dry-goods houses of San Francisco, most of which were conducted by very fine Jewish-American owners. They came to know us extremely well. They called Father "Lowe Fat" because his full name was Lowe Fat Yuen, meaning Source of Prosperity. As Father's girth increased, this name was used more frequently. When he had time enough to wax his whiskers, some of the younger salesmen, feeling that his mustache and his appearance gave him a seignorial aspect, called him "The Duke" or "The Count." Father was always pleased with these titles. Sometimes they would even call Father by the name of his store. It was a constant source of merriment to hear him addressed as "Mr. Sun Loy," which, when translated, meant "Mr. The Letter Always Comes."

Father's methods of winning American friends were different, although equally wise and intelligent. To begin with, he always made it a point to emphasize his knowledge, thereby winning the respect of the Barbarians.

Father, it appeared, loved the old-fashioned tradition of haggling over each sale. In his business deals, he always insisted upon a fair price even if it required a terrific siege of bargaining. He would finger each piece of merchandise with the utmost care. Sometimes he drew it beneath his nose, or across his cheek, or over his tongue. When he ran it down, even the hardest of Jewish shopkeepers turned weak with despair. They claimed that Chinatown could outhaggle any ghetto and it took two Jewish businessmen to outsmart one Chinese.

The wholesale merchants could ill afford not to let him have his way. Besides buying in such large quantities they knew that once Father made a bargain there would be no further worry. "Mr. The Letter Always Comes" never failed to discount his bills before the tenth of the month. Prompt payment and the tremendous volume of Father's business made generous treatment necessary. But, as Father put it: "The secret of business is simple. If you have money you are the Master. You can buy low and sell high."

Before the coming of the Republic, when the old Chinese New Year was more generally celebrated, these American firms would remember Father and his establishment magnificently. It gratified Father immensely to realize that they appreciated his business so much they remembered it in what amounted to a lavish Chinese manner. In the year that Sun Loy shifted from gas jets to electric-light bulbs, I remember, no fewer than fifty elaborate fruit cakes, adorned with glowing inscriptions of happiness and good luck, and countless bottles of wines and champagnes and boxes of rare Havana cigars were showered upon him. Father never made it a point to reciprocate with these American firms. "They have my business," he said. "That's gratitude enough."

His gifts to Westerners usually took the form of very lovely Chinese vases or art objects. He personally bought them at Sing Fat's, Chinatown's largest bazaar, for his doctor and lawyer friends, to whom he was deeply obligated. Invariably, I was taken along to make the final presentation. "Why?" I questioned. "*Hoh Tay,*" Father said. (It looks well.) When I asked Father why he was so generous with such gifts, he answered: "In commerce each article has a price, which is paid for in coin. In personal relations no such set values exist. But this does not preclude expressing materially one's deep appreciation for kindnesses granted." Adding: "Never forget that without the rain of generosity no friendship blooms."

At Christmas and Chinese New Year, the volume of money and energy Father and Mother spent for presents astounded me. I learned that the Chinese, even the poorest, were a gift-bearing and gift-giving folk. Soon I became a part of that system. The giving of presents as a visible expression of gratitude became an integral part of my own life.

I remember all too vividly the first occasion on which I practised this good-neighbor policy. It was the last week of my first year in Markham Grammar School. I had been there since September. My report card had been good, and Father was pleased. When I informed him that I would be given a vacation for Christmas, he had a long conference with Mother and Aunt Lillian. They concluded that something should be done.

On the last day before vacation, Aunt Lillian accompanied

me to school, followed by Uncle Jack who bore on his back a huge wicker basket. Reaching school, Aunt Lillian told me to gather all my teachers in the principal's office. When they assembled Uncle Jack opened his basket. It contained a profusion of Oriental curios—carved brass candlesticks and incense burners, muttonfat jade desk weights, oxblood vases, rice-patterned ginger jars, and mother-of-pearl and ivory snuff-boxes. The gifts were much more valuable, I appreciated even in my childishness, than the family could afford. I looked at Aunt Lillian in amazement, but she told me not to be such a busybody and to hand out the gifts.

The teachers were overwhelmed with delight and embarrassment. "The Board does not allow us to accept such expensive gifts," they chorused. "Besides, if we ever did, then other children might also think it is necessary."

For a long time Aunt Lillian and white-haired Miss Williams, the school principal, argued this point. Father and Mother would feel highly insulted, Aunt Lillian explained, if the gifts were not accepted. This made Miss Williams pause, and listen to the rest of Aunt Lillian's argument. It proved irresistible. In China, she said, next to the parent stood the teachers. Since they cherished as well as instructed their pupils, nothing was too good for them. The fact that I, "Glorious Descendant," was being taught by Barbarians at the Markham Grammar School did not excuse our family from observing the traditional social code.

Miss Williams accepted Aunt Lillian's explanation. That evening Aunt Lillian told my parents that the gifts made my teachers very happy. They smiled. I later discovered that in addition to making friends for me among my teachers, Father and Mother had also improved racial relations.

I shall never forget Father's ideas on good neighborliness. Our people, he said, can win the friendship of Americans forever by showing tolerance and understanding. Moreover, we Chinese must hold our heads high even though we comply with their demands. What they do we must learn to do better. Proudly, Father recalled how he had won the respect and friendship of the merchants of Battery, Sansome, and Mission Streets with his knowledge and understanding.

"Always remember," he emphasized, "that you, a Chinese, could not have attended Markham Grammar were it not for Miss Williams. She could have been harsh and compelled you and Sister Mabel to attend the segregated school in this city many miles away. But Miss Williams was tolerant and democratic. Because we appreciate her generous feelings towards us we gave her a gift in your name. Gifts should always represent the material symbols of friendship. In this case it won for you an eternal friend."

The fact that for years my brothers and sisters and I went unchallenged to Markham Grammar while Chinese children living in other American neighborhoods of East Belleville were compelled to attend the segregated public schools in Chinatown made a tremendous impression upon me.

I grew up to respect more and more Father's beliefs on social relationships. He certainly knew how to be a good neighbor.

22. WALTER REUTHER

*Too Old to Work; Too Young to Die**

Walter P. Reuther was born in 1907 in Wheeling, West Virginia, the second son of an immigrant from Germany who had arrived in the United States in 1892. While the family was Lutheran, it had long been influenced by German Social Democratic ideas and the father had been active in the Brewery Workers Union. Walter left high school at the age of twelve, worked in a steel mill and then moved to Detroit, attracted by the opportunities of the automobile industry. His ambition carried him through part-time studies in high school and at Wayne State University. The Depression had a marked influence on him; he was active in the League for Industrial Democracy and in 1933 toured the Soviet Union and worked for a while in the Gorki automobile plant. He returned to the United States in the fall of 1935, in time to join the new United Auto Workers Union. He was active in the sit-down strikes, helped organize General Motors, and in 1946 became president of the Union. The experience of organization left him doubts about the socialist program; he became anti-Communist and more inclined to emphasize democratic methods. But he remained an active, dynamic force in the labor movement.

One of labor's long-range objectives is to achieve in every basic industry a guaranteed annual wage so that the consumers of this country can have a sustained income month in and month out, because only on that basis can we sustain an econ-

* Walter P. Reuther, "Opening Address of the Twelfth Constitutional Convention of the United Automobile . . . Workers of America" (Milwaukee, July 10, 1949), *Selected Papers*, Henry M. Christman, ed. (New York, 1961), pp. 36–43.

omy of full employment and full production and full distribution.

When we drafted the economic demands of our union in January of this year, we said that the workers in our industry needed a pension plan, that every day they were getting older and every day insecurity was clouding their future. We said that when a worker had worked twenty-five years and reached the age of sixty he was entitled to a minimum of one hundred dollars on top of the federal Social Security payments in order to be able to retire with a semblance of security and human dignity in his old age. We said that industry had to pay the bill because the workers have created the wealth that makes possible these great industries. We said that we wanted a hospital medical program financed on the basis of 5 per cent of payroll to give our workers and their families complete hospital and medical care. We said we wanted a wage increase to reestablish our real wage position back to where it was in June of 1946 when OPA was destroyed.

When we drafted these demands, we drafted them because they reflected the basic needs of our workers and they also reflected the basic needs of our nation's economy. Since we drafted these demands the economic picture in America has worsened. There are soft spots developing. Unemployment is developing in serious proportions in many communities, like Muskegon, for example, and because of these worsening economic factors, these negative factors, the high priests in Wall Street say to us, "This is no time to rock the boat. Labor ought to demonstrate real statesmanship. Withdraw your demands and let's kind of weather the storm together."

And we in the UAW say to these people in industry, to the coupon clippers in Wall Street, every reason that necessitated our drafting our demands in January has been reemphasized and reinforced by the fact that we are getting into economic difficulty with growing unemployment. This is not the time for people in the leadership of American labor to be men of little faith or little courage. This is the time for labor to stand up and say we are getting in trouble in America because the little guy hasn't got enough, and therefore, he has to fight harder now to get what he is entitled to in order to avoid going into a depression. We have to say that loud and clear.

Industry tells us, when we are in a period of inflation, that we should not demand wage increases when prices are going up because they will create more inflation. Then when the inflation is leveling off and we are getting into trouble because people are being laid off, they say, "You should not do it now."

It is a good system: they get you coming and get you going.

We say the needs of our workers are simple and compelling, and we are not going to permit those demands to be ignored or postponed. We are going after them in 1949.

Big business again has welded a united front. The steel industry told Philip Murray and the Steelworkers the other day the answer was "no" on their wage and economic demands. The Ford Motor Company has told the Ford Motor workers "no." The Chrysler people have indicated their answer will be "no." And across America in industry you have this united front in the making.

We are going into these negotiations on the basis that we would like to see a situation in America where we can raise collective bargaining above the status of a struggle between competing economic pressure groups. We would like to resolve our economic demands on the basis of the economic facts and not upon economic power; but whether it is done one way or another is a decision and responsibility which industry must make.

We talk a great deal in our union about economic facts, and every time I get a chance to talk to you fellows I talk economic facts, because the kind of complex problems we have to solve cannot be solved just by table pounding or by picket line marching, no matter how militant you may be. Table pounding and picket line marching are part of the problem, but you have to base your demands and struggle on sound economic facts. We keep saying to our workers they have to understand these facts because these facts are the arithmetic of our future.

What are the facts of the current economic situation as they relate to our demands? American industry has made profits higher than at any time in the history of America. Thirty-two billion dollars before taxes in 1948 and twenty billion after taxes, more than five times the profit rate of American industry before the war.

Profits have gone up three times as fast as wages and salaries. In the auto industry, eight companies, excluding the Ford Motor Company, in 1948 made profits 51 per cent higher than they did in 1947. In the first quarter of 1949, they made profits 35 per cent higher than in 1948, and these eight companies together made a return on their investment after taxes of 28 per cent. And that includes the little companies, Studebaker, Hudson, Packard, Willys-Overland, Kaiser-Frazer, in addition to General Motors and Chrysler. And despite these profits they are back at their old game of trying to cut corners and cut costs by sweating more work out of the workers. And I say to you the record of this union in its historic struggle in resisting speed-up with every weapon we have is clear. We have authorized 409 strikes since the last convention, the largest number in the history of this union, and almost 50 per cent of them involved the question of speed-up. We take the position we will mobilize our union to fight against speed-up wherever it raises its ugly head, whether it be in the small plant or Ford Motor Company or General Motors or Chrysler, or any other company. The boys who are now making propaganda about the speed-up unfortunately are the same boys who tried to sell us piecework and were ready to lay their all on the altar for Joe Stalin at the Buffalo convention. They are not fooling anybody.

We say our economic demands are sound economically, and they are right morally. We have talked for a long time about destroying the double standards, and now we are finally in a position where we are going to do something about it. The trouble is that industry operates on the basis of these double economic and moral standards. They say to the worker when he is too old to work and too young to die, "You cannot have security in your old age: that is reserved to only the blue bloods, only the ones who were smart enough to pick the right grandfather before they were born. They can have security, but if you live on the wrong side of the railroad tracks you are not entitled to it."

And we say they are economically and morally and stupidly wrong.

Let me give you some of the figures. C. E. Wilson in 1948 got $516,000 in salary and bonus. He made, on the basis of a 40-hour week and 50 weeks a year, $258 an hour. Yet the Board of Directors of General Motors when they met in Wilmington said, "Poor old C. E., he is having a rough time of it, he can't get along on $516,000 a year; General Motors will give him $25,000 a year when he is too old to work but too young to die."

If you make $258 an hour they give it to you; if you make $1.65 an hour they say, "You don't need it, you are not entitled to it, and we are not going to give it to you."

We are going to change that in America, and we are going to start in the next couple of weeks.

Now don't get the idea C. E. Wilson is lonely. He has a lot of company in General Motors in this highly paid group. If you take the salary and bonuses of the top seven executives in General Motors, they averaged $426,799 last year. They averaged $213 per hour on a 40-hour work week, 50-week basis.

General Motors has made so much profit they declared a $48,000,000 bonus. Eight million was laid aside for a rainy day, and forty million divided up. They had so much money they ran out of executives. They never run out of workers—just executives. And then they gave bonuses to people not on the pay roll of the General Motors Corporation, and they wrote a letter to the Chairman of the Securities and Exchange Commission to keep this information a secret. They didn't want anybody to know who got these bonuses, and why they got them and how much they were.

We have written the Securities and Exchange Commission, and we want this convention to pass a resolution, demanding they publish the information as to who is being bribed by the General Motors Corporation of America.

I don't want the Chrysler boys to feel badly, because I know they all love K. T. Keller. The four top officials in the Chrysler Corporation made last year an average of $225,000, or $113 per hour. And that does not include bonuses.

Let me tell you what happened on that. You fellows are all stockholders in the Chrysler Corporation. All of us together own one share. We bought one share of stock in every company under contract with our union, so that our Research Department could sit in on every Board of Directors' meeting, and see if we could not peep behind the Iron Curtain.

A brother from the Research Department went to the Chrysler stockholders' meeting, and after they went through all the rigamarole that they have at such meetings, the Chairman of the Board of Directors of the Chrysler Corporation stood before the meeting with a big brown envelope sealed tight. He said, "The Board of Directors has voted bonuses to some of the executives, and we want you to approve these bonuses. They are in the sealed envelope. We won't tell you who is getting how much. It is all in the envelope." And the fellow representing your one share of stock got up and said, "Mr. Chairman, I make a motion that we open up the envelope, so we can see who is getting how much of this bonus melon." He did not have enough shares—one share did not carry—and they voted him down. Imagine this! They voted themselves bonuses that are secret in a stockholders' meeting. I would just like to say to Brother Mazey and the other officers and Board Members, if we came before this convention, which is the stockholders' meeting of our union, and we had in a sealed envelope some bonuses for the top officers, and we said, you vote for them and approve them, without telling you who is getting what, I would want a jet plane out here to jump into and take off, because I would need it pretty quickly.

Now look at the Nash-Kelvinator Corporation. This is one of the little independents that is having a hard time getting along in the world. Mr. G. W. Mason of Nash-Kelvinator Company last year, got $300,925—$150 per hour, yet he got a pension plan.

International Harvester—so that the International Harvester

boys do not feel slighted—Fowler McCormick made $161,000 last year, and when he is too old to work and too young to die he gets $40,000 a year pension from International Harvester.

And so the aircraft boys don't think that their industry is excluded, Mr. Leonard Hobbs of United Aircraft Company—he is just a measly vice-president—made $95,000 last year, and when he gets too old to work and he is too young to die, he will get a $12,337 per year pension. I just say to you people and we say to America—we say to American industry, if you can afford to pay pension plans to people who don't need them, then by the eternal gods you are going to have to pay them to people who do need them, the guys in the shop.

We want a hospital and medical plan. We want to remove the economic barriers which block good health to the average family in America. I don't speak with simply academic knowledge on this problem. I lay in four different hospitals over a period of months, and I tell you, you have to be a millionaire to afford medical care in America.

Let me just tell you the sort of things I have seen. I went into a hospital one morning to be treated and I met a young fellow twenty-eight years of age, a clean-cut looking boy with a smile in his eye, lying there on a hospital bed. The nurse asked me to go over and say hello to him and cheer him up, and I did. This boy has been paralyzed for nine years, and he lay at home. He could not afford hospital and medical treatment. I talked to him every morning, and after he had laid in the hospital about a month, after being paralyzed for nine years, I came in one morning and he was just overcome with joy. He said to me, "I have been reborn this morning." I said, "What do you mean?" And he said to the nurse, "Pull this sheet back so I can show Mr. Reuther." And the nurse pulled the sheet back and he could wiggle his big toe. It was the first time in nine years that he could wiggle his toe, and he was just like a kid on Christmas morning. I watched him every morning making progress, getting a new grip on life, with a whole new world opening up before him. Sometime later I came in to see him and he was crying like a kid. He was brokenhearted, and I said to the nurse, "What's the matter, hasn't he been doing so well?" And she said, "He hasn't got any more money; he goes home tomorrow."

I say there is something wrong in America when, if you happen to be born on the wrong side of the railroad tracks as these kids were, and you are paralyzed and you lie on your back for nine years because you can't afford the treatment that medical science can give you, I say that is morally wrong. No nation that has an ounce of self-respect or human decency, no nation that can spend $400,000,000,000 for war, can stand idly by and tolerate a continuation of that kind of double standard in America. And I say this convention has got to stand up and fight for these kids and give our people the kind of care to which they are entitled.

What made this thing so ironic—and you begin to see what is wrong in America—the same week this happened the *Free Press* came out with a story about C. E. Wilson's bull. C. E. Wilson had a bull and the bull had a bad back. We are sorry about that. But what happened to C. E. Wilson's bull compared to this boy who was paralyzed for nine years? In the case of C. E. Wilson's bull, the General Electric Company sent a special 140,000-volt X-ray machine into Detroit on a special chartered airplane. It was picked up by a General Motors truck and taken out to C. E. Wilson's farm. The bull didn't even have to leave home to get medical care. Then when they got the 140,000-volt machine there they couldn't operate it because they didn't have enough power, so the Detroit Edison Company ran a special power line out to C. E. Wilson's farm.

Then medical specialists flew in from all over the country and they gave this bull the best medical care that modern medicine and science knows how to deliver. Now why? Why? I ask that simple, honest question. Why did C. E. Wilson's bull get the best of medical care while millions of these kids all over America are not getting that kind of care? It is because C. E. Wilson's bull cost $16,000, and you get boys and workers for free. It is the age-old struggle between human rights and property rights, between people and profits, and this is just a dramatic illustration of how completely wrong some of our moral values are in America.

In the coal mines—and there are a lot of former coal diggers in this convention—they used to lay the coal miners off and they went hungry, but they always fed the mine mules because they owned the mine mules. They had to buy them but they didn't have to buy the coal miners. They got them for free.

That is the trouble in America, and we have got to change these things. We have to renew our faith in basic human values. We have to reassert the sovereignty of people above profits in America, and this convention has to do that. We want the pension plans and the medical plans and the wage increase. We need them. We are willing to sit down and do everything we can to resolve these problems intelligently and constructively, based upon the economic facts of life. But management must accept their responsibility in these coming negotiations, because if they try to continue the double standards we say to them here and now we are prepared to use all the weapons possessed by free labor in America in these negotiations. We know that we can't solve all of our problems through collective bargaining over the conference table.

23. WILLIAM SAROYAN

*Believing in Every Religion**

William Saroyan was born in Fresno, California, in 1908, the son of immigrants from Bitlis, Armenia. He was educated in the public schools and early took to writing. He has turned out a steady flow of plays, stories, and essays, much of it autobiographical in nature. See also William Saroyan, The Twin Adventures *(New York, 1950).*

One of the many curious and delightful things about our country is the ease with which our good people move from one religion to another, or from no particular religion at all to any religion that happens to come along, without experiencing any particular loss or gain, and go right on being innocent anyhow.

Myself, I was born, for instance, a kind of Catholic, although I was not baptized until I was thirteen, a circumstance which, I remember clearly, irritated the priest very much and impelled him to ask my people if they were crazy, to which my people replied, We have been away.

Thirteen years old and not baptized! the priest shouted. What kind of people are you?

For the most part, my uncle Melik replied, we are an agricultural people, although we have had our brilliant men, too.

It was a Saturday afternoon. The whole thing took no more than seven minutes, but even after I was baptized it was impossible for me to feel any change.

Well, my grandmother said, you are now baptized. Do you feel any better?

For some months, I believe I ought to explain, I had been

* William Saroyan, *My Name Is Aram* (New York, 1940), pp. 113–30.

feeling intelligent, which led my grandmother to suspect that I was ill with some mysterious illness or that I was losing my mind.

I think I feel the same, I said.

Do you believe now? she shouted. Or do you still have doubts?

I can easily *say* I believe, I said, but to tell you the truth I don't know for sure. I want to be a Christian of course.

Well, just believe then, my grandmother said, and go about your business.

My business was in some ways quaint and in other ways incredible.

I sang in the Boys Choir at the Presbyterian Church on Tulare Street. For doing so I received one dollar a week from an elderly Christian lady named Balaifal who lived in sorrow and solitude in the small ivy-covered house next to the house in which my friend Pandro Kolkhozian lived.

This boy, like myself, was loud in speech. That is to say, we swore a good deal—in all innocence of course—and by doing so grieved Miss or Mrs. Balaifal so much that she sought to save us while there was still time. To be saved was a thing I for one had no occasion to resent.

Miss Balaifal (I shall call her that from now on, since while I knew her she was certainly single, and since I do not know for sure if she ever married, or for that matter if she ever thought of marrying, or if she ever so much as fell in love—earlier in life of course, and no doubt with a scoundrel who took the whole matter with a grain of salt)—Miss Balaifal, as I began to say, was a cultured woman, a reader of the poems of Robert Browning and other poets and a woman of great sensitivity, so that coming out on the porch of her house to hear us talk she could stand so much and no more, and when the limit had been reached, cried out, Boys, boys. You must not use profane language.

Pandro Kolkhozian, on the one hand, seemed to be the most uncouth boy in the world and on the other—and this was the quality in him which endeared him to me—the most courteous and thoughtful.

Yes, Miss Balaifum, he said.

Balaifal, the lady corrected him. Please come here. Both of you.

We went to Miss Balaifal and asked what she wanted.

What do you want, Miss Balaifum? Pandro said.

Miss Balaifal went into her coat pocket and brought out a sheaf of pamphlets, and without looking at them handed one to each of us. My pamphlet was entitled *Redemption, The Story of a Drunkard*. Pandro's was entitled *Peace at Last, The Story of a Drunkard.*

What's this for? Pandro said.

I want you boys to read those pamphlets and try to be good, Miss Balaifal said. I want you to stop using profane language.

It doesn't say anything here about profane language, Pandro said.

There's a good lesson for each of you in those pamphlets, the lady said. Read them and don't use profane language any more.

Yes, ma'am, I said. Is that all?

One thing more, Miss Balaifal said. I wonder if you boys would help me move the organ from the dining room to the parlor?

Sure, Miss Balaifum, Pandro said. Any time.

So we went into the lady's house and, while she instructed us in just how to do it without damaging the instrument or ourselves, we moved it, by slow degrees, from the dining room to the parlor.

Now read those pamphlets, Miss Balaifal said.

Yes, ma'am, Pandro said. Is that all?

Well, now, the lady said. I want you to sing while I play the organ.

I can't sing, Miss Balaifum, Pandro said.

Nonsense, the lady said. Of course you can sing, Pedro.

Pandro, not Pedro, Pandro said. Pedro is my cousin's name.

As a matter of fact Pandro's name was Pantalo, which in Armenian means pants. When he had started to school his teacher hadn't cared for, or hadn't liked the sound of, the name, so she had written down on his card Pandro. As for his cousin's name, it was Bedros, with the *b* soft, which in turn had been changed at school to Pedro. It was all quite all right of course, and no harm to anybody.

Without answering him, the elderly lady sat on the stool, adjusted her feet on the pedals of the organ, and without any instructions to us, began to play a song which, from its dullness, was obviously religious. After a moment she herself began to sing. Pandro, in a soft voice, uttered a very profane, if not vulgar, word, which fortunately Miss Balaifal did not hear. Miss Balaifal's voice was, if anything, not impressive. The pedals squeaked a good deal louder than she sang, the tones of the organ were not any too clear, but even so, it was possible to know that Miss Balaifal's voice was not delightful.

Galilee, bright Galilee, she sang.

She turned to us, nodded, and said, Now sing. Sing, boys.

We knew neither the words nor the music, but it seemed that common courtesy demanded at least an honest effort, which we made, trying as far as possible to follow the music coming out of the organ and the dramatic words coming out of Miss Balaifal.

Ruler of the storm was He, on the raging Galilee, she sang.

In all, we tried to sing three songs. After each song, Pandro would say, Thank you very much, Miss Balaifum. Can we go now?

At last she got up from the organ and said, I'm sure you're the better for it. If evil friends invite you to drink, turn away.

We'll turn away, Miss Balaifum, Pandro said. Won't we, Aram?

I will, I said.

I will too, Pandro said. Can we go now, Miss Balaifum?

Read the pamphlets, she said. It's not too late.

We'll read them, Pandro said. Just as soon as we get time.

We left the lady's house and went back to the front yard of Pandro's house and began to read the pamphlets. Before we were half through reading, the lady came out on the porch and in a very high and excited voice said, Which of you was it?

Which of us was *what*? Pandro said.

He was very bewildered.

Which of you was it that *sang?* Miss Balaifal said.

We both sang, I said.

No, Miss Balaifal said. Only one of you sang. One of you has a beautiful Christian voice.

Not me, Pandro said.

You, Miss Balaifal said to me. Eugene. Was it you?

Aram, I said. Not Eugene. No, I don't think it was me either.

Boys, come here, Miss Balaifal said.

Who? Pandro said.

Both of you, the lady said.

When we were in the house and Miss Balaifal was seated at the organ again Pandro said, I don't want to sing. I don't like to sing.

You sing, the lady said to me.

I sang.

Miss Balaifal leaped to her feet.

You are the one, she said. You must sing at church.

I won't, I said.

You mustn't use profane language, she said.

I'm not using profane language, I said, and I promise not to use profane language again as long as I live, but I won't sing in church.

Your voice is the most Christian voice I have ever heard, Miss Balaifal said.

It isn't, I said.

Yes, it is, she said.

Well, I won't sing anyway, I said.

You must, you must, Miss Balaifal said.

Thanks very much, Miss Balaifum, Pandro said. Can we go now? He doesn't want to sing in church.

He must, he must, the lady insisted.

Why? Pandro said.

For the good of his soul, the lady said.

Pandro whispered the profane word again.

Now tell me, the lady said. What is your name?

I told her.

You are a Christian of course? she said.

I guess so, I said.

A Presbyterian of course, she said.

I don't know about that, I said.

You are, the lady said. Of course you are. I want you to sing in the Tulare Street Presbyterian Church—in the Boys' Choir —next Sunday.

Why? Pandro said again.

We need voices, the lady explained. We must have young voices. We must have singers. He must sing next Sunday.

I don't like to sing, I said. I don't like to go to church either.

Boys, Miss Balaifal said. Sit down. I want to talk to you.

We sat down. Miss Balaifal talked to us for at least thirty minutes.

We didn't believe a word of it, although out of courtesy we kept answering her questions the way we knew she wanted us to answer them, but when she asked us to get down on our knees with her while she prayed, we wouldn't do it. Miss Balaifal argued this point for some time and then decided to let us have our way—for a moment. Then she tried again, but we wouldn't do it. Pandro said we'd move the organ any time, or anything else like that, but we wouldn't get down on our knees.

Well, Miss Balaifal said, will you close your eyes?

What for? Pandro said.

It's customary for everybody to close his eyes while someone is praying, Miss Balaifal said.

Who's praying? Pandro said.

No one, *yet,* Miss Balaifal said. But if you'll promise to close your eyes, *I'll* pray, but you've got to promise to close your eyes.

What do you want to pray for? Pandro said.

I want to pray for you boys, she said.

What for? Pandro said.

A little prayer for you won't do any harm, Miss Balaifal said. Will you close your eyes?

Oh! all right, Pandro said.

We closed our eyes and Miss Balaifal prayed.

It wasn't a little prayer by a long shot.

Amen, she said. Now, boys, don't you feel better?

In all truth, we didn't.

Yes, we do, Pandro said. Can we go now, Miss Balaifum? Any time you want the organ moved, we'll move it for you.

Sing for all you're worth, Miss Balaifal said to me, and turn away from any evil companion who invites you to drink.

Yes, ma'am, I said.

You know where the church is, she said.

What church? I said.

The Tulare Street Presbyterian Church, she said.

I know where it is, I said.

Mr. Sherwin will be expecting you Sunday morning at nine-thirty, she said.

Well, it just seemed like I was cornered.

Pandro went with me to the church on Sunday, but refused to stand with the choir boys and sing. He sat in the last row of the church and watched and listened. As for myself, I was never more unhappy in my life, although I sang.

Never again, I told Pandro after it was all over.

The following Sunday I didn't show up of course, but that didn't do any good, because Miss Balaifal got us into her house again, played the organ, sang, made us try to sing, prayed, and was unmistakably determined to keep me in the Boys' Choir. I refused flatly, and Miss Balaifal decided to put the whole thing on a more worldly basis.

You have a rare Christian voice, she explained. A voice needed by religion. You yourself are deeply religious, although you do not know it yet. Since this is so, let me ask you to sing for *me* every Sunday. I will *pay* you.

How much? Pandro said.

Fifty cents, Miss Balaifal said.

We usually sang four or five songs. It took about half an hour altogether, although we had to sit another hour while the preacher delivered his sermon. In short, it wasn't worth it.

For this reason I could make no reply.

Seventy-five cents, Miss Balaifal suggested.

The air was stuffy, the preacher was a bore, it was all very depressing.

One dollar, Miss Balaifal said. Not a cent more.

Make it a dollar and a quarter, Pandro said.

Not a cent more than a dollar, Miss Balaifal said.

He's got the best voice in the whole choir, Pandro said. *One* dollar? A voice like that is worth *two* dollars to any religion.

I've made my offer, Miss Balaifal said.

There are other religions, Pandro said.

This, I must say, upset Miss Balaifal.

His voice, she said bitterly, is a Christian voice, and what's more it's Presbyterian.

The Baptists would be glad to get a voice like that for two dollars, Pandro said.

The Baptists! Miss Balaifal said with some—I hesitate to say it—contempt.

They're no different than the Presbyterams, Pandro said.

One dollar, Miss Balaifal said. One dollar, and your name on the program.

I don't like to sing, Miss Balaifal, I said.

Yes, you do, she said. You just think you don't. If you could see your face when you sing—why—

He's got a voice like an angel, Pandro said.

I'll fix you, I told Pandro in Armenian.

That's no one-dollar voice, Pandro said.

All right, boys, Miss Balaifal said. A dollar and fifteen cents, but no more.

A dollar and a quarter, Pandro said, or we go to the Baptists.

All right, Miss Balaifal said, but I must say you drive a hard bargain.

Wait a minute, I said. I don't like to sing. I won't sing for a dollar and a quarter or anything else.

A bargain is a bargain, Miss Balaifal said.

I didn't make any bargain, I said. Pandro did. Let *him* sing.

He *can't* sing, Miss Balaifal said.

I've got the worst voice in the world, Pandro said with great pride.

His poor voice wouldn't be worth ten cents to anybody, Miss Balaifal said.

Not even a nickel, Pandro said.

Well, I said, I'm not going to sing—for a dollar and a quarter or anything else. I don't need any money.

You made a bargain, Miss Balaifal said.

Yes, you did, Pandro said.

I jumped on Pandro right in Miss Balaifal's parlor and we began to wrestle. The elderly Christian lady tried to break it up, but since it was impossible to determine which of us was the boy with the angelic voice, she began to pray. The wrestling continued until most of the furniture in the room had been knocked over, except the organ. The match was eventually a draw, the wrestlers exhausted and flat on their backs.

Miss Balaifal stopped praying and said, Sunday then, at a dollar and a quarter.

It took me some time to get my breath.

Miss Balaifal, I said, I'll sing in that choir only if Pandro sings too.

But his voice, Miss Balaifal objected. It's horrible.

I don't care what it is, I said. If I sing, he's got to sing too.

I'm afraid he'd ruin the choir, Miss Balaifal said.

He's got to go up there with me every Sunday, I said, or nothing doing.

Well, now, let me see, Miss Balaifal said.

She gave the matter considerable thought.

Suppose he goes up and stands in the choir, Miss Balaifal said, but *doesn't* sing? Suppose he just *pretends* to sing?

That's all right with me, I said, but he's got to be there all the time.

What do *I* get? Pandro said.

Well, now, Miss Balaifal said, I surely can't be expected to pay you, too.

If I go up there, Pandro said, I've got to be paid.

All right, Miss Balaifal said. One dollar for the boy who sings; twenty-five cents for the boy who doesn't.

I've got the worst voice in the world, Pandro said.

You must be fair, Miss Balaifal said. After all, you won't be singing. You'll just be standing there with the other boys.

Twenty-five cents isn't enough, Pandro said.

We got off the floor and began rearranging the furniture.

All right, Miss Balaifal said. One dollar for the boy who sings. Thirty-five cents for the boy who doesn't.

Make it fifty, Pandro said.

Very well, then, Miss Balaifal said. A dollar for *you.* Fifty cents for *you.*

We start working next Sunday? Pandro said.

That's right, Miss Balaifal said. I'll pay you here after the services. Not a word of this to any of the other boys in the choir.

We won't mention it to anybody, Pandro said.

In this manner, in the eleventh year of my life, I became, more or less, a Presbyterian—at least every Sunday morning. It wasn't the money. It was simply that a bargain had been made, and that Miss Balaifal had her heart set on having me sing for religion.

As I began to say six or seven minutes ago, however, a curious thing about our country is the ease with which all of us—or at least everybody I know—are able to change our religions, without any noticeable damage to anything or anybody. When I was thirteen I was baptized into the Armenian Catholic Church, even though I was still singing for the Presbyterians, and even though I myself was growing a little skeptical, as it were, of the whole conventional religious pattern, and was eager, by hook or crook, to reach an understanding of my own, and to come to terms with Omnipotence in my own way. Even after I was baptized, I carried in my heart a deep discontent.

Two months after I was baptized my voice changed, and my contract with Miss Balaifal was canceled—which was a great relief to me and a terrible blow to her.

As for the Armenian Catholic Church on Ventura Avenue, I went there only on Easter and Christmas. All the rest of the time I moved from one religion to another, and in the end was none the worse for it, so that now, like most Americans, my faith consists in believing in every religion, including my own, but without any ill-will toward anybody, no matter what he believes or disbelieves, just so his personality is good.

24. NELSON ALGREN

*The Trouble with Daylight**

Nelson Algren was born in Detroit in 1909 of Scandinavian parents. Educated in the public schools of Chicago and at the University of Illinois, he early encountered the effects of the Depression and worked as a migratory laborer in the Southwest before his writing won recognition. His first novels treated the proletarian life of the industrial cities and particularly the effects of poverty on youth. His subjects were frequently Poles, they having been among the worst victims of the distress he observed. Beneath the harsh realism of his fiction lies a sympathetic, almost sentimental, concern for the quest of the young for love and understanding. Bruno Lefty Bicek, however brutalized by existence in Chicago's North West Side, never loses the longing for human dignity.

The lefthander's Mama stirred restlessly on her cot in the rear of Bicek's Imperial Milk Depot and Half-Price Day-Old Bakery. She heard the lefthander getting empty bottles back into their cases, listened for the faint tinkle that heralded a customer's entrance, and hoped the boy would stay in the store until the driver arrived.

Though it was bright autumn and the sky cloudless, Mama Bicek always felt, in the low-roofed rear of the little store, that outside a cold wind rose and an all-night rain began. She touched the crucifix at her throat and drew the army blanket closer about her.

* Nelson Algren, *Never Come Morning* (New York, 1942), pp. 11–16, 33–8.

Bruno Lefty Bicek, ace southpaw of the 26th Ward Warriors, squatted forward on a milk bottle case, as he had seen Benkowski squat in the seconds before the bell, working the fingers of his right hand about a red sponge ball. With the left—the hand that was already strong enough—he filled the cases that happened to be nearest. The fingers that worked the sponge ball flexed regularly, strenuously, with an unremitting ambition; those that handled the empty bottles did so with absent-minded indifference, as though possessed of the knowledge that Bruno Lefty planned higher uses for them than that of pleasing milk drivers.

Bruno Lefty was divided in his ambitions between being a big-league hurler and becoming a contender for the heavyweight championship of the world. Somehow or other, no White Sox scout had shown up the time he had held the Wonders to a single hit, so he was slightly more inclined to the ring. And why hadn't anyone called him "Iron-Man" the day he'd shut out the Logan Squares and then relieved Fireball Kodadek in the fifth inning of the second game? Why, they'd almost won the second game behind him as well!

That Fireball was through, the boy reflected with satisfaction now. When Bicek was on the mound the boys would play any team on the Near Northwest Side for thirteen dollars a side, and when Fireball was in there they wouldn't put up more than a quarter apiece, against anybody.

"I hope that Kodadek gets beaned for keeps 'n never comes to," Lefty hoped without malice, as he hoped for any possibility which would clear a pathway to being known throughout the ward as "Iron-Man."

Or maybe the barber would get him a fight with some headshy boogie, like that Big-Ink Martin from the Savoy, and he'd ice the jig with a punch. Then the *Chicagoski* might call him One-Punch Bicek, the undefeated white hope of Chicago Avenue or something; maybe the *Daily Times* would pick it up and tell just how he did it. The boy had a sort of super punch, they'd say. He sat looking vacantly into space, sponge ball and milk bottles equally forgotten.

When the doorbell tinkled he did not rise; he recognized the black bombazine and pince-nez of the middle-aged caseworker from the Sangamon Street Relief. She hustled past him into the rear, without recognition; she had learned that if she so much as said "Good afternoon, Bruno," he lied to her in reply. She was curing him of the habit by not recognizing him at all. For the boy's part, he didn't seem to notice that anyone had entered, and that irked the woman a little. While sitting with Mama Bicek, notebook in hand, she concluded that she'd better have a heart-to-heart talk with the boy before she left. Perhaps all he needed was Social Guidance. He was leaning on the handle of a broom when she came out, apparently absorbed in his shoes. "I know everythin' she's goin' t' tell me, like it's a big discovery," he thought. He knew it all by rote, and he listened patiently while she dinned it in his ear anew:

Mama Bicek needed an orange.

Mama Bicek needed meat.

Mama Bicek needed medicine.

Mama Bicek should get sunshine.

But Mama Bicek couldn't have those things from the relief, for she had a son and a store besides. Now if Mama Bicek had no store, and Mama Bicek's boy wasn't old enough to work on W.P.A., then things could be different. Then the black bombazine would take care of everything personally.

Bruno had never taken advantage of the fact that he was a year younger than the woman credited him with being. He enjoyed being taken for eighteen. "At least you don't lie about your age," she had once assured him.

The implication, that he lied as fast as a dog can trot about everything else, was true so far as she was concerned. Why he lied to her the boy didn't know. Perhaps it was, in part, distrust of her notebook and pince-nez; perhaps it was partly her consistent failure to regard him as the Warriors' mainstay; perhaps it was chiefly his realization that she came from the same world as did detectives and truant officers and park policemen. Perhaps too he had sensed that she stopped to question him chiefly in order that she might be able to leave feeling she had been most deliberately, brazenly and wantonly betrayed by a client she had trusted completely.

"You didn't show up Wednesday morning," she apprized him now, "Why not?"

He had promised her faithfully that, when she got him assigned, at fifty-five a month, to a project on the Outer Drive, he would be as certain to appear on the job as the foreman himself. Now he rested his cheek on the end of the broom handle and mumbled sleepily.

"I'm in trainin'. Had to go to bed early 'n sleep late. That was orders."

Seeing the full-grown slouch of his shoulders, she found herself hoping that he'd lie more outrageously than ever before. But she kept that out of her voice.

"Training for *what?* Orders from *whom?*"

It wouldn't pay to let him think she was being fooled for one minute. But one would think, by those shoulders, that he was twenty-one; she surveyed his face to make certain that he wasn't over eighteen: a wholesome, placid, sallow Polish face with cheekbones set high and widely to protect the nose and eyes. And what in the world was he up to, at that age, squeezing a sponge ball?

"For a fight. From my manager."

"You mean you fight pro*fess*ionally?"

"Uh-huh."

Anyhow, he was going to get a money fight pretty soon, wait and see. If the barber didn't get him on at the Garden, Benkowski would.

She jotted something in the book, and he took time out to fancy himself climbing through the ropes at the City Garden. Then she'd see his picture in the paper the next morning and would write him a letter of apology addressed to "*Mister* Bicek." He found himself waiting for her to call him "Mister"; as he waited, among the boys, for someone to call him "Iron-Man."

"What do you earn when you fight?"

The boy had no one to whom he could boast freely but an underage girl friend, and she didn't count.

"I wouldn't pull on a glove fer less 'n a hunerd," he heard himself saying. And if she had the nerve not to call him "Mister" after that one, he'd raise the ante until she did.

"Of course," he added, looking her squarely in the pince-nez, "there's trainin' expenses, gym expenses, travel expenses, manager's cut, handler's fee, sparrin' partners—they're gettin' harder fer me t' get since I developed my super punch—the word's gettin' around about that——"

"How often do you fight, *Mister* Bicek?"

There! He'd gotten that much out of her. He felt almost grateful. Some day he'd get her a couple free passes to the Garden.

"Ever' chance I get. If I can't get a ring match I pick up a street fight just t' keep in shape. I'm sharp as a razor right now."

He leaned the broom against the counter and jab-jabbed for her with his right.

"How often in the ring?" she asked, notebook poised. If this hunky thought he was going to be able to deny any of this later, he had another think coming. She retreated a step to give him more room.

"And you always get a hundred dollars?"

He leaned indolently against the counter.

"So help me."

"Why isn't your mother getting better attention then?"

As though she had heard, Mama Bicek groaned appropriately. Bruno hung his head in mock repentance. The old lady had been doing that, sick or well, all her life.

"I spend it all on myself—I guess I'm just a mug."

He heard the door slam behind her, a proper slam; righteousness had been betrayed again.

Well, he reflected, she wasn't going to help the old lady anyhow; now she had a good excuse not to. He heard his mother call for water and brought her a glass. After she drank he sat unconcernedly on the side of the bed.

"T'morrow I get up," she told him. "Do a little work, feel better." She had the peasant faith in work as a cure-all. When a woman got sick all she had to do was work a little harder than usual, till the sick was gone. Not enough work was why she was sick—washing Bruno's dishes and sweeping the floor and selling a bottle of milk—Was that a day's work for a woman? No wonder she was sick. Not enough work to keep her well; not enough work ever to make her well again. If the other children had lived, there would be enough work. She heard a peddler passing in the alley and opened her eyes.

"*Obarzanki! Obarzanki!*"

A *zyd* selling bagles. Out in front a horn honked, and the boy straightened up, hoping Finger wouldn't honk again. Mama Bicek felt the bedspring give as he rose. All the health that had been denied her three other children had been given this one—it seemed to Mama Bicek—the only one who had lived past ten years. She heard the bell tinkle faintly as he closed the door behind him.

She turned and faced the wall, remembering a time when two policemen had come for him, their numbered badges and the flashlight on the wall. That had been the summer he was fourteen. On the cot on the other side of the room, he had pulled the covers over his head and feigned sleep.

"Get him up, Missis, or we'll get him up for you."

She had yanked the covers back and there he was, fully clothed, with blood on the front of his shirt.

"Just shootin' dice, Mom . . ." he had turned to the officers sullenly: "The fella got me in the game 'n I lost a autograph *Al Simmons* bat, 'n I hold the dice up to the light 'n sure enough, they was missouts, they was engineered, he couldn't have sevened with those in a month."

Mama Bicek had not understood. Two days later, when he was released, he had tried to explain. She had waved him away. Fourteen years old and he had thought nothing of being two days in a jail. She had taken no pleasure in him since. She had never been certain, since, whether his friends weren't detectives when they entered the store.

If they had stayed in the Old World, she felt, her son would have been a good son. There a boy had to behave himself or be put in the army.

"You! Bruno!" She called, to be certain he was gone.

Boys in the army were good boys. The army made them good. She turned painfully on her side and a car door slammed and he was gone again; for a day or two weeks or two months or forever. That was the way with poor folks' boys. She felt in the pocket of the army coat: the forty cents was gone, so he wouldn't be back that day. And the front door open. Well, what was there to take? A few day-old rolls? Would the driver come today or tomorrow? She pulled the coat over her head so as not to hear any who entered. Half in sleep and half in waking, she heard a cold wind moaning to itself through the alleyway. And heard an all-night rain begin. . . .

His thoughts returned to Steffi. If a girl was really a good girl she ought to have sense enough not to bother with a Polack who had barely finished eighth grade, just because he'd been born on the same block. And hadn't had a job, outside of freight handling, since.

And freight handling wasn't a real job, because you never knew from day to day whether you had it or not. You walked over to Kinzie Street to save carfare, with your lunch under your arm, and hung around half a day waiting for them to tell you either to get yourself a truck or go home. So the next day you went with only two sandwiches and a date with Steffi at six, and had to work sixteen straight hours and leave her standing up.

She hadn't forgiven him for that one for a week; she hadn't understood, at first, that he had had no way of getting away without losing the hours already put in. The shippers were never able to tell a man how long he was going to work because they never knew themselves. They unloaded the cars, loaded them again, trying to get everything into the least possible number; it was well worth their while to save one car even though it meant paying six men for an extra hour each. They did not pay for the hours that elapsed while the men waited for the extra hour.

Standing Steffi up hadn't bothered him too much, however. That was good for a dame, kept her from getting stuck up. Nor was it the way you had to work for that forty cents an hour or their way of never letting you know whether you were on the job or not, that had made him throw it up. He hadn't done that until they'd cut the rate to thirty. A few men with families had stayed in the face of the cut, feeling that thirty was better than nothing at all. The others had left, and the next morning the company had a full gang working at the new rate. They had picked men off the street, from the agencies around Grand and Halsted and from the Green Street Shelter—any man with two arms and two legs could learn how to shove a truck, and the right place to shove it, in five minutes.

"Grzmoty zabili diabla," he hummed idly to himself, *"a diabla zabili rzyda."*

It was the barber's tune. "When the thunder kills a devil." He hummed it without remembering where he had heard it.

Why hang around a crumby relief station, with a mob of crumby greenhorns, for a fifty-five a month pick-and-shovel job, when you could get by never going near the relief, beating some sprout at rotation in back of the widow's for a quarter a game or pitching softball on Saturday afternoons for a dollar a man or league ball on Sundays; or by picking up a half dollar off Mama Tomek for bringing her a couple customers?

Once Mama Tomek had given him a horse called Lonely Road, when he'd had no money to play a horse himself. So he'd given it, in turn, to the ticket taker at the Little Pulaski, who was the wife of the owner of the show. She had played ten across the board, the horse had won in a photograph finish, and Bruno had been awarded ten dollars for his advice.

When that was gone he had stopped by the poolroom and shot a free game with Steffi while her mother was upstairs and then had asked the girl to loan him a dollar.

"Ask your old lady to borrow you out a buck," he had suggested.

"She'll want to know what for."

"Tell her it's for a special intention."

"But she knows I done five 'Our Fathers' 'n five 'Hail Marys' Sunday toward it, so she'll think I really been up to something since if I need a buck so soon afters—she won't let me out of the house all week if I give her that one."

"Don't tell her nothin' then. Just hook it."

"I wouldn't steal from Ma. You shouldn't ask me. I don't earn nothin' for her. Least I could do is not steal off her."

"You'll pay it back. It's just borrowin'. I'll borrow it back to you before she misses it."

"What's the matter with your own old lady? Borrow off her."

"She'd miss it sooner 'n yours. Don't you trust me?"

"Where would you get it to pay back, Bunny?"

"Never mind where. I'd just get it."

"Stealin'?"

"I said I'd get it, didn't I?"

"You always say that, 'n you never have a dime."

"I had a ten-spot last Saturday."

"That's why I didn't see you till it was spent."

"Forget I even said anything." He had thrown his cue across the table and turned away: she saw him going, his cap too far back on his head and his shoulders like a wall.

"Bunny!"

He had turned toward her, in the doorway, waiting; she had seen there was no use moving toward him. She had gone to the cash register instead.

"I'll make that up to her, too," he resolved now. "I'll take her to community singin' on double-feature night. She's a *good* girl."

But what could you do with a good girl once she was yours? You couldn't keep on just sleeping around, above a poolroom or on the beach or in a corner as though she were some Clark Street tramp. If you did you'd make a Clark Street tramp out of her. He decided fiercely that no one else was going to sleep with her ever; as though others, unseen, were already challenging his exclusive right to any girl.

"I'll make it *all* up. I'll take her on the *Bluestreak*."

But he remained troubled. She had put trust in him, who had no trust in himself. He felt irritated with her for that; a girl ought not to trust anyone these days. Why should she trust him any more than he trusted the barber, he wondered as he walked. How could you trust the barber, who was nobody's friend, when you couldn't trust Benkowski, who was anybody's friend? You couldn't trust the barber because he kept Mama T. running a fourth-rate house by the Northwestern tracks, because he never took chances and yet would buy anything, from a bicycle to a radio, if it wasn't too hot. And he always knew, somehow, what was hot and what had cooled off. He knew the right people, he knew too much. And you couldn't trust a Benkowski because he didn't have anything. You couldn't trust the ones with brains, because they had them, and you couldn't trust the ones without, because they didn't.

"All the hoods on *Div*ision got guts," Benkowski had once told him—"but they got no brains to go with them. If they had the brains they wouldn't be hoods, they'd be like Bonifacy. How many guys, beside me, you think got brains in the whole Triangle, Left'?" Benkowski had asked.

Bruno considered the answer now: the alderman had brains, the democratic committeeman had brains, One-Eye Tenczara at Potomac Street had brains. Even the precinct captain, Figura, had some brains. And the barber had brains or he wouldn't be getting twenty cents off every two dollars that Mama Tomek's women earned. But that was all. That covered the ward. That's all the brains there were between Chicago Avenue and *Div*ision Street. That took care of all the penny matchers, all the jackpot sneaks, all the buck priests, the Gallaghers just off the boat, the bartenders and all the spooks on W.P.A. That took care of the widow and her half-wit kid Udo and that good-looking little Steffi R. That took care of Bruno Bicek's old lady for living her life behind Bicek's Imperial Half-Price Bakery. It took care of Finger Idzikowski for training to be a hex-man by pointing at fellows from the Polish Wonders to make them lose their next game. It took care of Fireball Kodadek for practicing a spitball the year round, with a dime-store rocket against a warehouse wall, when spitballing hadn't been allowed in the majors since the Dodgers had released

Burleigh Grimes. That took care of Bibleback for thinking he was going to make a living for the whole year by peddling tomatoes during the summer, when he didn't have either a wagon or a license. It took care of Knothole Chmura from the Viaduct for trying to stay off relief by selling song sheets in front of Goldblatt's with one knee knocked a little against the other to give the impression he was lame without making it look too lame—in case a citizen dress man from the Potomac Street station was on the prowl for an arrest.

It had taken good care of Dumb Kunka and Poor Andy Bogats, the night Kunka had shot the cop. Bruno remembered Andy lying alone in the front room of his mother's house the night after he and Kunka had burned: the yellow all-night flares of the vigil lights and the hoarse sounds of the drinking in the kitchen. Andy's forehead and nose were burned a rust-yellow and the cheeks were sunken, as though he had taken it too hard, and there were great dark pouches under his eyes. Bruno had remembered him as a grinning, high-spirited, round-cheeked eighteen-year-old. The man in the casket had looked forty-five.

The single-car local to Humboldt Park slowed up overhead and clattered lamely west; to the boy's ears the clatter became a crescendo of applause. He jabbed with his right and threw the left—that's the hand they were cheering. A right to the heart and a left to the jaw. He bobbed, ducked, covered, swung and straightened up: the applause was faint and far away and then it was gone. He shoved his hands down his pockets and shuffled on.

There was only the dumb September dark about him and the places where everything looked the same as always and so looked a little like he'd always wanted them to; a fellow didn't get so mad at himself when he was alone like this. This way things didn't seem to matter, as they did at the sidewalk shed when everybody had a pair of dice and nobody had a dime; or when shooting pool with Steffi when the fellows weren't around.

"It's best for a Polack who ain't got much not to think too

much about gettin' more," he philosophized easily. "After all, I got a place to sleep 'n there's still a couple cans on the shelf. I'm settin' pretty you." First thing you know, if a fellow got too big for his shoes, he'd wind up with some Dago judge throwing the book at him. "It's a free country. You always got enough to eat 'n a place 'sleep." He felt pleased with himself for having thought of that; it was always easier to think of such answers in the dark. Then you could feel yourself not caring so much after all, like just before falling asleep to dream you were driving a cream-colored roadster like those the state police drove.

Bruno Bicek from Potomac Street had his own cunning. He'd argue all day, with anyone, about anything, in daylight, and always end up feeling he'd won, that he'd been right all along. He'd refute himself, in daylight, for the mere sake of an argument.

But at night, alone, he refuted no one, denied nothing. He saw himself close up and clearly then, too clear for any argument. As clear, as close up, as the wolf's head in the empty window.

That was the trouble with daylight.

25. JERRE MANGIONE

*Talking American**

Jerre Mangione was born in 1909 in Rochester, New York, and studied at Syracuse University. The Depression compelled him to shift about to a variety of jobs—ditchdigger, usher in a burlesque show, librarian, and magazine staff writer. His first book, autobiographical in character, was widely read, and he ultimately became a member of the faculty of the University of Pennsylvania.

My father could be more severe than my mother, but usually he was gentle with us and even conspired with us occasionally when we tried to avoid some of the household rules my mother laid down. Probably the most repugnant rule of all was that we eat everything she cooked for us, regardless of whether or not we liked the food or were hungry.

Unless my father protested, she persistently fed us *verdura*, in the interests of health, usually dandelion or escarole or some other bitter member of the vegetable family. The more we complained about such dishes the more convinced she became that they were good for us. She was without mercy about such things. If one of us dared protest while we were at the table, she would inflict a second helping on him. In time, we learned the wisdom of pretending to look fairly enthusiastic about everything she cooked for us, regardless of how distasteful it seemed.

Another unpopular rule she vigorously enforced was that we speak no other language at home but that of our parents. Outside the house she expected us to speak English, and often

* Jerre Mangione, *Mount Allegro* (Boston, 1943), pp. 51–69.

took pride in the fact that we spoke English so well that almost none of our relatives could understand it. Any English we spoke at home, however, was either by accident or on the sly. My sister Maria, who often talked in her sleep, conducted her monologues in English, but my mother forgave her on the ground that she could not be responsible for her subconscious thoughts.

My mother's insistence that we speak only Italian at home drew a sharp line between our existence there and our life in the world outside. We gradually acquired the notion that we were Italian at home and American (whatever that was) elsewhere. Instinctively, we all sensed the necessity of adapting ourselves to two different worlds. We began to notice that there were several marked differences between those worlds, differences that made Americans and my relatives each think of the other as foreigners.

The difference that pained me most was that of language, probably because I was aware of it most often. Child that I was, I would feel terribly embarrassed whenever my mother called to me in Italian while I was playing on the street, with all my playmates there to listen; or when she was buying clothes for me and would wrangle in broken English with the salesmen about the price.

My mother took no notice of such childish snobbery. As long as I remained under her jurisdiction, she continued to cling to her policy of restricting the family language to Italian. 'I might as well not have my children if I can't talk with them,' she argued. She considered it sinful for relatives to permit their children to speak a language which the entire family could not speak fluently, and claimed that if she were to cast aside Italian, the language of her forefathers, it would be like renouncing her own flesh and blood.

There was only one possible retort to these arguments but no one dared use it: the language we called Italian and spoke at home was not Italian. It was a Sicilian dialect which only Sicilians could understand. I seldom heard proper Italian spoken, except when my Uncle Nino made speeches or when one of my relatives would meet an Italian or another Sicilian for the first time. Proper Italian sounded like the melody of church bells and it was fresh and delicate compared to the earthy sounds of the dialect we spoke. Yet it was hard to understand how two persons could carry on an honest conversation in a language so fancy.

My Uncle Nino claimed that Italian was 'feminine' and Sicilian 'masculine.' He also said that the only reason Sicilians ever addressed each other in proper Italian was to show off their schooling and prove to each other that they were not peasants. He probably was right, for I noticed that the ostentation of speaking proper Italian was dropped as soon as two Sicilians had known each other for an evening and showed any desire to be friends. Anyone who persisted in speaking Italian after that was considered a prig or, at least, a socialist.

But if my relatives were under the impression that they were speaking the same dialect they brought with them from Sicily, they were mistaken. After a few years of hearing American, Yiddish, Polish, and Italian dialects other than their own, their language gathered words which no one in Sicily could possibly understand. The most amazing of these were garbled American words dressed up with Sicilian suffixes—strange concoctions which, in later years, that non-Sicilian pundit, H. L. Mencken, was to include in his book, *The American Language.*

Mr. Mencken's collection of Italian-American words is a good indication of what happened to the vocabulary of my relatives. Such words as *minuto* for minute, *ponte* for pound, *storo* for store, *barra* for bar, *giobba* for job were constantly used as Sicilian words.

One word that Mr. Mencken should include in the next edition of his book is *baccauso,* which has been in my relatives' vocabulary as far back as I can remember. My parents probably picked it up from other American Sicilians when they first arrived in Rochester. Certainly, the word had no relation to their current mode of city life. It was used when referring to 'toilet' and was obviously derived from the American 'backhouse' that flourished in earlier and more rural America. Not until a few years ago when I first visited Italy, a nation without backhouses, and mystified Sicilians there by using the word, did I become aware of its Chic Sale derivation. Yet I had been using *baccauso* for a lifetime, always under the impression it was an authentic Sicilian word.

While the gradual effect of such bastard words was to break down the differences between the dialects my relatives spoke, there were enough differences of accent and vocabulary left to lend the various dialects their own peculiarities. Usually, the more distant the relative the greater was the difference between the dialect he spoke and the one we used at home. The relatives who came from towns on the sea (like my father) still talked as though they were hurling words against the wind or through the fog, in a piercing singing accent. Those from towns far inland talked as though they had never heard gay music, and their speech was heavy with mournful and burly sounds.

I gathered that every Italian town left its individual stamp on the language of its people. My Uncle Luigi liked to tell the story of the American priest who spoke perfect schoolroom Italian. When he went to Italy for the first time, the priest decided that the best way of seeing the country and meeting its people was to travel the whole length of the nation, listening to confessions as he went from town to town. He got along famously in northern Italy. Although he found the confessions rather dull, he had no trouble understanding the sins described to him.

Below Rome he began to have difficulties. The confessions were more interesting but the dialects he heard were harder to understand, and on several occasions, he suspected that the penance he imposed on sinners was entirely out of proportion to the sins they had committed. 'It must have been very annoying when he got to Naples,' my uncle said, 'for Neapolitans are some of the most fascinating sinners in the world.'

When the priest reached Sicily, he was at a complete loss. He could not understand a word of the dialects he heard and was obliged to conduct all his confessions in sign language.

When anyone who had not heard the story was gullible

enough to ask Uncle Luigi how that was possible, he would gleefully grab the opportunity to show off his histrionic talents and act out a sin or two in pantomime. Invariably, of course, they were sins of the flesh.

There was never any effort made to keep any Sicilian words secret from us, no matter how heretical or bawdy. Yet my parents would be shocked whenever we repeated a word they did not consider proper. Once I horrified my parents with a word which my father often used in his speech. The experience taught me to regard every Sicilian idiom thereafter with a wary eye.

One evening my Aunt Giovanna gave a party for some of the women who worked with her at the tailor factory. She invited my family but, since my parents were expecting visitors that evening, they begged off and sent me, the oldest son, to represent them. Like so many women gathered together away from their husbands, my aunt's guests were inclined to be boisterous.

I was the only male present, but I was only eleven years old and did not inhibit them at all. They were all very attentive to me. My aunt let me drink a glass of wine, and when no one was looking, the buxom woman sitting next to me gave me more. After dinner, I pumped the player-piano while the women danced the schottische and the polka. By the time I was ready to leave, I felt quite stimulated by the gaiety of the evening.

I came into the house, my face radiant with the wine and the crisp wintry air. After introducing me to the guests, my mother asked about her sister's health.

'Aunt Giovanna is fine,' I said. 'Her *risotto* was good–and I had wine and nuts,' I rattled on enthusiastically.

'Did you drink much of the wine?' my father asked with a sly smile.

I avoided the question. 'There were lots of people there and I played the piano for them.' Without stopping to catch my breath I continued, 'The ladies danced and made a lot of noise and it all sounded like a *bordello*.'

My father's face suddenly went grim. My mother gasped,

and one of the visitors giggled. My father said: 'Hold your tongue and go to bed at once. You've said enough.'

'But Papa,' I protested, 'it did sound like a *bordello*.'

'Stop using that word!' he thundered. 'Go to bed!'

I went upstairs and brooded. *Bordello* was a word I often heard my father use when he complained about noise. Why should he object to my using it? Downstairs I heard the visitors departing; one of them was telling my mother that boys will be boys and not to worry about me. There was an ominous silence after they left. I heard my mother puttering around the kitchen, and my father angrily creaking his rocking-chair.

It was all too much for me. I decided that I had probably committed some hideous and mysterious crime. My father had once told me the legend of a man who could destroy the world by uttering a single word, secret to everyone but himself. As I cried myself to sleep, I was sure that *bordello* was the word.

The next morning my mother said: 'You used a bad word last night. It is a word that only grownups are allowed to use.'

'But Papa uses it all the time.'

'Yes, but he's a grownup, my little squash.'

'What does the word mean?'

'The word wouldn't have any meaning for you now. I'll tell you when you get older. Now hurry to school or you'll be late.'

My mother would never explain adult words to me, though she saw no harm in exposing me to them. Her theory seemed to be that if her children went to church regularly, they would surely develop an instinct that would teach them to tell the difference between good and bad. So far as vocabulary was concerned, the theory worked out pretty well. I had a secret vocabulary of dozens of words I would never dare use at home, even though I had heard many of them there originally. Most of them were terrifying curses involving God, the Virgin Mary, and various kinds of barnyard animals. They frightened me, so much so that I used them only when it seemed necessary to impress new playmates with my bravery.

Even my father felt inhibited by my mother's determination to keep English out of the house, and would only speak the language when it was absolutely necessary or when my mother was not present. My father's English was like no one else's in the world. Yet it could be understood more easily than the English spoken by most of my Sicilian relatives. All that he knew of the language he managed to pick up during his first six months in America. His first factory *bosso*, a noisy Irishman, provided the incentive. My father wanted to learn enough English so that he could talk back to him. He was most successful; the boss fired him the first time he understood what he was saying.

So elated was my father with the amount of English he absorbed in a half-year that he stopped learning the language then and there and never made any further conscious effort to add to his vocabulary or improve his grammar. But he made the most of what he knew, and in a few years had developed a system of speaking English which defied all philological laws but could be understood by most Americans after about five minutes of orientation. Probably the most astonishing aspect of his system was that he used only one pronoun—'she'—and only one tense—the present.

The little English my mother knew she acquired from my father. But she spoke the language without any system, groping for nearly all the words she used, without any of my father's wonderful sureness. Although she had been in America as long as he, she had never had daily contact with persons who spoke only English. The tailor factories, where she worked when she arrived, were nearly all filled with men and women who had recently come from Italy and spoke only their native tongue.

The stores where she did her shopping every day were operated by Italians whose customers were all Italians. The Poles and the Jews who made up a large part of Mount Allegro stuck to their native languages most of the time. My mother had little to do with them. She exchanged greetings with all of them, but you did not need to know much English to keep on friendly terms with a neighbor. A smile or an occasional gift of cooked spaghetti served the purpose just as effectively.

My Uncle Luigi, more than any other of my relatives, had to depend on his smiles and charms to maintain good relations with Americans. His English was so rudimentary that it could be understood only by Sicilians. In view of his burning ambition to marry a slim widow with a fat bank account, his scant knowledge of the language proved something of a handicap. Most of the Italian widows he knew were fat and had very slim bank accounts. The few widows he met who qualified did not know a word of Italian.

It is possible that had he been able to speak English with any fluency, he might have married one of them, for he was six feet tall, and handsome in a gaunt and silvery way. He had been a widower for such a long time that his eyes had begun to dance again like those of a young bachelor. Yet despite all this and his most earnest efforts, he found that his sign language and his eye-rolling were not sufficient to establish communication with a rich widow's heart.

There was the time he fell in love with an Australian-born widow who lived on a five-hundred-acre farm on the outskirts of town and was said to own seven cows. People claimed she had so much money that every few years she imported a kangaroo from Australia and donated it to the city zoo. My uncle flirted with her in church for a month before she gave him a tumble. After that, she did most of the flirting and he decided it was time to carry matters a step further.

One evening he cornered me alone. 'My nephew,' he said gravely, 'I want you to do me a brotherly favor. I will pay you well for it. Do you think you could write a passionate love letter for me?'

At the mention of pay I became thoroughly interested and assured him I could write such a letter, if he told me what he wanted to say.

He became a little impatient. 'You, a young man with eleven years of life behind you, at least six of which have been squandered watching countless movies, have the gall to tell me that you don't know what to say in a love letter? Very well, I shall describe what I want said.' He paused to take a pinch of snuff.

'Her name is Belle. After I marry her I shall call her Bella. Tell Belle I love her, of course. It might be a good idea to repeat that in the letter a few times. Tell her, too, that I like the country and fresh vegetables and have a great fondness for cows—I detest milk, but don't mention that. You might reminisce a bit—women like nostalgic men—and let her know that I used to milk goats in my youth and probably would have no difficulty at all with cows. Have I made myself clear?'

I wrote the letter and promptly received my first fee as a ghost writer, twenty-five cents. But Uncle Luigi never received a reply to the letter, and when he saw the Australian widow at church the following Sunday she turned crimson and lifted her nose as high as it would go.

'What in God's name did you say in that letter, squash head?' he asked. 'Why, I could almost see the froth gathering at her lips when she caught sight of me!'

I mumbled that I had only written what he had asked me to. It was not until a few years later, when I was more qualified to think of the opposite sex as such, that I realized you could not woo a lady effectively by devoting most of your first letter to a discourse on your passion for milking cows.

Uncle Luigi was not discouraged. Within a short time he was campaigning for the heart and bank account of another widow. This one lived in Pennsylvania. For once she happened to be an Italian, an immigrant from Calabria, so that he was able to do his own letter-writing for a change. The correspondence progressed pretty well at first. They immediately struck a topic of mutual interest: their disapproval of their children. Each letter would be given to a thorough and heartless analysis of the faults of one of the children.

In their eagerness to show each other that they saw eye to eye, each one tried to outdo the other in stripping the children clean of any virtues they might have. They both had several sons and daughters, and the correspondence would probably have continued in this morbid vein indefinitely if my Uncle Nino had not stepped in with a piece of advice.

'You will never get anywhere that way,' he told Uncle Luigi. 'You must say more about love and less about your children. Children are the bane of all romance.'

Uncle Luigi, who had great respect for Uncle Nino's opinions on such matters, tried to follow his advice. The main difficulty with that was that the widow was well educated and he was not. This became more and more apparent as the correspondence grew more intimate. Uncle Luigi hesitated to mail her his crudely expressed declarations of love and had to consult frequently with Uncle Nino, who claimed to know more about love than Boccaccio. Uncle Nino would edit each letter, improving the phraseology considerably and adding two or three flowery paragraphs of his own, all of which Uncle Luigi laboriously copied.

The amorous sentiments of my Uncle Nino raised the correspondence to new romantic heights. One letter to which he contributed heavily had such a pronounced effect on the widow that she replied to it with a five-page poem. My Uncle Luigi was so enormously pleased with what he considered his own success that he gave readings of the poem whenever he found an audience.

But when the widow began to write all her letters in poetry, he became plainly disgusted. The correspondence was rapidly getting out of hand. Except for his handwriting and the postage, he was able to contribute nothing to it, for he was incapable of writing a couplet, let alone a letterful of rhymes, and was obliged to depend entirely on my Uncle Nino. When he threatened to go back to prose, my Uncle Nino pointed out that when a lady takes the trouble to address you in poetry, she expects to be answered in kind.

Uncle Luigi's only consolation was that up till that point he had managed to conceal the address of the widow from my Uncle Nino. 'You never can tell,' he confided in my father. 'Nino is an honorable man, but he might take it into his head to start a correspondence with her on his own. After all, he knows as well as I do that, in addition to being palatable, she is heavily insured and has a nice steady income. Frankly, I'm getting tired of this whole letter-writing business. Fancy phrases get you nowhere if they are not followed up with action. I must pay the lady a visit soon.'

But before he could save enough money for the train fare, he made the mistake of quarreling violently with Uncle Nino about the merits of their respective home towns. Uncle Nino, feeling bested, got back at him by refusing to write any more poems for him.

Uncle Luigi tried valiantly to maintain something of the poetic quality of the correspondence, but his literary style was too primitive and quite inappropriate for anything but the bluntest declarations. Having become a devout admirer of Uncle Nino's luxuriant phrases, the widow was repulsed by Uncle Luigi's sudden lack of literary grace and insisted on interpreting his bad grammar and crude sentences as signs of growing indifference.

The more my Uncle Luigi protested, the more ungrammatical he became. Finally, she could no longer tolerate the crudeness of his letters and gave up writing to him altogether.

In spite of his superior intellect, Uncle Nino never learned much English—chiefly because of an old grudge he bore against his wife. Whenever he quarreled with her he would shout that he had never intended to come to America in the first place and only did so because she so 'blinded' him that he could not distinguish between love and common sense. Even when he was not quarreling with her, you would have surmised from hearing him talk that he was through with America and was returning to Sicily the very next day.

Since he had ranted in much the same way for nearly twenty years, none of his relatives, least of all his wife, took him seriously. Yet the fact remained that during all that time Uncle Nino considered himself little more than a transient who would some day persuade his wife that it would be far more comfortable to return to Sicily and live on the fat of the land he owned there than to exist in a callow city like Rochester and slave all week for a few strands of spaghetti.

His arguments did not impress his wife, possibly because it was she and not he who slaved all week. My Aunt Giovanna sewed buttonholes in a tailor factory, while he ran a small jewelry trade from his living-room, an occupation that left him with considerable time and energy to play briscola and threaten to leave America.

It was quite true that if he had not met my Aunt Giovanna, he probably would never have set foot outside of Sicily. As a young man he was managing a prosperous importing business in Palermo—so prosperous, my mother said, that he could bribe judges to change their decisions. And then my Aunt Giovanna came along. She was in the throes of conspiring to secure admission into the United States after having failed twice before. Both times her application had been rejected in the belief that she had trachoma, the eye disease that was often contracted by Sicilians living in towns where the water was bad.

On her first attempt to get to America she actually got as far as Ellis Island. But American officials seemed less susceptible to her beauty than the Italian officials who had gallantly helped to smuggle her through the red tape in Palermo. Ellis Island was little more than a prison in those days. For eight days she spent her time looking through iron bars at the Statue of Liberty and the New York skyline, and weeping.

Every morning an Irish policewoman who spoke Italian tried to make her tell how she had got on the boat without a passport. But my aunt never told. Finally the immigration officials realized they were wasting their time and shipped Aunt Giovanna back to Palermo.

When my Uncle Nino proposed three days after he met her, she consented, but only on condition that he take her to America. He gave up his thriving business, married her, and took her on a honeymoon to France, where they thought she would stand a better chance of getting a passport. At Havre she was again turned down. Uncle Nino got his passport without any trouble, but he saw little point in leaving his bride behind to go to a country that did not particularly attract him.

My Aunt Giovanna was never lacking in stubbornness. Against his better judgment, she persuaded him to sail alone, arguing that once he was in the United States it would be a simple matter for him to make arrangements to send for her. Was she not his wife? Surely, American officials could not be so heartless as to permit red tape to separate newlyweds. Uncle Nino loved his wife too much to argue with her.

Her reasoning proved to be faulty. Uncle Nino's presence in the United States did not stir up any sentiments American officials might have for young newlyweds. He spent a miserable year in New York filling out endless forms, pining for his bride, and cursing the moment he had given in to her arguments. He was about to return to Europe and take her back to Sicily, when word came that Aunt Giovanna had been able to persuade the French immigration officials that there was nothing wrong with her eyes that a less tearful existence could not remedy.

He had never forgiven her for those lonely months he spent in New York waiting for her. And after twenty years of America he was still angry with her for having wrenched him away from a successful career to a makeshift existence in a strange land where he had to depend largely on his wife's earnings.

If it had not been for this old grudge, Uncle Nino might have mastered English.

'He who knows the English language will go forward,' he was fond of saying. But he himself made not the slightest effort to learn it. 'Why should I try to master a language as difficult as English? By the time I learned to speak it properly, it would be time for me to die. If your demands are as simple as mine, it is not hard to get whatever you want without knowing the language.'

He liked to illustrate this point with a story he heard about the first Italians who came to Rochester.

'In the early days Italians were disliked far more than they are now,' he said. 'They could not speak a word of English; at least I can fool an American into believing that I know what he is talking about, but they didn't even know enough English to do that. Nor did they get much chance to associate with Americans.

'The men were good strong workers but the Americans regarded them as bandits and intruders, and their employers treated them as though they were nothing but workhorses. They all forgot that they had been foreigners once too, and they made life as miserable as possible for them.

'Although the Italians had money, the storekeepers would not sell them food and the landlords would not rent them homes. For many weeks they were forced to live in boxes and tents and depend on *cicoria* for their main food. Now, *cicoria* is one the most nutritious foods God planted in this earth, but even *cicoria* can become boring as a steady diet.

'The men had tried praying to God, begging Him to remind the Americans that they were *Cristiani* like themselves. But that didn't help. They became desperate. What was the use of earning money if you could not buy the things you needed most? One afternoon they armed themselves with pickaxes and marched into one of the largest grocery stores in town. While they stood by with their pickaxes poised over their heads, their leader addressed himself to the chief clerk.

'The leader did not know a word of English. He made motions with his hands and his mouth to show that they were all very hungry. He also made it clear that unless the men were allowed to purchase food, they would tear up the store with their pickaxes. The clerk was a very understanding fellow and sold them all the food they wanted.

'Their success went to their heads. Now that they could buy food, they began to wish for real houses to eat it in. Even then Rochester was a miserably damp and rainy town, and a tent or a box was no way to keep snug. Once more the men got out their pickaxes and called on the grocery clerk. Again the clerk had no difficulty making out what they wanted. He begged them to calm down and indicated that he would try to help them.

'A few minutes later the police arrived. The clerk told them what the Italians wanted. The police told the Town Council, and the authorities told the landlords. In a few days the men were moved from their tents and shanties into real homes. These same Italians now have children who are some of the leading doctors, lawyers, and druggists in town. There's no doubt about it: you have to ask for whatever you want in this world, and prayer isn't always the way to ask.'

26. PETER DE VRIES

*Without Those Consolations Called Religious**

Peter De Vries was born in 1910, the son of Dutch immigrants who had settled in a tightly knit Calvinist community in Chicago's South Side. He studied in a high school of the Reformed Church and in Calvin College, Grand Rapids, Michigan—both institutions that sustained ethnic piety. A succession of jobs on newspapers and in radio led to a position as associate editor of Poetry *magazine in 1939 and finally to* The New Yorker *where he developed a biting ironic humor. Most of his writing touched on the foibles of suburban life, but the selection that follows is drawn from a novel in which the protagonist, having lost his ancestral faith, faces the tragic death of his only child.*

So we were back in the Children's Pavilion, and there was again the familiar scene: the mothers with their nearly dead, the false face of mercy, the Slaughter of the Innocents. A girl with one leg came unsteadily down the hall between crutches, skillfully encouraged by nurses. Through the pane in a closed door a boy could be seen sitting up in bed, bleeding from everything in his head; a priest lounged alertly against the wall, ready to move in closer. In the next room a boy of five was having Methotrexate pumped into his skull, or, more accurately, was watching a group of mechanics gathered solemnly around the stalled machine. In the next a baby was sitting up watching a television set on which a panel show was in progress. Three experts were discussing the state of the contemporary theater. I paused in the doorway to listen. "I think

* Peter De Vries, *The Blood of the Lamb* (Boston, 1961), pp. 205–14, 231–41.

writers like Tennessee Williams exaggerate the ugly side of life, the seamy side, it seems to me," observed a well-dressed female participant. "I fail to see what purpose is gained by that." A mother keeping watch at the next crib rose from her chair and turned the dial. There was a squawk of protest from the baby, who was evidently fascinated by the speaker's hat or the tone of her voice, or something else about the program, and the woman quickly tuned it back, making a comic face at me.

Among the parents and children, flung together in a hell of prolonged farewell, wandered forever the ministering vampires from Laboratory, sucking samples from bones and veins to see how went with each the enemy that had marked them all. And the doctors in their butchers' coats, who severed the limbs and gouged the brains and knifed the vitals where the demon variously dwelt, what did they think of these best fruits of ten million hours of dedicated toil? They hounded the culprit from organ to organ and joint to joint till nothing remained over which to practice their art: the art of prolonging sickness. Yet medicine had its own old aphorism: "Life is a fatal disease."

I rejoined in time the endless promenade of visitors pushing their treasures in wheel chairs. Among these was a beatnik adolescent trundling his younger sister. They were both very gay; one knew from their manner that she was going home soon. The youth was dressed in jeans and a black sweater. The beard was no doubt intended to be Bohemian but recalled, instead, the traditional figure of the hayseed. The pleasant spirit given off by their companionship made us join them, wheeling along side by side, up and down, back and forth, until some countertraffic forced us to break ranks. In one of these oncoming chairs was black-eyed Rachel Stein, propelled by her mother. The two girls instantly renewed the friendship begun the first time in, and it was obvious that they preferred now to be left together in the recreation room, where in any case a birthday party for another patient was in full swing. Mrs. Stein excused herself to dart after a disappearing doctor, and I looked around for Stein. As I neared the main lounge I heard voices raised in argument.

"These people who want to tell God how to run the universe," a man with a brick-red neck was saying, "they remind me of those people with five shares in some corporation who take up the entire stockholders' meeting telling the directors how to run their business."

I might have guessed who the object of the dressing down would be. Stein stood cornered behind the telephone booth, a carton of coffee in one hand and a smile on his face, obviously enjoying himself enormously. This was what he liked, proof of idiocy among the Positive Thinkers.

"I suppose you're going to tell me next I never met a payroll," he said, throwing me only the faintest sign of greeting so as not to interrupt the debate. Several visitors, mostly parents in various stages of vigil and dishevelment, listened or chimed in.

"You ought to be ashamed," a woman in an Easter bonnet told Stein. "Your race gave us our religion. It's a good thing the ancient prophets weren't like you or we wouldn't have any." Stein drank from his carton and waited; she had not yet delivered herself into his hands. "From ancient polytheism, the belief in lots of gods," the woman continued a little more eruditely, "the Hebrew nation led us on to the idea that there is only one."

"Which is just a step from the truth," said Stein, and dropped his carton into a wastebasket.

The woman began to show anger, squirming a bit on her leather chair. "We with our finite . . ."

"What baffles me is the comfort people find in the idea that somebody dealt with this mess. Blind and meaningless chance seems to me so much more congenial—or at least less horrible. Prove to me that there is a God and I will really begin to despair."

"It comes down to submitting to a wisdom greater than ours," said the man who had been attempting to focus the problem in terms of a stockholders' meeting. "A plan of which we can no more grasp the whole than a leaf can the forest of which it is a rustling part, or a grain of sand the seashore. What do you think when you look up at the stars at night?"

"I don't. I have enough to occupy me here."

"The Lord giveth and the Lord taketh away. What do you think of that?"

"I think it's a hell of a way to run a railroad."

"You ought to be ashamed!" the woman repeated with a further rise in spirit, not noticing a four-year-old patient watching the argument from a tricycle in the doorway. "Have you ever read your Bible?"

I nearly laughed. Where did she think he had got his pessimism? On what had he nurtured his despair if not on "Vanity of vanities," "All flesh is grass," "My tears have been my meat day and night," and "Is there no balm in Gilead; is there no physician there?"

Stein left his persecutors to join me in the hall, sending little Johnny Heard off on his tricycle with a pat on the head. We stood a moment comparing notes. Rachel was in for the very same thing as Carol, after all these months of solid remission on Methotrexate and the 6-MP still to go. We sought out the girls in the recreation room, where they were getting on beautifully together. They didn't want any part of us. "How about a drink?" Stein proposed.

In my present need Stein might seem the last company I ought to seek. Yet in another sense he was precisely what I wanted at my side, the Devil's advocate off whom to bounce my speculations, the rock against which to hurl my yearnings and my thoughts, to test and prove them truly, an office that mealy-mouthed piety could not have performed. He was the goalkeeper past whom I must get my puck.

"There is so much we don't know," I said as, walking down the street, we resumed the debate where we had left off last time. "Newton knew it, who told us so much we do know. We play like children on the shore—out there is the measureless sea. How do you explain—well, a thing like what happened on the road to Damascus?"

"Do I have to explain every case of hysterical blindness?

How do we know it happened, anyway? It's related only in the Acts, which Luke wrote. Paul himself never mentions it, and him a man who talked about himself at the drop of a hat."

"He said Christ was revealed to him, as to a child born untimely. That may be what he's referring to. I think it's in Corinthians. And there's the incident of the viper and the fire."

"I'm told Orientals walk barefoot across hot coals with no ill effects."

"So such things happen." Something made me look up. I saw, her arms spread along the parapet of the second-story roof from which the mice were visible, the woman with the Easter bonnet, gazing up into the dirty spring evening. "Do you believe any of the miracles attributed to Christ?" I said quickly, perhaps because I had looked just in time to see her brush her eye, under the cheap pink veil.

Stein gave his snort, this time somewhat more finely shaded than usual. He jerked his head back toward the hospital. "Who do you expect to see take up his bed and walk in there?"

As we strolled along, for all the world like friends out taking the evening air rather than two men wringing each other's hearts like empty dishrags, we encountered a phenomenon that under the circumstances could hardly be ignored. A street-corner evangelist was hurling plangent metaphors rapidly into space.

"Would you like to call Heaven tonight? You can reverse the charges, you know. Oh, yes, brother, reverse the charges." He swung from his audience, a girl with a jump rope and a Chinese laundryman pausing in the gutter with his pushcart to eat a candy bar, toward us as we approached. "Oh, yes, brother, reverse the charges. *He'll* accept them. He's paid for your call with the ultimate price—His Son Jesus Christ! It's all paid for, all on the house, all for free! Just pick up the phone and tell the operator—that's the Holy Ghost, you know—'Get me Heaven, please. Put me through to God Almighty!'"

We shuffled on in silence. Stein had the grace not to smile at the ally I had picked up along the way. I observed after a moment:

"Someone has pointed out that nothing proves the validity of the Church so much as its ability to survive its own representatives. It's got to be divine to stand up against them."

"I have never been convinced by that argument—it's from one of the witty Catholics, isn't it? You might as well say it about the Ku Klux Klan."

"That's no analogy. In that case the members are no worse than the principles. In this, the principle is always supremely there for us to match up to or fall short of."

Stein shrugged and gave a grunt. I felt I had gotten past the goalkeeper and scored a point. We were passing a pushcart vendor selling sprigs of dogwood. I had brought plenty of that from the country this morning. I asked Stein, after another silence, whether he had ever heard the legend that the Cross had been made of dogwood and that supposedly explained the cross shaped vaguely into the grain of its heartwood, like that on the back of the Sardinian donkey for its having borne Our Lord into Jerusalem on his triumphal day. Stein said that he had never heard either of those things.

In the bar, I chided Stein for what he had said to the woman in the Easter hat, on the ground that Westminster Hospital was no place to pull rugs out from under mothers. He agreed, with the assurance that he never did that to mothers, or even to men unless they could take it, but informed me that the woman in this case was not the mother but an aunt—the mother was on another floor in the same hospital, having a malignancy edited from her foot. This brought Stein perilously close to his role of clown, and I could feel my shoulders threaten to shake in preparation for the only response possible to this eager trowel work with the Absurd. It didn't take much.

"Was the man who talked about stockholders' meetings the father?"

"No," said Stein, as though he had been waiting for me to ask that question, "the father is in a mental institution."

Stein watched me until my sobs of laughter had subsided, smiling uneasily as I gasped, "Have you no heart, man?" and brushing cigarette ashes from his horrible green sleeve.

Wiping my eyes, I asked whether he didn't think even aunts deserved to have their belief that those who mourned would be comforted, safeguarded from the scourge of intellect. Here I sensed a quiver of indignation as he launched a review of the Beatitudes aimed at finding one—"just one"—that held water when examined squarely in the light of reality. The poor in spirit would have to imagine for themselves any kingdom of heaven, as the pure in heart would any God for themselves; the merciful obtained no more mercy than the cruel; the meek would have to inherit anything they ever got, and so on. There was, however, one Beatitude with which one need not quarrel —could I guess which it was? It was not one of the official nine, having been delivered separately on the road to Calvary. I gave up. " 'Blessed are the wombs that never bare, and the paps that never gave suck,' " Stein said. "Could this be the Son of Man preparing himself for those final words against the black sky, the last, cosmic turn of the wheel of agony, the hoax at last seen through: 'My God, my God, why hast thou forsaken me?' "

"You mean you're not *sure*? Why, man, that's great! For the rest of us, who like to hug that little doubt we so desperately need today—what faith was to folk of another time—the ray of hope. Oh, how grateful we are for that uncertainty! Our salvation almost. Go thy way, thy doubt hath made thee whole. Bartender, two more!"

My spirits began to rise—genuinely, not in another spasm of unstable mirth. From nowhere, I had suddenly that conviction that we would beat the rap, that Carol and Rachel would be among those who were around when the Drug came. *Some* would; why not they? My mood continued to ascend. The wall-motto moralists quite rightly call bottom the place from which there is nowhere to go but up, the floor against which the swimmer kicks himself lightly toward the surface once again.

As we left the tavern, I remarked, "Well, we could go on arguing for hours, I suppose. As man has in fact for centuries about these things. There's as much to be said for one side as for the other. Fifty-fifty."

"Not quite. One charge can be brought against your point of view that can't against mine: wishful thinking. Believers believe what they want to believe. I would like to believe it, too, but deny that an honest man can. Unbelief is to that extent less suspect than faith."

We trudged along a moment longer, during which I debated with myself whether to say what I was thinking. I spoke up.

"One doubts that you don't enjoy thinking or saying what you do, at least a little, Stein. The side of man that loves to hate, to rub in the horrible, even revel in it. Psychiatrists have even got a name for it, I think. Algolagnia, or something like that."

We passed in due course the church of St. Catherine, from which a pair of people were contentedly emerging after their evening devotionals. Here a vibration of anger escaped Stein that was not put into words, but that I felt had given me a flash of illumination into his spirit—something that might even be held to confirm the theory of my friend to which I had been needled into giving audible expression. Stein resented the sedative power of religion, or rather the repose available to those blissfully ignorant that the medicament was a fictitious blank. In this exile from peace of mind to which his reason doomed him, he was like an insomniac driven to awaken sleepers from dreams illegitimately won by going around shouting, "Don't you realize it was a placebo!" Thus it seemed to me that what you were up against in Stein was not logic rampant, but frustrated faith. He could not forgive God for not existing.

When we returned to the Pavilion of Children, Mrs. Stein greeted us in the corridor. "You should see the two of them playing together," she said. "Come look."

We stood in the recreation room doorway. In a pandemonium of television noise, piano music being thumped out by a volunteer as youngsters banged drums and shook tambourines to its rhythm, Rachel and Carol sat side by side at a table, twisting into being paper flowers for children less fortunate. Mrs. Stein had quoted us that bit as we came down the hall with a surprising minimum of rue. "Aren't they just too sweet together?" she beamed in the doorway.

"Lifelong friends," said Stein, who gave, and asked, no quarter. . . .

"The trouble with doubling recipes," said Mrs. Brodhag, "is that some ingredients do a little more than double when you put in twice as much of them. Matter of proportion. Like the fellow says about people being created equal, well, some are more equal than others."

I laughed extendedly at this, watching her complete her handiwork. From the pastry bag she squeezed eight green rosettes around the rim of the cake with meticulous care, then cleaned out the bag thoroughly for the eight red rosettes which were to alternate with them. The field of the frosting was white. Once again she washed out the bag to write, with a blue icing also separately mixed, Carol's name in her flawless Palmer Method. She had been up since dawn.

"See that she gets plenty but the other kids do too," Mrs. Brodhag said as she set the creation in my two hands. "It's not the kind of thing I like to see ice cream glopped on top of, but if that's what they want to do I guess we can't object. And tell her there'll be another ready for her when she comes home, though I don't imagine she has to be told that. Don't lay things on too thick, like I keep telling you."

After parking the car in New York, I picked the boxed cake up carefully from the seat and, pushing the door shut with my knee, carried it down the street. A short distance up ahead I could see Mrs. Morano, the night nurse, turn into the church of St. Catherine for her morning prayers. I shifted the package to one hand in order to open the door. I walked to the front of the church, which had its normal smattering of worshipers. I set the cake down on an empty pew and joined the kneeling figures.

When I rose, Mrs. Morano was standing at the edge of the chancel. We whispered together a moment in greeting as we moved up the aisle.

"You heard about Carol," I said.

"Yes, it's exciting. That's why I'm so sorry about this."

"What?"

"The infection. It's been going through the ward like wildfire. Half of the kids are in oxygen tents."

"Carol?"

She nodded. "They had me phone you this morning, but you'd left. The new drug does depress the white count so terribly, of course, and leave them wide open to infection. It's the old story—you can pick anything up in a hospital."

"Staph?"

"I don't know. They took a blood culture, but it takes a while for the organisms to grow out. They're putting Chloromycetin into her, I think. Maybe you'd better go up."

I hurried into the hospital. One look at Carol and I knew it was time to say good-by. The invading germ, or germs, had not only ravaged her bloodstream by now, but had broken out on her body surface in septicemic discolorations. Her foul enemy had his will of her well at last. One of the blotches covered where they were trying to insert a catheter, and spread down along a thigh. By afternoon it had traveled to the knee, and by the next, gangrened. Dr. Scoville could not have been kinder.

"Someone has ordered another tank of oxygen," he told me that afternoon in the corridor, "but I think you'll agree it won't be necessary. . . . Well, hello there, Randy, you're going home today." Up, up, my head, for the sake of that childhood whom there is none in heaven to love, and none to love on earth so much as you. Up, up! "I've left orders for all the morphine she needs. She'll slip away quietly. She doesn't know us now. It's just as well, because there isn't much in the new drug, if it's any consolation. We have a co-operative study on it, and the remissions are few and brief, and suspect because of the incidence of Meticorten administered with it. We can never be sure it wasn't the Meticorten in this case. It would only have meant another short reprieve—no pardon." He sighed and went his busy way, to the ends of the earth.

I went back into the room. The nurse was taking her blood

pressure. "Almost none at all," she whispered. "It's just as well. Only a matter of hours now at the most." The wig was on a globe of the world on the table. The hands were free of needles now, spread out quietly on the counterpane, with their stigmata to which no more would be added. Her breathing slowed, each breath like a caught sob. But once she smiled a little, and, bending closer, I heard her call something to a comrade on another bicycle. They were flying home from school together, down the hill. "All her dreams are pleasant," the nurse murmured. I was thinking of a line of old poetry. "Death loves a shining mark." Now the flower-stem veins were broken, the flower-stalk of the spine destroyed. But through the troll I saw the fairy still, on her flying wheels, the sun in her hair and in the twinkling spokes. I had seen her practicing the piano in her leotard, there were so many things to do and so little time to do them in. I remembered how little labor the sprite had given her mother, so eager was she to be born, so impatient To Be.

The nurse stepped outside a moment, and I moved quickly from the foot of the bed around to the side, whispering rapidly in our moment alone:

"The Lord bless thee, and keep thee: The Lord make his face shine upon thee, and be gracious unto thee: The Lord lift up his countenance upon thee, and give thee peace."

Then I touched the stigmata one by one: the prints of the needles, the wound in the breast that had for so many months now scarcely ever closed. I caressed the perfectly shaped head. I bent to kiss the cheeks, the breasts that would now never be fulfilled, that no youth would ever touch. "Oh, my lamb."

The lips curled in another smile, one whose secret I thought I knew. I recognized it without the aid of the gaze, now sealed forever from mine, with which it had come to me so often throughout her childhood. It was the expression on her face when her homework was going well, the shine of pride at a column of figures mastered or a poem to spring successfully forged. It was the smile of satisfaction worn at the piano when a new composition had been memorized, on her bicycle when, gripping its vanquished horns, she had ridden past me on her first successful solo around the yard. Sometimes, as on that Saturday morning, she would turn the smile shyly toward me, taking added pleasure in my approval.

But this time the experience was not to be shared. She was going alone. Even without the eyes to help communicate it, there was a glow of the most intense concentration on her face, with that wariness of error or shortcoming that had always made it so complete and so characteristic. She had never seemed more alive than now, when she was gathering all the life within her for the proper discharge of whatever this last assignment might have been. Was it a sum of figures or a poem to nature she was undertaking in her dream? Or a difficult, delicate spray of notes, or the first ecstatic journey on the two-wheeler, with the promise of liberty on summer roads unfolding far ahead? I bent again to whisper a question in her ear, but there was no answer—only the most remote sense of flight upon the face. It shone like a star about to burst and, in bursting, yield me all its light at once—could I but bear the gift.

Even her wearied limbs had for the moment this tension, a vibrancy as of a drawn bow. But as the hours wore on, they seemed to slacken, and her features to relax as well. Perhaps the mission had been accomplished, and the hour of rest was at hand. Once, later that afternoon, the smile parted her lips again, this time widely enough to show that her gums were dripping. The enemy was pouring out of every crevice at last. The sight of these royal children pitted against this bestiality had always comsumed me with a fury so blind I had had often to turn my face away. Now I was glad Carol could not see me standing there, alone, at last, on holy ground.

She went her way in the middle of the afternoon, borne from the dull watchers on a wave that broke and crashed beyond our sight. In that fathomless and timeless silence one does not look rather wildly about for a clock, in a last attempt to fix the lost spirit in time. I had guessed what the hands would say. Three o'clock. The children were putting their schoolbooks away, and getting ready to go home.

After some legal formalities I went into the room once more to say good-by. I had once read a book in which the hero had complained, in a similar farewell taken of a woman, that it was like saying good-by to a statue. I wished it were so now. She looked finally like some mangled flower, or like a bird that had been pelted to earth in a storm. I knew that under the sheet she would look as though she had been clubbed to death. As for the dignity of man, this one drew forth a square of cloth, and, after honking like a goose, pocketed his tears.

The bartender had finished cleaning up after some last late lunchers and was polishing the glasses for the evening's trade. After I'd had six or seven drinks, he said to me, "No more. That must be the tenth muddler you've snapped in two." Perhaps he was hearing the voices too . . .

Passing the church of St. Catherine on the way to the car, I suddenly remembered the cake. I went inside, out of curiosity. It was still there on the pew, undisturbed. I picked it up and started out with it. An incoming worshiper took frowning note of my unsteady career through the lobby door.

Outside, I paused on the sidewalk, one foot on the bottom step. I turned and looked up at the Figure still hanging as ever over the central doorway, its arms outspread among the sooted stones and strutting doves.

I took the cake out of the box and balanced it a moment on the palm of my hand. Disturbed by something in the motion, the birds started from their covert and flapped away across the street. Then my arm drew back and let fly with all the strength within me. Before the mind snaps, or the heart breaks, it gathers itself like a clock about to strike. It might even be said one pulls himself together to disintegrate. The scattered particles of self—love, wood thrush calling, homework sums, broken nerves, rag dolls, one Phi Beta Kappa key, gold stars, lamplight smiles, night cries, and the shambles of contemplation—are collected for a split moment like scraps of shrapnel before they explode.

It was miracle enough that the pastry should reach its target at all, at the height from the sidewalk. The more so that it should land squarely, just beneath the crown of thorns. Then through scalded eyes I seem to see the hands free themselves of the nails and move slowly toward the soiled face. Very slowly, very deliberately, with infinite patience, the icing was wiped from the eyes and flung away. I could see it fall in clumps to the porch steps. Then the cheeks were wiped down with the same sense of grave and gentle ritual, with all the kind sobriety of one whose voice could be heard saying, "Suffer the little children to come unto me . . . for of such is the kingdom of heaven."

Then the scene dissolved itself in a mist in which my legs could no longer support their weight, and I sank down to the steps. I sat on its worn stones, to rest a moment before going on. Thus Wanderhope was found at that place which for the diabolists of his literary youth, and for those with more modest spiritual histories too, was said to be the only alternative to the muzzle of a pistol: the foot of the Cross.

Summer passed into autumn, and when in November a few white flakes sifted down out of the sky, Mrs. Brodhag decided to make the journey to her sister in Seattle of which she had for so long restively spoken. Perhaps she would make "other connections" there, in view of my having the house on the market. If I sold it—a result little foreshadowed by the processions marching through it behind an ever-changing leadership of brokers—and did move into a city apartment, I would hardly be needing her help. The trip to the airport was the first down the Parkway since the days when we had made so many. "—In both our prayers—" she raged in my ear against the roar of the jets. I pressed into her hand a St. Christopher medal, extricated with difficulty from the chain of the crucifix with which it had become entangled in my pocket. We smiled as she nodded thanks. Then she was a bird in the sky, then a bee, then nothing.

It was as many months again before I could bring myself to explore at any length the bright front bedroom, then only because the sudden sale of the house required its cleaning out.

Dresses and toys and bureau articles were put into boxes and carried into the garage for the charity truck to haul away. Among the books and papers in the large desk drawer was a class letter from the sixth grade, a monumental scroll on which each individual note was pasted, wound upon two sticks like an ancient document. I read a few before stowing it into a carton of things to be kept for a still further future. One was a note from a boy reputed to have lost his heart to her, commanding her early return and with a P.S. reading, "You and I up in a tree, K-I-S-S-I-N-G." Into the carton were also tucked the home movies still sealed in their original tins. At last I found the courage to turn on the tape recorder.

I carried it down into the living room, of which the windows were open, the year being now once again well advanced into spring. It was twilight, and I turned on all the lamps.

After a whir of scratches and laughing whispers began some absurd dialogue Carol had picked up between Mrs. Brodhag and me, without our knowing it, about leaking eaves and how they should be got at. "You might as well be married the way she nags you," Carol said into the machine she had herself initiated with this prank. Then followed some of her piano pieces, including the Chopin *Nocturne* I had managed to get on the tape the night of the unfortunate television program. I stood at the window with a heavy drink as each molten note dropped out of nowhere onto my heart. There was a long silence after the music, and I was about to end the entertainment as a poor idea when my hand was arrested at the switch by the sound of her voice. This time she read a selection to which she had a few words of preface:

"I want you to know that everything is all right, Daddy. I mean you mustn't worry, really. You've helped me a lot—more than you can imagine. I was digging around in the cabinet part at the bottom of the bookshelves for something to read that you would like. I mean, not something from your favorite books of poetry and all, but something of your own. What did I come across but that issue of the magazine put out by your alma mater, with the piece in it about your philosophy of life.

Do you remember it? I might as well say that I know what's going on. What you wrote gives me courage to face whatever there is that's coming, so what could be more appropriate than to read it for you now? Remember when you explained it to me? Obviously, I don't understand it at all, but I think I get the drift:

"I believe that man must learn to live without those consolations called religious, which his own intelligence must by now have told him belong to the childhood of the race. Philosophy can really give us nothing permanent to believe either; it is too rich in answers, each canceling out the rest. The quest for Meaning is foredoomed. Human life 'means' nothing. But that is not to say that it is not worth living. What does a Debussy *Arabesque* 'mean,' or a rainbow or a rose? A man delights in all of these, knowing himself to be no more—a wisp of music and a haze of dreams dissolving against the sun. Man has only his own two feet to stand on, his own human trinity to see him through: Reason, Courage, and Grace. And the first plus the second equals the third."

27. JOHN FANTE

The Odyssey of a Wop[*]

John Fante was born in Denver, Colorado, in 1911 and spent much of his early life there and in San Juan, California. His writing which dealt with his earthy Italian-American background early earned considerable recognition: and although he spent some time as a scenario writer in Hollywood, he returned to an autobiographical theme in his Full of Life *(Boston, 1952).*

I pick up little bits of information about my grandfather. My grandmother tells me of him. She tells me that when he lived he was a good fellow whose goodness evoked not admiration but pity. He was known as a good little Wop. Of an evening he liked to sit at a table in a saloon sipping a tumbler of anisette, all by himself. He sat there like a little girl nipping an ice-cream cone. The old boy loved that green stuff, that anisette. It was his passion, and when folks saw him sitting alone it tickled them, for he was a good little Wop.

One night, my grandmother tells me, my grandfather was sitting in the saloon, he and his anisette. A drunken teamster stumbled through the swinging doors, braced himself at the bar, and bellowed:

"All right, everybody! Come an' get 'em! They're on me!"

And there sat my grandfather, not moving, his old tongue coquetting with the anisette. Everyone but he stood at the bar and drank the teamster's liquor. The teamster swung round. He saw my grandfather. He was insulted.

"You too, Wop!" said he. "Come up and drink!"

[*] John Fante, "The Odyssey of a Wop," *American Mercury,* XXX (September, 1933), pp. 89–97.

Silence. My grandfather arose. He staggered across the floor, passed the teamster, and then what did he do but go through the swinging doors and down the snowy street! He heard laughter coming after him from the saloon and his chest burned. He went home to my father.

"*Mamma mia!*" he blubbered. "Tummy Murray, he calla me Wopa."

"*Sangue de la Madonna!*"

Bareheaded, my father rushed down the street to the saloon. Tommy Murray was not there. He was in another saloon half a block away, and there my father found him. He drew the teamster aside and spoke under his breath. A fight! Immediately blood and hair began to fly. Chairs were drawn back. The customers applauded. The two men fought for an hour. They rolled over the floor, kicking, cursing, biting. They were in a knot in the center of the floor, their bodies wrapped around each other. My father's head, chest and arms buried the teamster's face. The teamster screamed. My father growled. His neck was rigid and trembling. The teamster screamed again, and lay still. My father got to his feet and wiped blood from his open mouth with the back of his hand. On the floor the teamster lay with a loose ear hanging from his head. . . . This is the story my grandmother tells me.

I think about the two men, my father and the teamster, and I picture them struggling on the floor. Boy! *Can* my father fight!

I get an idea. My two brothers are playing in another room. I leave my grandmother and go to them. They are sprawled on the rug, bent over crayons and drawing-paper. They look up and see my face flaming with my idea.

"What's wrong?" one asks.

"I dare you to do something!"

"Do what?"

"I dare you to call me a Wop!"

My youngest brother, barely four, jumps to his feet, and dancing up and down, screams, "Wop! Wop! Wop! Wop!"

I look at him. Pooh! He's too small. It's that other brother, that bigger brother, I want. He's got ears too, he has.

"I bet *you're* afraid to call me Wop."

But he senses the devil in the woodpile.

"Nah," says he. "I don't wanna."

"Wop! Wop! Wop! Wop!" screams the little brother.

"Shut your mouth, you!"

"I won't neither. You're a Wop! Wop! Woppedy Wop!"

My older brother's box of crayons lies on the floor in front of his nose. I put my heel upon the box and grind it into the carpet. He yells, seizing my leg. I back away, and he begins to cry.

"Aw, that was sure dirty," he says.

"I dare you to call me a Wop!"

"Wop!"

I charge, seeking his ear. But my grandmother comes into the room flourishing a razor-strop.

II

From the beginning, I hear my mother use the words Wop and Dago with such vigor as to denote violent disrepute. She spits them out. They leap from her lips. To her, they contain the essence of poverty, squalor, filth. If I don't wash my teeth, or hang up my cap, my mother says, "Don't be like that. Don't be a Wop." Thus, as I begin to acquire her values, Wop and Dago to me become synonymous with things evil. But she's consistent.

My father isn't. He's loose with his tongue. His moods create his judgments. I at once notice that to him Wop and Dago are without any distinct meaning, though if one not an Italian slaps them on to him, he's instantly insulted. Christopher Columbus was the greatest Wop who ever lived, says my father. So is Caruso. So is this fellow and that. But his very good friend Peter Ladonna is not only a drunken pig, but a Wop on top of it; and of course all his brothers-in-law are good-for-nothing Wops.

He pretends to hate the Irish. He really doesn't, but he likes to think so, and he warns us children against them. Our grocer's name is O'Neil. Frequently and inadvertently he makes errors when my mother is at his store. She tells my father about short weights in meats, and now and then of a stale egg.

Straightway, my father grows tense, his lower lip curling. "This is the last time that Irish bum robs me!" And he goes out, goes to the grocery-store, his heels booming.

Soon he returns. He's smiling. His fists bulge with cigars. "From now on," says he, "everything's gonna be all right."

I don't like the grocer. My mother sends me to his store every day, and instantly he chokes up my breathing with the greeting, "Hello, you little Dago! What'll you have?" So I detest him, and never enter his store if other customers are to be seen, for to be called a Dago before others is a ghastly, almost a physical humiliation. My stomach expands and recedes, and I feel naked.

I steal recklessly when the grocer's back is turned. I enjoy stealing from him: candy bars, cookies, fruit. When he goes into his refrigerator I lean on his meat scales, hoping to snap a spring; I press my toe into egg baskets. Sometimes I pilfer too much. Then, what a pleasure it is to stand on the curb, my appetite gorged, and heave *his* candy bars, *his* cookies, *his* apples into the high yellow weeds across the street. . . . "Damn you, O'Neil, you can't call me a Dago and get away with it!"

His daughter is of my age. She's cross-eyed. Twice a week she passes our house on her way to her music lesson. Above the street, and high in the branches of an elm tree, I watch her coming down the sidewalk, swinging her violin case. When she is under me, I jeer in sing-song:

Martha's croooooss-eyed!
Martha's croooooss-eyed!
Martha's croooooss-eyed!

III

As I grow older I find out that Italians use Wop and Dago much more than Americans. My grandmother, whose vocabulary of English is confined to the commonest of nouns, always employs them in discussing contemporary Italians. The words never come forth quietly, unobtrusively. No; they bolt forth. There is a blatant intonation, and then in the sense of someone being scathed, stunned.

I enter the parochial school with an awful fear that I will be called Wop. As soon as I find out why people have such things as surnames, I match my own against such typically Italian cognomens as Bianci, Borello, Pacelli—the names of other students. I am pleasantly relieved by the comparison. After all, I think, people will say I am French. Doesn't my name sound French? Sure! So thereafter, when people ask my nationality, I tell them I am French. A few boys begin calling me Frenchy. I like that. It feels fine.

Thus I begin to loathe my heritage. I avoid Italian boys and girls who try to be friendly. I thank God for my light skin and hair, and I choose my companions by the Anglo-Saxon ring of their names. If a boy's name is Whitney, Brown, or Smythe, then he's my pal; but I'm always a little breathless when I am with him; he may find me out. At the lunch hour I huddle over my lunch pail, for my mother doesn't wrap my sandwiches in wax paper, and she makes them too large, and the lettuce leaves protrude. Worse, the bread is homemade; not bakery bread, not "American" bread. I make a great fuss because I can't have mayonnaise and other "American" things.

The parish priest is a good friend of my father's. He comes strolling through the school grounds, watching the children at play. He calls to me and asks about my father, and then he tells me I should be proud to be studying about my great countrymen, Columbus, Vespucci, John Cabot. He speaks in a loud, humorous voice. Students gather around us, listening, and I bite my lips and wish to Jesus he'd shut up and move on.

Occasionally now I hear about a fellow named Dante. But when I find out that he was an Italian I hate him as if he were alive and walking through the classrooms, pointing a finger at me. One day I find his picture in a dictionary. I look at it and tell myself that never have I seen an uglier bastard.

We students are at the blackboard one day, and a soft-eyed

Italian girl whom I hate but who insists that I am her beau stands beside me. She twitches and shuffles about uneasily, half on tiptoe, smiling queerly at me. I sneer and turn my back, moving as far away from her as I can. The nun sees the wide space separating us and tells me to move nearer the girl. I do so, and the girl draws away, nearer the student on her other side.

Then I look down at my feet, and there I stand in a wet, spreading spot. I look quickly at the girl, and she hangs her head and looks at me in a way that begs me to take the blame for her. We attract the attention of others, and the classroom becomes alive with titters. Here comes the nun. I think I am in for it again, but she embraces me and murmurs that I should have raised two fingers and of course I would have been allowed to leave the room. But, says she, there's no need for that now; the thing for me to do is go out and get the mop. I do so, and amid the hysteria I nurse my conviction that only a Wop girl, right out of a Wop home, would ever do such a thing as this.

Oh, you Wop! Oh, you Dago! You bother me even when I sleep. I dream of defending myself against tormentors. One day I learn from my mother that my father went to the Argentine in his youth, and lived in Buenos Aires for two years. My mother tells me of his experiences there, and all day I think about them, even to the time I go to sleep. That night I come awake with a jerk. In the darkness I grope to my mother's room. My father sleeps at her side, and I awaken her gently, so that he won't be aroused.

I whisper, "Are you sure Papa wasn't *born* in Argentina?"

"No. Your father was born in Italy."

I go back to bed, disconsolate and disgusted.

IV

During a ball game on the school grounds, a boy who plays on the opposing team begins to ridicule my playing. It is the ninth inning, and I ignore his taunts. We are losing the game, but if I can knock out a hit our chances of winning are pretty strong. I am determined to come through, and I face the pitcher confidently. The tormentor sees me at the plate.

"Ho! Ho!" he shouts. "Look who's up! The Wop's up. Let's get rid of the Wop!"

This is the first time anyone at school has ever flung that word at me, and I am so angry that I strike out foolishly. We fight after the game, this boy and I, and I make him take it back.

Now school days become fighting days. Nearly every afternoon at 3:15 a crowd gathers to watch me make some guy take it back. This is fun; I am getting somewhere now, so come on, you guys, I dare you to call me a Wop! When at length there are no more boys who challenge me, insults come to me by hearsay, and I seek out the culprits. I strut down the corridors. The smaller boys admire me. "Here he comes!" they say, and they gaze and gaze. My two younger brothers attend the same school, and the smallest, a little squirt, seven years old, brings his friends to me and asks me to roll up my sleeve and show them my muscles. Here you are, boys. Look me over.

My brother brings home furious accounts of my battles. My father listens voraciously, and I stand by, to clear up any doubtful details. Sadly happy days! My father gives me pointers; how to hold my fist, how to guard my head. My mother, too shocked to hear more, presses her temples and squeezes her eyes and leaves the room.

I am nervous when I bring friends to my house; the place looks so Italian. Here hangs a picture of Victor Emmanuel, and over there is one of the cathedral of Milan, and next to it, one of St. Peter's, and on the buffet stands a wine-pitcher of medieval design; it's forever brimming, forever red and brilliant with wine. These things are heirlooms belonging to my father, and no matter who may come to our house, he likes to stand under them and brag.

So I begin to shout at him. I tell him to cut out being a Wop and be an American once in a while. Immediately he gets his razor-strop and whales hell out of me, clouting me from room to room and finally out the back door. I go into the woodshed and pull down my pants and stretch my neck to examine the blue slices across my rump. A Wop! that's what my father is! Nowhere is there an American father who beats his son this way. Well, he's not going to get away with it; some day I'll get even with him.

I begin to think that my grandmother is hopelessly a Wop. She's a small, stocky peasant who walks with her wrists criss-crossed her belly, a simple old lady and fond of boys. She comes into the room and tries to talk to my friends. She speaks English with a bad accent, her vowels rolling out like hoops. When, in her simple way, she confronts a friend of mine and says, her old eyes smiling. "You lika go the Seester scola?" my heart roars. *Mannaggia!* I'm disgraced; now they all know that I'm an Italian.

My grandmother has taught me to speak her native tongue. By seven, I know it pretty well, and I always address her in it. But when friends are with me, when I am twelve and thirteen, I pretend to ignorance of what she says, and smirk stiffly; my friends daren't know that I can speak any language but English. Sometimes this infuriates her. She bristles, the loose skin at her throat knits hard, and she blasphemes with a mighty blasphemy.

V

When I finish in the parochial school my people decide to send me to a Jesuit academy in another city. My father comes with me on the first day. Chiseled into the stone coping that skirts the roof of the main building of the academy is the Latin inscription: *Religioni et Bonis Artibus.* My father and I stand at a distance, and he reads it aloud and tells me what it means.

I look up at him in amazement. Is this man my father? Why,

look at him! Listen to him! He reads with an Italian inflection! He's wearing an Italian mustache. I have never realized it until this moment, but he looks exactly like a Wop. His suit hangs carelessly in wrinkles upon him. Why the deuce doesn't he buy a new one? And look at his tie! It's crooked. And his shoes: they need a shine. And for the Lord's sake, will you look at his pants! They're not even buttoned in front. And oh, damn, damn, damn, you can see those dirty old suspenders that he won't throw away. Say, mister, are you really my father? you there, why, you're such a little guy, such a runt, such an old-looking fellow! You look exactly like one of those immigrants carrying a blanket. You can't be *my* father! Why, I thought, . . . I've always thought . . .

I'm crying now, the first time I've ever cried for any reason except a licking, and I'm glad he's not crying too. I'm glad he's as tough as he is, and we say goodbye quickly, and I go down the path quickly, and I do not turn to look back, for I know he's standing there and looking at me.

I enter the administration building and stand in line with strange boys who also wait to register for the Autumn term. Some Italian boys stand among them. I am away from home and I sense the Italians. We look at one another and our eyes meet in an irresistible amalgamation, a suffusive consanguinity; I look away.

A burly Jesuit rises from his chair behind the desk and introduces himself to me. Such a voice for a man! There are a dozen thunderstorms in his chest. He asks my name, and writes it down on a little card.

"Nationality?" he roars.

"American."

"Your father's name?"

I whisper it, "Luigi."

"How's that? Spell it out. Talk louder."

I cough. I touch my lips with the back of my hand and spell out the name.

"Ha!" shouts the registrar. "And still they come! Another Wop! Well, young man, you'll be at home here! Yes sir! Lots of

Wops here! We've even got kikes! And, you know, this place reeks with shanty Irish!"

Dio! How I hate that priest!

He continues, "Where was your father born?"

"Buenos Aires, Argentina."

"Your mother?"

At last I can shout with the gusto of truth.

"Chi-cag-oo!" Aye, just like a conductor.

Casually, by way of conversation, he asks, "You speak Italian?"

"Nah! Not a word."

"Too bad," he says.

"You're nuts," I think.

VI

That semester I wait on table to defray my tuition fee. Trouble ahead; the chef and his assistants in the kitchen are all Italians. They know at once that I am of the breed. I ignore the chef's friendly overtures, loathing him from the first. He understands why, and we become enemies. Every word he uses has a knife in it. His remarks cut me to pieces. After two months I can stand it no longer in the kitchen, and so I write a long letter to my mother; I am losing weight, I write; if you don't let me quit this job, I'll get sick and flunk my tests. She telegraphs me some money and tells me to quit at once; oh, I feel so sorry for you, my boy; I didn't dream it would be so hard on you.

I decided to work just one more evening, to wait on table for just one more meal. That evening, after the meal, when the kitchen is deserted save for the cook and his assistants, I take off my apron and take my stand across the kitchen from him, staring at him. This is my moment. Two months I have waited for this moment. There is a knife stuck into the chopping block. I pick it up, still staring. I want to hurt the cook, square things up.

He sees me, and he says, "Get out of here, Wop!"

An assistant shouts, "Look out, he's got a knife!"

"You won't throw it, Wop," the cook says. I am not thinking of throwing it, but since he says I won't, I do. It goes over his head and strikes the wall and drops with a clatter to the floor. He picks it up and chases me out of the kitchen. I run, thanking God I didn't hit him.

That year the football team is made up of Irish and Italian boys. The linemen are Irish, and we in the backfield are four Italians. We have a good team and win a lot of games, and my team-mates are excellent players who are unselfish and work together as one man. But I hate my three fellow-players in the backfield; because of our nationality, we seem ridiculous. The team makes a captain of me, and I call signals and see to it my fellow-Italians in the backfield do as little scoring as possible. I hog the play.

The school journal and the town's sport pages begin to refer to us as the Wop Wonders. I think it an insult. Late one afternoon, at the close of an important game, a number of students leave the main grandstand and group themselves at one end of the field, to improvise some yells. They give three big ones for the Wop Wonders. It sickens me. I can feel my stomach move; and after that game I turn in my suit and quit the team.

I am a bad Latinist. Disliking the language, I do not study, and therefore I flunk my examinations regularly. Now a student comes to me and tells me that it is possible to drop Latin from my curriculum if I follow his suggestion, which is that I fail deliberately in the next few examinations, fail hopelessly. If I do this, the student says, the Jesuits will bow to my stupidity and allow me to abandon the language.

This is an agreeable suggestion. I follow it out. But it backtracks, for the Jesuits are wise fellows. They see what I'm doing, and they laugh and tell me that I am not clever enough to fool them, and that I must keep on studying Latin, even if it takes me twenty years to pass. Worse, they double my assignments and I spend my recreation time with Latin syntax. Before examinations in my junior year the Jesuit who instructs me calls me to his room and says:

"It is a mystery to me that a thoroughbred Italian like yourself should have any trouble with Latin. The language is in your blood, and believe me, you're a darned poor Wop."

Abbastanzia! I go upstairs and lock my door and sit down with my book in front of me, my Latin book, and I study like a wild man, tearing crazily into the stuff until, lo! What is this? What am I studying here? Sure enough, it's a lot like the Italian my grandmother taught me so long ago—this Latin, it isn't so hard, after all. I pass the examination. I pass it with such an incredibly fine grade that my instructor thinks there is knavery somewhere.

Two weeks before graduation I get sick and go to the infirmary and am quarantined there. I lie in bed and feed my grudges. I bite my thumbs and ponder old grievances. I am running a high fever, and I can't sleep. I think about the principal. He was my close friend during my first two years at the school, but in my third year, last year, he was transferred to another school in the Province. I lie in bed thinking of the day we met again in this, the last year. We met again on his return that September, in the principal's room. He said hello to the boys, this fellow and that, and then he turned to me, and said:

"And you, the Wop! So you're still with us."

Coming from the mouth of the priest, the word had a lumpish sound that shook me all over. I felt the eyes of everyone, and I heard a giggle. So that's how it is! I lie in bed thinking of the priest and now of the fellow who giggled.

All of a sudden I jump out of bed, tear the fly-leaf from a book, find a pencil and write a note to the priest. I write, "Dear Father: I haven't forgotten your insult. You called me a Wop last September. If you don't apologize right away there's going to be trouble." I call the brother in charge of the infirmary and tell him to deliver the note to the priest.

After a while I hear the priest's footsteps rising on the stairs. He comes to the door of my room, opens it, looks at me for a long time, not speaking, but only looking querulously. I wait for him to come in and apologize, for this is a grand moment for me. But he closes the door quietly and walks away. I am astonished. A double insult!

I am well again on the night of graduation. On the platform the principal makes a speech and then begins to distribute the diplomas. We're supposed to say, "Thank you," when he gives them to us. So thank you, and thank you, and thank you, everyone says in his turn. But when he gives me mine, I look squarely at him, just stand there and look, and I don't say anything, and from that day we never speak to each other again.

The following September I enroll at the university.

"Where was your father born?" asks the registrar.

"Buenos Aires, Argentina."

Sure, that's it. The same theme, with variations.

VII

Time passes, and so do school days.

I am sitting on a wall along the plaza, watching a Mexican *fiesta* across the street. A man comes along and lifts himself to the wall beside me, and asks if I have a cigarette. I have, and lighting the cigarette, he makes conversation with me, and we talk of casual things until the *fiesta* is over. Then we get down from the wall, and still talking, go walking through the Los Angeles Tenderloin. This man needs a shave and his clothes do not fit him; it's plain that he's a bum. He tells one lie upon another, and not one is well told. But I am lonesome in this town, and a glad listener.

We step into a restaurant for coffee. Now he becomes intimate. He has bummed his way from Chicago to Los Angeles, and has come in search of his sister; he has her address, but she is not at it, and for two weeks he has been looking for her in vain. He talks on and on about this sister, seeming to gyrate like a buzzard over her, hinting to me that I should ask some questions about her. He wants me to touch off the fuse that will release his feelings.

So I ask, "Is she married?"

And then he rips into her, hammer and tongs. Even if he does find her, he will not live with her. What kind of a sister is she to let him walk these streets without a dime in his pocket, and she married to a man who has plenty of money and can give him a job? He thinks she has deliberately given him a false address so that he will not find her, and when he gets his hands on her he's going to wring her neck. In the end, after he has completely demolished her, he does exactly what I think he is going to do.

He asks, "Have *you* got a sister?"

I tell him yes, and he waits for my opinion of her; but he doesn't get it.

We meet again a week later.

He has found his sister. Now he begins to praise her. She had induced her husband to give him a job, and tomorrow he goes to work as a waiter in his brother-in-law's restaurant. He tells me the address, but I do not think more of it beyond the fact that it must be somewhere in the Italian Quarter.

And so it is, and by a strange coincidence I know his brother-in-law, Rocco Saccone, an old friend of my people and a *paesano* of my father's. I am in Rocco's place one night a fortnight later. Rocco and I are speaking in Italian when the man I have met on the plaza steps out of the kitchen, an apron over his legs. Rocco calls him and he comes over, and Rocco introduces him as his brother-in-law from Chicago. We shake hands.

"We've met before," I say, but the plaza man doesn't seem to want this known, for he lets go my hand quickly and goes behind the counter, pretending to be busy with something back there. Oh, he's bluffing; you can see that.

In a loud voice, Rocco says to me, "That man is a skunk. He's ashamed of his own flesh and blood." He turns to the plaza man.

"Ain't you?"

"Oh, yeah?" the plaza man sneers.

"How do you mean—he's ashamed? How do you mean?"

"Ashamed of being an Italian," Rocco says.

"Oh, yeah?" from the plaza man.

"That's all he knows," Rocco says. "Oh, yeah? That's all he knows. Oh, yeah? Oh, yeah? Oh, yeah? That's all he knows."

"Oh, yeah?" the plaza man says again.

"Yah," Rocco says, his face blue. "*Animale codardo!*"

The plaza man looks at me with peaked eyebrows, and he doesn't know it, he standing there with his black, liquid eyes, he doesn't know that he's as good as a god in his waiter's apron; for he is indeed a god, a miracle worker; no, he doesn't know; no one knows; just the same, he is that—he, of all people. Standing there and looking at him, I feel like my grandfather and my father and the Jesuit cook and Rocco; I seem to have come home, and I am surprised that this return, which I have somehow always expected, should come so quietly, without trumpets and thunder.

"If I were you, I'd get rid of him," I say to Rocco.

"Oh, yeah?" the plaza man says again.

I'd like to paste him. But that won't do any good. There's no sense in hammering your own corpse.

28. DELMORE SCHWARTZ

America! America![*]

Delmore Schwartz was born in Brooklyn, New York, in 1913, the son of Jewish immigrants from Eastern Europe. He studied at the University of Wisconsin, New York University, and Harvard and taught for brief intervals at Harvard and Syracuse. But he was dedicated to poetry and impatient with the life of a teacher. He was a thoughtful critic who for a time edited The Partisan Review, *a sensitive poet, and a short-story writer with a gift for characterization. The story that follows describes the hopes and the problems of the generation affected by the Depression and the war.*

When Shenandoah Fish returned from Paris in 1936, he was unable to do very much with himself, he was unable to write with the great fluency and excitement of previous years. Some great change had occurred in the human beings he knew in his native city, whom he had sought out before his stay in Europe. The depression had occurred to these human beings. It had reached the marrow at last; after years, the full sense of the meaning of the depression had modified their hopes and their desires very much. The boys with whom Shenandoah had gone to school no longer lived in the same neighborhood, they no longer saw much of each other, they were somewhat embarrassed when they met, some of them were married now, and many of them were ashamed of what they had made or what had been made of their lives. After visits which concluded in perplexity, Shenandoah ceased to try to renew his old friend-

[*] Delmore Schwartz, *The World Is a Wedding* (Norfolk, Conn., 1948), pp. 106–29.

ships. They no longer existed and they were not going to rise from the grave of the dead years.

Yet Shenandoah was not troubled by his idleness. He would have liked to be in Paris again, and he expected to go back next year. He did not know then that it would be impossible for him to go back. Meanwhile, as his mother said, he was taking it easy, and enjoying an indolence and a relaxation which, though peculiar in him, seemed unavoidable after the prolonged and intense activity of the year before.

He slept late each morning, and then he sat for a long time at the breakfast-table, listening to his mother's talk as she went about her household tasks. It was simple and pleasant to shift attention back and forth between what his mother said and the morning newspaper, for in the morning sunlight, the kitchen's whiteness was pleasant, the newspaper was always interesting in the strength of attention possible in the morning, and Shenandoah found his mother's monologue pleasant too. She spoke always of her own life or of the lives of her friends; of what had been; what might have been; of fate, character and accident; and especially of the mystery of the family life, as she had known it and reflected upon it.

After two months of idleness, Shenandoah began to feel uneasy about these breakfast pleasures. The emotion which often succeeded extended idleness returned again, the emotion of a loss or lapse of identity. "Who am I? what am I?" Shenandoah began once more to say to himself, and although he knew very well that this was only the projection of some other anxiety, although he knew that to work too was merely to deceive himself about this anxiety, nonetheless the intellectual criticism of his own emotions was as ever of no avail whatever.

On the morning when this uneasiness of the whole being overtook Shenandoah seriously, his mother's monologue began to interest him more and more, much more than ever before, although she spoke of human beings who, being of her own generation, did not really interest Shenandoah in themselves. She began to speak of the Baumanns, whom she had known well for thirty years.

The Baumanns, said Mrs. Fish, had given Shenandoah a silver spoon when he was born. Mrs. Fish brought forth the silver and showed Shenandoah his initials engraved in twining letters upon the top of the spoon. Shenandoah took the spoon and toyed with it nervously, looking at the initials as he listened to his mother.

The friendship of the Fish family with the Baumann family had begun in the period just before the turn of the century. Shenandoah's father, who was now dead, had gone into what was then entitled the insurance *game.* The word rang in Shenandoah's mind, and he noted again his mother's fine memory for the speech other people used. Mr. Baumann who was twenty years older than Shenandoah's father, had already established himself in the business of insurance: he had been successful from the start because it was just the kind of business for a man of his temperament.

Shenandoah's mother proceeded to explain in detail how insurance was a genial medium for a man like Mr. Baumann. The important thing in insurance was to win one's way into the homes and into the confidences of other people. Insurance could not be sold as a grocer or a druggist sells his *goods* (here Shenandoah was moved again by his mother's choice of words); you could not wait for the customer to come to you; nor could you like the book salesman go from house to house, plant your foot in the doorway, and start talking quickly before the housewife shut the door in your face. On the contrary, it was necessary to become friendly with a great many people, who, when they came to know you, and like you, and trust you, take your advice about the value of insurance.

It was necessary to join the lodges, societies, and associations of your own class and people. This had been no hardship to Mr. Baumann who enjoyed groups, gatherings, and meetings of all kinds. He had in his youth belonged to the association of the people who came from the old country, and when he married, he joined his wife's association. Then he joined the masonic lodge, and in addition he participated in the social life of the neighborhood synagogue, although he was in fact an admirer of Ingersoll. Thus he came to know a great many people, and visited them with unfailing devotion and regularity, moved by his love of being with other human beings. A visit was a complicated act for him. It required that he enter the house with much amiability, and tell his host that he had been thinking of him and speaking of him just the other day, mentioning of necessity that he had just *dropped* in for a moment. Only after protestations of a predictable formality, was Mr. Baumann persuaded to sit down for a cup of tea. Once seated, said Mrs. Fish (imposing from time to time her own kind of irony upon the irony which sang in Shenandoah's mind at every phase of her story), once seated it was hours before Mr. Baumann arose from the dining-room table on which a fresh table-cloth had been laid and from which the lace cover and the cut-glass had been withdrawn.

Mr. Baumann drank tea in the Russian style, as he often explained; he drank it from a glass, not from a cup: a cup was utterly out of the question. And while he drank and ate, he discoursed inimitably and authoritatively upon *every topic of the day,* but especially upon his favorite subjects, the private life of the kings and queens of Europe, Zionism, and the new discoveries of science. A silent amazement often mounted in his listeners at the length of time that he was capable of eating, drinking, and talking; until at last, since little was left upon the table, he absentmindedly took up the crumbs and poppyseeds from the tablecloth.

Mrs. Fish had not known Mr. Baumann until he was near middle age. But she had heard that even in his youth, he had looked like a banker. As he grew older and became quite plump, this impression was strengthened, for he took to pince-nez glasses, and handsome vests with white piping. Shenandoah remembered that Mr. Baumann resembled some photographs of the first J. P. Morgan. His friends were delighted with all the aspects of his being, but they took especial satisfaction in his appearance. They were shamed often enough into allowing him to *write* a new insurance policy for them, for it was a time of general prosperity for these people: most of them were rising in the world, after having come to America as grown or half-grown children. Their first insecurity was passed and hardly borne in mind, except in the depths of consciousness; and now they were able to *afford* an insurance policy, just as they were able to look down on newcomers to America, and their own early lives in America, a state of being which was expressed by the word, *greenhorn.* Mr. Baumann's friendship was a token of their progress; they liked him very much, they were flattered by his company, and when he paid them a visit, he conferred upon the household a sense of the great world, even of intellectuality. This pleased the husband often because of what it implied to his wife; it implied that although he, the husband, was too busy a man in the dress business to know much of these worldly matters, yet he was capable of having the friendship and *bringing into the house* this amiable and cultivated man who spoke English with a Russian accent which was extremely refined.

Shenandoah's mother explained then that in the insurance business a good man like Mr. Baumann soon arrives at the point where there is no urgent need to acquire new customers and to write new policies. One can live in comfortable style off the commissions due you as the premiums continue to be paid from year to year. You must maintain your friendship with the policy-holders, so that the stress of hard times as it recurs does not make them give up their policies or stop paying the premiums. But this need of reassuring and cajoling policyholders did not for Mr. Baumann interfere with a way of life in which one slept late in the morning and made breakfast the occasion for the most painstaking scrutiny of the morning newspaper. One can go for vacations whenever one pleases, and Mr. Baumann went often with his family, on religious holidays and on national holidays. In fact, Mr. Baumann had frequently written some of his best policies during the general high spirits which are the rule on vacations and at resorts. He was at his best at such times and amid such well-being.

Here Shenandoah recognized in his mother's tone the resentment she had always felt toward those who lived well and permitted nothing to stop their enjoyment of life. It was the resentment of one who had herself never felt the inclination to live well, and regarded it as unjustified, except on the part of the very rich, or during holidays.

Mrs. Fish continued, saying that an insurance man is faced with one unavoidable duty, that of putting in an appearance at the funerals of human beings with whom he has been acquainted, even though he has not known them very well. This is a way of paying tribute to one of the irreducible facts upon which the insurance business is founded. And it provides the starting-point for useful and leading conversation.

"Yes," Mr. Baumann often said, "I was at L——'s funeral today." His tone implied the authoritative character of his presence.

"Yes," he reiterated with emphasis, squeezing the lemon into his tea, "we all have to go, sooner or later!"

Then he dwelt on the interesting incidents at the funeral, the children's lack of understanding, the widow's hysterical weeping, the life-like appearance of the corpse.

"He looked," said Mr. Baumann, "just like he was taking a nap."

And indeed, apart from *doing business,* Mr. Baumann enjoyed funerals for their own sake, for they were comprehensive gatherings of human beings with whom he had everything in common and to whom he was a very interesting and very *well-informed* man, even a man, as he seemed to some and to himself, who was a sage although without rabbinical trappings.

Here, having said this with unconscious disdain, Mrs. Fish finished ironing a tablecloth, folded it carefully, placed it with other ironed linens, took a new piece, and permitted herself no pause in her monologue.

She said that Mrs. Baumann was the one person who was unable to take Mr. Baumann with the seriousness he expected and received in all quarters. She preferred the neighborhood rabbi as a sage. She and her husband shared so many interests that there was a natural and extensive antagonism between them. Whatever gentleman occupied the rabbinical position in the neighborhood synagogue surpassed her husband at his own game, as far as she was concerned: surpassed him in unction, suavity, and fecundity of opinion.

Next to her husband, Mrs. Baumann seemed small and almost tiny. She was nervous and anxious, while he was always assured; and he merely smiled when she attacked him or criticized him before other people, or told him that he was talking too much, or said that he did not know what he was talking about. However, they loved the same things, and some of her resentment of her husband had as its source his freedom to have a full social life while she had to take care of the children. For her children, her friends, and all things Jewish, she had an inexhaustible charity, indulgence, and attentiveness, and consequently she sometimes neglected her household in order to make many visits and tell many stories, stories of patient detail and analysis which had to do with her friends. In the time before the World War, Freud and Bergson were celebrated in Jewish newspapers as Jews who had made a great fame for themselves in the Gentile world. Mrs. Baumann relished their fame to the point of making out a misleading and mistaken version of their doctrines; and in this way, Shenandoah's father, who visited the Baumann household very often before his marriage, learned of the teachings of Freud and passed them on to the salesmen who worked for him in the real estate business.

Only one thing excited Mrs. Baumann more than the success of a musician or an inventor who was Jewish; and that one thing was a new fad, especially fads about food. She often spoke of herself as having a new *fad,* and she often said that everyone should have fads. For the word pleased her, and some of its connotations had never occurred to her. She said often that she wished that she were a vegetarian.

As Shenandoah listened to his mother, he became nervous. He was not sure at any given moment whether the cruelty of the story was in his own mind or in his mother's tongue. And his own thoughts, which had to do with his own life, and seemed to have nothing to do with these human beings, began to trouble him.

What is it, he said to himself, that I do not see in myself, because it is of the present, as they did not see themselves? How can one look at oneself? No one sees himself.

As the Baumann children grew up, they seemed to gain vitality from the intensive social life of the household. For their small apartment near a great park came to be a kind of community center on Sunday nights. All whom Mr. Baumann met on his leisurely rounds were invited to come at any time. Both husband and wife knew very well how glad lonely human beings are to have a house to visit, a true household; and especially the human beings who have gone from the community life of the old country and foundered amid the immense alienation of metropolitan life. And the Baumanns also knew, although they were too wise to express the belief, that it was very important to have something to eat amid the talk, for people do not continue very long without the desire to eat; and in addition, the conversations, the jokes and the comments are improved, heightened, or excited by food and drink, by sandwiches, cake, and coffee; and the food one gets in another's household seems *exceptionally appetizing*.

Shenandoah as he listened tried to go back by imagination or imaginative sympathy to the lives of these people. Certainly in the old country there had been periods when food was scarce, so that one of the most wonderful things about America was the abundance of food. But it was impossible for Shenandoah, who had always been well-fed, to convince himself that he knew what their feelings about food had been. He returned to his mother who had begun genre studies of Sunday nights in the Baumann household.

Each of the Baumann children as they grew up amid these scenes of much sociability acquired social talents which gained them gratifying applause from the visitors, who were expected, in any case, in a profound, unspoken understanding, to make much of the children of any household. Dick, the oldest of the three children, learned to play the piano very cleverly, and he recited limericks and parodies. Sidney, the youngest one, was enchanted by the Sunday nights to the extent that he brought his neighborhood cronies to the house, which was a revelation most children avoided and dreaded because they were ashamed that their parents spoke broken English or a foreign tongue.

Sidney was less gifted than his brother; yet he was liked a good deal because he was small and *cute.* Martha, the girl, suffered from the intense aversions, shames, and frustrations of girlhood; and, as her father remarked, she *took it out* upon the piano, playing romantic music from morning to night. She was very smart and clever; and her remarks were often so biting that she was scolded helplessly, vainly, and tirelessly by her mother. Visitors, however, were charmed and not annoyed, when she was *fresh.* And as she became older, she defended herself by saying that she had learned her wit and irony at the Sunday night school of gossip, when all who were present analyzed the failings of their absent friends. Nonetheless, despite her bitter remarks about the household, she loved its regime very much, though annoyed to see how she depended upon it to nourish the depths of her being.

It was when Dick and Martha were old enough to need jobs that Shenandoah's father and Mr. Baumann went into partnership in the real estate business. Shenandoah's father had been in business *for himself* for some time and he had prospered greatly. It was his need of capital, which however he might have secured elsewhere, and his fondness for the Baumann's household which had made him suggest the partnership. The suggestion was made in a moment of weakness and well-being, when Mr. Fish had just enjoyed a fine dinner at the Baumann's. Whenever Shenandoah's father was pleased and had enjoyed himself very much, he suffered from these generous and unexpected impulses; but this did not prevent him from repairing the evil consequences of his magnanimity with an equally characteristic ruthlessness as soon as it was obvious that it not only had been costly (for then, he might forget about it), but that the cost would continue.

The difficulty soon showed itself, for Mr. Baumann and Dick made it clear that their habits of life were not going to be changed merely because they were now part of a *going concern.* Father and son arrived at work an hour before noon, which permitted them just enough time to look at the mail before departing for an unhurried lunch. They *drew* handsome salaries, and this was what troubled Shenandoah's father most of all. When it was a question of making a sale, Mr. Baumann often allowed his interests of the moment, which were often international in scope, to make him oblivious of *the deal.* He ingratiated himself with the customer very well, but this process ingratiated the customer with Mr. Baumann, and thus the mutual bloom of friendship, made business matters unimportant or a matter for tact and delicacy. Dick followed in his father's footsteps. He took customers to the ball game, which was well enough except that he too forgot the true and ulterior purpose of this spending of the firm's money. In three months, Shenandoah's father appreciated his error to the full; and for a week of half-sleepless nights, he strove to think of a way to free himself of his pleasure-loving partner. In the end, and as often before, he found only a brutal method; he sent Mr. Baumann a letter stating his grievances and dissolving the partnership. For a time, this summary dismissal ended the friendship of the two families. But Mr. Baumann was utterly unable to sustain a grudge, although his wife was unable to forget one, and *pestered* him about his weakness in forgiving those who had injured him.

Dick Baumann seemed to be unable to keep a job and he showed few signs of being able to make his way in the world. But he was popular, he had an *immense* number of friends, he was in request all over because he was always truly and literally the life of every party. At one such party, he met his future wife, an extremely beautiful girl who was also successful and had her own business. She was the only child of a mother deserted by her husband, and never had she been so charmed as by Dick, by Dick's parodies, imitations, out-goingness, and his fine air of well-being and happiness. Although somewhat perplexed by the girl's intense and fond looks, since he had not paid much attention to her, Dick had invited her to the Baumann ménage, where Mrs. Baumann immediately fell in love with her. Dick was pliant and suggestible, Mrs. Baumann was the only strong-willed one in the family, and soon she had arranged matters in such a way that after a certain amount of urging on her part, everyone recognized the inevitability of the marriage.

First, however, Dick had to make a living. His intended had her handsome business, which she *ran* with a cousin. But this did not seem right to Mrs. Baumann; it offended her sense of propriety. She expected that it would end very soon, and she spoke of its ending all the time. She insisted that it must end before the marriage took place, since it was not only intolerable that a wife should make her own living, should go to work each day, but it was wrong that the wife should earn more money than the husband. As it happened, Dick was in no hurry to get married. He wished to please his mother, as he wished to please all. But from morning until night, he enjoyed being *single;* yet he did not conceive of his marriage as bringing about any great change in his habits, or any new goodness.

Shenandoah listened with an interest which increased continuously; and yet his own thoughts intervened many times. He reflected upon his separation from these people, and he felt that in every sense he was removed from them by thousands of miles, or by a generation, or by the Atlantic Ocean. What he cared about, only a few other human beings, separated from each other too, also cared about; and whatever he wrote as an author did not enter into the lives of these people, who should have been his genuine relatives and friends, for he had been surrounded by their lives since the day of his birth, and in an important sense, even before then. But since he was an author of a certain kind, he was a monster to them. They would be pleased to see his name in print and to hear that he was praised at times, but they would never be interested in what he wrote. They might open one book, and turn the pages; but then perplexity and boredom would take hold of them, and they would say, perhaps from politeness and certainly with humility, that this was too *deep* for them, or too *dry*. The lower middle-class of the generation of Shenandoah's parents had engendered perversions of its own nature, children full of contempt for every thing important to their parents. Shenandoah had thought of this gulf and perversion before, and he had shrugged away his unease by assuring himself that this separation had nothing to do with the important thing, which was the work itself. But now as he listened, as he felt uneasy and sought to dismiss his emotion, he began to feel that he was wrong to suppose that the separation, the contempt, and the gulf had nothing to do with his work; perhaps, on the contrary, it was the center; or perhaps it was the starting-point and compelled the innermost motion of the work to be flight, or criticism, or denial, or rejection.

Mrs. Fish had gone to the roof for more wash. She told Shenandoah as she returned that it was time for him to dress (for he had been in dressing-gown and pajamas all the while), and in her imperative tone, he recognized the strain and the resistance which was part of the relationship of mother and son; which had its cause in the true assumption that mother and son would disagree about what was the right thing to do, no matter what the problem might be.

The *engagement* of Dick and Susan was a protracted one; and after two years, the youthful couple had begun to take their intermediate state for granted. Mrs. Baumann in pride told her friends that Susan *practically* lived with them. It was by no means unusual for Susan to be at the Baumann household on every weekday evening, and on such evenings, as Dick read the sport pages with care, his mother interrupted him persistently to demand that he admire Susan's profile as she sat near the window, sewing. Susan was very beautiful indeed; and her business grew more and more prosperous as Dick went from job to job, unperturbed that a girl waited for him, a fact to which Mrs. Baumann often summoned his attention.

At last, being impatient, Mrs. Baumann arranged that the

marriage should occur at the beginning of one of Dick's business ventures, the capital for which had been provided by Mr. Baumann and Susan. It was as if, remarked Shenandoah's mother, Mrs. Baumann was afraid to await the outcome of the new venture. And she had been right, for within eight months the business had to be given up to avoid bankruptcy, and Susan had to return to work as an assistant where before she had been *her own boss*, a humiliation which left Susan without any further illusions about her mother-in-law. The two never again managed to get along very well, although Mrs. Baumann's admiration of her daughter-in-law remained undisturbed. Mrs. Baumann was unable to understand Dick's failure to get rich, for no one failed to be delighted by his charm and his intelligence, and he always seemed to have a great deal of information about each new business. But somehow he was unable to make a success of it, or even to make it *pay*.

After his marriage, Dick frequented his parents' household as often as before marriage, a simple enough matter since he and his bride had taken an apartment near the parents to please Mrs. Baumann. And when Susan had to go back to work, it became convenient for the young married couple to have dinner every night with the whole Baumann family, a procedure Susan resented very much, although she was of a divided heart, since she too often enjoyed the conviviality of the family circle as much as before marriage.

One subject prevailed above others in the Baumann circle, the wonders of America, a subject much loved by all the foreign-born, but discussed in the Baumann household with a scope, intensity, subtlety, and gusto which was matchless, so far as Mrs. Fish knew. One reason for this subject's triumph was Mr. Baumann's interest in science, and one reason was that he was very much pleased with America.

When the first plane flew, when elevators became common, when the new subway was built, some newspaper reader in the Baumann household would raise his head, announce the wonder, and exclaim:

"You see: America!"

When the toilet-bowl flushed like Niagara, when a suburban homeowner killed his wife and children, and when a Jew was made a member of President Theodore Roosevelt's cabinet, the excited exclamation was:

"America! America!"

The expectations of these human beings who had come in their youth to the new world had not been fulfilled in the least. They had above all expected to be rich, and they had come with a very different image of what their new life was to be. But a thing more marvellous than fulfillment had transformed their expectations. They had been amazed to the pitch where they knew that their imaginations were inadequate to conceive the future of this incredible society. They expected and did not doubt that all the wonders would continue and increase; and Mr. Baumann maintained, against rising and rocking laughter, that his grandchildren would return from business by a means of transit which resembled the cash carriers which fly through tubes in department stores. Mrs. Baumann's conception of the future was less mechanical and scientific. She hoped and expected her grandchildren would be millionaires and grandsons, rabbis, or philosophers like Bergson.

Sidney, the youngest child, had arrived at the age when it was expected that he too should earn a living for himself. But the disappointments Dick had caused were nothing to the difficulties Sidney made. Dick had been an indifferent student, but Sidney flatly refused to continue school at all after a certain time, and he displayed unexampled finickiness about the job Mr. Baumann's friends gave him, or helped him to get. He left his job as a shipping clerk because he did not like *the class of people* with whom he had to work, and he refused to take a job during July and August on the ground that he suffered greatly from the summer heat, a defense natural to him after the many family discussions of health, food, and exercise. His mother always defended and *humored him,* saying that his health was delicate. But Mr. Baumann was often made furious and at times of an insane anger by his youngest son's indolence. Mrs. Baumann pointed out that Sidney was to be admired, after all, since in being unable to work he showed a sensitivity to *the finer things in life*. But Mr. Baumann knew too much of the world not to be concerned about the fact that both of his sons appeared to be unable to make out well in the world. In anger, he blamed his wife and his wife's family; but on other occasions, he discussed the problem with his friends, once with Shenandoah's father after the two were reconciled.

"I'll tell you what to do," said Mr. Fish, "but you won't do it."

"Tell me," said Mr. Baumann, although he knew well enough he was not likely to take his friend's advice.

"Ship Sidney out into the world," said Shenandoah's father, "make him stand on his own two feet. As long as he has a place to come home to and someone else to give him money for cigarettes, and plenty of company in the house, he's not going to worry about losing a job."

"But if a boy does not have ambition," Mr. Baumann replied, "is that enough? I always say, it all depends on the individual. His home has nothing to do with it. It is always the character of the person that counts."

"Sure it depends on character," said Mr. Fish, "but a fellow only finds out about his own character when he's all by himself, with no one to help him. Why if I had been your son," said Shenandoah's father, flattered that his advice was asked and wishing to please his friend, "I would have quit work myself and taken it easy and enjoyed the pleasant evenings."

A year later, Sidney was sent to Chicago to be *on his own*, although not before he had been given the addresses of many friends and relatives of the family. In three months, he was back; he had quarreled with his boss about working hours and he had exhausted his funds. He was welcomed into the bosom of the family with unconcealed joy. Although Mr. Baumann grumbled, and Martha addressed habitual ironic remarks to her brother as *a captain of industry*, no one had failed to feel his absence keenly and to be pleased deeply by his return.

"Well: you can try in New York as well as Chicago," said

Mr. Baumann, "a smart boy like you is bound to get started sooner or later."

Mrs. Baumann believed that Sidney would fall in love one day, and this would prove the turning point. Either he would meet a rich girl who would be infatuated with *his personality,* or he would meet some poor girl and his desire to marry her would inspire him. In America, everyone or almost everyone was successful. Mrs. Baumann had seen too many fools make out very well to be able to believe otherwise.

And now all he had heard moved Shenandoah to remember all he knew himself of the Baumann family. The chief formal occasions of the Fish family had always been marked by the presence of the Baumanns. Each incident cited by his mother suggested another one to Shenandoah, and he began to interrupt his mother's story and tell her what he himself remembered. She would seize whatever he mentioned and augment it with her own richness of knowledge and experience.

As a girl, Martha had suffered an attack of polio, which left her with a curvature of the spine, which in turn made it unlikely that she would be able to have children. Martha had then decided that this defect and her plainness of appearance, a plainness which, although she did not know this truth, disappeared in her natural vivacity and wit—would prevent her from getting a husband. She would be an old maid, the worst of shames from the point of view of a Jewish mother. The belief that she would never marry heightened Martha's daring wit and *nerve.* She was the one who continued her father's intellectual interests. As he would cite the authors he had read in Russia as a young man, Pushkin, Lermontov, and Tolstoy, so she was much taken with Bernard Shaw and H.G. Wells, and spoke with bitter passion about women's suffrage.

And then, to the amazement of all, a young doctor who had frequented the household, a very shy young man who was already very successful, asked Martha to marry him, pale with fear that she would laugh at him and attack him with her famous sharpness and scorn. When she told him that he would have to go through life without children, he replied with a fine simplicity that he loved her and expected her to make a home for him which would be like her mother's household.

This marriage became the greatest satisfaction of the Baumanns' life, although it did not *compensate* for the shortcomings of the sons in business. Mrs. Baumann tirelessly praised her son-in-law, and marvelled infinitely at his magnanimity in marrying a girl who was unable to have children. She took especial pride in his being a very good doctor, a fact which impressed the women of her acquaintance because they wished most of all for sons or sons-in-law who were doctors. But it was for Mrs. Baumann a triumph chiefly because of her passionate interest in health.

Martha's harshness and sharpness rose to new heights with her marriage, and she became more relentless than ever with her brother, while often Maurice, her husband, found it necessary to protest gently, from a profound gentleness of heart, because she had once again called both brothers *failures*. Maurice had an admiration for the arts which gave him the conventional independence of conventional business values. He tried to argue with Martha that she was being *very conventional* and accepting conventional views of what *success* was. Martha, inspired by an enjoyment of her own brutality of speech, replied that there was one thing the Baumanns were wonderfully successful at, and that was marriage: they made first-class marriages. She was referring then not only to her own husband's prosperity and generosity, but also to Susan, who had started her own business again, and for years now had supported her husband and herself, and provided Dick with the capital for each new enterprise he attempted, spurred by his mother's anguish at the way things were.

Martha became more impatient with her family year by year, and after a time she did not wish to see them at all. But Maurice gently insisted that she pay her parents a weekly visit, and he sought to soothe the parents' hurt feelings when Martha saw to it that they lived in a suburb distant from the Baumann household.

America! America! The expression began to recur in Shenandoah's mind, like a phrase of music heard too often the day before. He was moved, and in a way shocked, as his mother was too, that Martha the family rebel, the one who had repudiated the family circle many times, should be the one who made out well in life. Shenandoah's mother amazed him by remarking that the two sons were unsuccessful because they were like their father, who had been successful, however, because of what he was. The sons had followed the father and yet for some unclear cause or causes, the way of life which had helped him to prosper prevented them from prospering.

And now Shanandoah remembered his last meeting with Mrs. Baumann, two years before. Late in the afternoon in October, as Shenandoah rewrote a poem, Mrs. Baumann's voice had come through the closed bedroom door. And he had been annoyed because he now had to come from his room, pale and abstracted, his mind elsewhere, to greet his mother's friends. It turned out that Mrs. Baumann had come with a friend, a woman of her own age, and when Shenandoah entered the living room, Mrs. Baumann, as voluble as Mrs. Fish, told Shenandoah in a rush the story of her friendship with this woman.

They had come to America on the same boat in the year 1888, and this made them *ship sisters*. And then, although their friendship had continued for some years, one day at a picnic of the old country's society, a sudden storm had disturbed the summer afternoon, everyone had run for cover, and they had not seen each other for the next nineteen years. And Mrs. Baumann seemed to feel that the summer thunderstorm had somehow been the reason for their long and unmotivated separation. The two old women drank tea and continued to tell the youthful author about their lives and how they felt about their lives; Shenandoah was suddenly relaxed and empty, now that he had stopped writing; he listened to them and drank tea too. Mrs. Baumann told Shenandoah that in her sixty-five years of life she had known perhaps as many as a thousand human beings fairly well, and when she tried to sleep at night, their faces came back to her so clearly that she believed she could draw their faces, if she were a painter. She was sickened and horrified by this plenitude of memory, although it was wholly clear why she found the past appalling. Yet these faces kept her from falling asleep very often, and consequently she was pleased and relieved to hear the milkman's wagon, which meant that soon the darkness would end and she would get up, make breakfast for her family and return to the world of daylight. Mrs. Baumann felt that perhaps she ought to see a psychoanalyst, like Freud, to find out what was wrong with her.

Her companion offered advice at this point; she said that everyone should have *a hobby*. Her own hobby was knitting and she felt that without her knitting in the morning, she would *go crazy*. This woman's daughter had married a *Gentile*, and she was permitted to visit her only child on monthly occasions when the husband had absented himself. Her one longing, one which she knew would never be satisfied, was to return and visit the old country.

"You would like it there," she said to Shenandoah, speaking of the country of her young girlhood. Shenandoah was flattered.

And as he listened to the two old women, Shenandoah tried to imagine their arrival in the new world and their first impression of the city of New York. But he knew that his imagination failed him, for nothing in his own experience was comparable to the great displacement of body and mind which their coming to America must have been.

Although almost finished with her ironing, Mrs. Fish was far from finished with her story. She was able to illustrate all that she said with fresh or renewed memories. And what she said bloomed in Shenandoah's mind in forms which would have astonished and angered her. Her words descended into the marine world of his mind and were transformed there, even as swimmers and deep-sea divers seen in a film, moving underwater through new pressures and compulsions, and raising heavy arms to free themselves from the dim and dusky green weight of underseas.

Shenandoah's mother now had progressed to the period of

great prosperity in America. The worst animosity had come to exist between Mr. Baumann and his son Sidney, for whenever Sidney was criticized by his father for not earning his own living, he replied by citing the success of his father's friends, many of whom were becoming rich. Few of them had the charm or presence of Mr. Baumann, but they were able to give their sons a start in life. Sidney, an avid reader of newspapers like his mother, had acquired a host of examples of immigrants who had made a million dollars. The movie industry was for Sidney a standing example of his father's ineptitude, his failure to make the most of opportunity in the land of promise. It seemed unfair to go outside the family circle of friends, but Sidney was merciless when criticized, and *stopped at nothing*. And Mr. Baumann was left helpless by Sidney's attack, for he felt there was something wrong not only with the comparisons his son made, but the repeated and absolute judgment that his life had not been successful. He himself was satisfied and felt successful. He had always provided for his wife and his children, and kept them in comfort. It was true that he did not work very hard, but then there was no need to work very hard, he made out well enough, since he had an income from the insurance policies he had written for the last thirty years, when the premiums were paid or when the policy was renewed. Yet Sidney used these professions as obvious admissions of weakness. He observed that the sons of other men had a *ten-dollar bill* to spend on a girl on Saturday nights, but he did not. The more unsuccessful he was, the more outrageous became his verbal assault upon his father for not having made a million dollars. He was provoked to these attacks by renewed efforts to get him to work, and by the citation of young men of his age who would soon be wealthy men in their own right, although they came from the households of parents who were really *common*.

During the period of great prosperity the Baumanns and Shenandoah's mother became intimate friends, since Shenandoah's father had left her. And often Mrs. Baumann and Mrs. Fish discussed the fate of the Baumann children. Mrs. Fish had once given Mrs. Baumann what she still regarded as very good advice, she had told her friend that the salvation of the family would have been the summer hotel business, which they had once considered seriously as an enterprise. No one would have been better suited for that business than the Baumanns, and this was indeed a *high compliment.*

When his mother said such things, Shenandoah suffered for the moment, at any rate, from the illusion that his mother had a far greater understanding of the difficulties of life than he had. It seemed to him at such times that the ignorance he saw in her was a sign of his own arrogant ignorance. Her understanding was less theoretical, less verbal and less abstract than his, and such privations were in fact virtues. She was never deceived about any actual thing by words or ideas, as he often was. And she had just perceived perfectly a profound necessity which he himself knew very well in literature, the necessity that the artist find the adequate subject and the adequate medium for his own powers. No one could deny that the proper medium for the gifted Baumanns was the summer hotel.

What Mrs. Baumann did not understand and sought to explain to herself and Mrs. Fish was the paradox that her sons, who had a good bringing-up unlike many successful young men, had made out so poorly in comparison with most of them. She wished to know whose fault it was, if it were her fault, if she ought to blame herself, as her husband blamed her, for *humoring* and *indulging* the boys. The head start, and the fine home which the boys had, seemed to be a handicap, but this was an impossible thing to think. Mr. Baumann had remembered the advice given him by Mr. Fish, that the boys would be more ambitious if they had no home to come to, and he had distorted this counsel into an explanation which declared that Mrs. Baumann had pampered her sons. Mrs. Baumann returned with this problem many times, eager to be reassured and anxious to be told that on the contrary she was a wonderful mother. Shenandoah's mother was already prepared to blame someone for everything that happened, but she had a general and theoretical interest in the problem which left her free of her natural prepossessions. She observed that one defect of the Baumann sons was their unwillingness to go from door to door for the sake of getting some business. They had not been reared to expect *hard knocks* and rebuffs, and here precisely was where boys of meaner families had the advantage. It was a strange and sad thing, both women agreed, that a certain refinement—nothing like the Four Hundred, *you understand,*—but merely a simple taste for the normal good things of life should be a severe and conclusive handicap. The greatest handicap, said Mrs. Fish, was the fine family circle; this was what had weakened the boys for a world where you had to fight for everything you wanted, and you had to fight all the time just to keep what you had. Mrs. Fish observed again that this was *a cut-rate cut-throat world,* an expression which was her version of the maxim, *dog eat dog.* The best preparation for such a world, as Mrs. Fish's experience had proved many times, was to be born into a family of thirteen children where there was never enough for everyone to eat.

After 1929, when those who had been successful lost so much, Sidney mounted to new summits of scorn. Before 1929, he had been contemptuous of *the system;* now that no one made out well Sidney took the national depression as a personal vindication. Every banker or broker caught in some kind of dishonesty became an instance to Sidney of his own integrity. He suggested that if he had been prepared to do such things, he too might have enjoyed their success.

And now Mr. Baumann was no longer able to support an idle son, for with the hard times people abandoned their insurance or borrowed on it. The father's difficulties and the son's arrogance made their quarrels more and more desperate. As Mr. Baumann dressed to pay a visit one Saturday night, he was unable to find the pair of shoes he wanted. As always, he was concerned about his appearance, and he became very irritated at being unable to find his shoes, and came into his son's bedroom to ask him if he had seen the shoes, and Sidney, outstretched upon his bed, reading and smoking, was annoyed to be interrupted, and replied that his father ought not to be concerned about such a cheap pair of shoes. The shoes were not cheap, in any case, and this typical judgment of his taste by his son, whose standards were derived from his Christmas jobs in fashionable clothing stores, infuriated Mr. Baumann. He hit Sidney with the flat of his hand, and only Mrs. Baumann's screaming entrance prevented a fist-fight. The day after, Sidney had a black eye which he tried to conceal with powder. It was a Sunday and the Baumanns were going to pay a visit. Sidney wished to go with them, being unable to endure solitude at any time, and having nowhere to go that afternoon. But his mother reminded him of his black eye and his father added that he had no clothes, especially no shoes, suitable for the visit they were going to make. When the Baumanns returned at midnight, they found an emergency wagon and the police in front of the apartment house. Sidney had tried to kill himself by turning on the gas in the kitchen, there had been an explosion, and he had not even been injured. Sidney was taken to Bellevue and kept there for a number of months. When visited by his mother, he told her *she should remember* that it was his father who had driven him to insanity. Hearing this, Mr. Baumann retaliated by saying that his son had been unable to be anything but a failure, even at suicide; and he reported to all that at the hospital, Sidney could not be made to take up any of the forms of occupational therapy. It seemed an epitome to Mr. Baumann that even at this extreme his son should refuse to do anything *remotely resembling work*. It was not customary for Mr. Baumann to be as harsh as this with any human being, but nothing would help Mr. Baumann to forget what Sidney had said to him during the early years of the depression, when Mr. Baumann's income had first begun to be sharply curtailed. He said to his father that *the old oil* no longer worked, and when his father said in perplexity and anger, *what oil? what is this oil?*, Sidney had replied, *banana oil!*, laughing with his whole body at his witticism and then explaining to his father that it was foolish to expect to persuade anyone that insurance was anything but *a gyp* by the old methods of striking up a friendship and paying long visits, *spouting* like the neighborhood sage.

Sidney remained under observation, and Dick assisted his wife in her thriving business. He had a child now. Martha and her husband prospered more and more because the practice of medicine was not as bound to general prosperity as business itself. And after an operation and much nervousness, Martha too had a child. Both grandchildren were daughters, which was a disappointment, but which showed, at any rate, that all disappointments were not financial in origin. As Dick often said,

"Money is not everything," to which his sister always replied, "Money helps," smiling at her own irony.

They were all ashamed of Sidney's *smash-up,* as Dick termed it, but this did not keep them from speaking of it openly with all their friends. Mr. Baumann at seventy was still able to eke out a living for himself and his wife, but he was a disappointed and disillusioned man. He blamed everything on the individual and on his sons' lack of will-power. Mrs. Baumann blamed everything on her husband. She said to Mrs. Fish, however, speaking of Sidney:

"You see: this is what we came to America for forty-five years ago, for this."

Shenandoah was exhausted by his mother's story. He was sick of the mood in which he had listened, the irony and the contempt which had taken hold of each new event. He had listened from such a distance that what he saw was an outline, a caricature, and an abstraction. How different it might seem, if he had been able to see these lives from the inside, looking out.

And now he felt for the first time how closely bound he was to these people. His separation was actual enough, but there existed also an unbreakable unity. As the air was full of the radio's unseen voices, so the life he breathed in was full of these lives and the age in which they had acted and suffered.

Shenandoah went to his room and began to dress for the day. He felt that the contemptuous mood which had governed him as he listened was really self-contempt and ignorance. He thought that his own life invited the same irony. The impression he gained as he looked in the looking-glass was pathetic, for he felt the curious omniscience gained in looking at old photographs where the posing faces and the old-fashioned clothes and the moment itself seem ridiculous, ignorant, and unaware of the period quality which is truly there, and the subsequent revelation of waste and failure.

Mrs. Fish had concluded her story by saying that it was a peculiar but an assured fact that some human beings seemed to be ruined by their best qualities. This shocking statement moved in Shenandoah's mind and became a generalization about the fate of all human beings and his own fate.

"What will become of me?" he said to himself, looking in the looking-glass.

"What will I seem to my children?" he said to himself. "What is it that I do not see now in myself?"

"I do not see myself. I do not know myself. I cannot look at myself truly."

He turned from the looking-glass and said to himself, thinking of his mother's representation of the Baumanns, "No one truly exists in the real world because no one knows all that he is to other human beings, all that they say behind his back, and all the foolishness which the future will bring him."

29. ISAAC ROSENFELD

*Passage from Home**

Isaac Rosenfeld was born in Chicago in 1918 and lived in that city until 1941. In the West Side community of lower middle class Jews of East European origins, he developed a commitment to the intellect and to sensibility that extended into his writing. At the University of Chicago, under the Hutchins regime, he was exposed to an education of considerable philosophic depth. And a youth spent during the Depression gave him a sensitivity to contemporary problems.

Rosenfeld came to New York at the age of twenty-three to work for the Ph.D. in philosophy at New York University. But a position on the New Republic *converted him into a literary journalist. He later moved on to teach at the Universities of Minnesota and of Chicago. A heart attack in July, 1956, cut short his life.*

His one novel has an autobiographical quality. Its subject is a sensitive fifteen-year-old boy, irked by the narrow confines of his Jewish home, who seeks an escape to freedom which he associates with an aunt who has rebelled against the family. In the end he returns to confront the father from whom he has fled, whom he resembles, and whom he cannot love because he does not know what love is.

Although he had been asleep and therefore might very well have been at a loss, my father showed neither shock nor surprise. He stood at the door while I mounted the stairs, stepped aside as I entered and closed the door behind me. His eyes were blinking, but perhaps only with sleep. He was bare-

* Isaac Rosenfeld, *Passage from Home* (New York, 1946), pp. 264–80.

foot and wearing a bathrobe, striped like an awning. His hair, which he combed every night before retiring, was still neat.

My stepmother, however, shrieked, rushed out of the bedroom, her robe coming apart, and fairly lifted me off my feet in a hug—and as quickly let me down. She looked at my father as if expecting him to indicate the proper manner of receiving me. He provided no clue, but stood to a side, shaking his head.

"So you're back." He did not know what else to say. Because he was my father he felt he should speak, judge me, pass immediate sentence, condemning or forgiving. This he felt he should do, just as I expected him to do it. But his emotion was the same as mine. In my embarrassment I avoided him, keeping my eyes averted to the floor, and while I still expected him to speak to me, it seemed to me that he, too, was staring at the floor. I saw him turn and leave and go to the front room. There, I knew, he would stand at the window, looking out.

My stepmother compressed her lips, wrinkled her chin like a peach pit, cupped her palm around it and rested her elbow in the palm of her other hand, an elaborate gesture which she employed only when, rarely, for lack of knowing what to express, she let the gesture express itself. But she soon recovered, whisked me into the kitchen, turned on the light and simulating a whisper, but loudly enough for my father to hear, began unburdening herself. "A fine son you are, shame on you! Can't you find something to say to your father? Go in right now and talk to him. Go on!"

I remained silent, avoiding her, and looking about the kitchen which had lost none of its brilliance during my absence. The checkered dish towels hung on their racks, the sink was gleaming, the jars of spice on the shelves above it had their old clean and sturdy air.

"What's the matter? Don't you know what to say? You can go in and say you're sorry. You can ask him to forgive you. Fine tricks! After making him suffer so much, all you can think of doing is to stand around with your hands in your pockets. Take your hands out of your pockets!"

She seldom ordered me about. It was usually "Please do this," or "Would you mind very much doing that?" I had forgotten the meaning of her politeness, and now that she had given a command, which I promptly obeyed, it recurred to me that her customary deference was a form of submission. She was only my stepmother, and did not want to presume. Even if I had been unaware of doing so, I had always exploited her deference. Old guilts were reopened before me, old habits whose significance I had ignored for years, were struck afresh with my re-entrance into the house, and I realized that to redeem my life with my father and with her I should have to begin, deep within myself, as if I were to question the uses to which I put the very air I breathed. For if I had wondered what love was while living with Minna and Willy, I now saw looming before me the more disquieting, if simpler, mystery—what was the relation between parent and child, what was a father, a mother?

"Don't be so proud and stubborn. If you realize you've done wrong, own up to it. And don't be afraid. For my part, I'm glad your back—and so is your father. Would he throw his own son out of the house?

"Although, I don't mind telling you, maybe you would deserve it, young man." She knotted the belt of her robe, which had come undone. She, too, was barefoot; her bunions seemed to have grown larger. "After all, what you did is unheard of, simply unbelievable! Imagine, planning it! Doing it on purpose! Inviting that woman—ptoo!—making her come when the whole family is together, so she can open her dirty drunken mouth, so all those terrible things can come pouring out like pitch! And she not even fit to stand in the same room with her father. Oh, let me tell you, you deserve it!"

I tried to interrupt her, to explain that I had not been responsible, but my stepmother, having discarded her politeness, having, in fact, become my mother, would not hear me.

"What makes it so bad is just that—that you planned it. You little sneak, you! Snot nose! You pissher! When I married your father you still used to wet your pants. You came home from second grade once with your pants full. You should do a thing like that? You should make plans, you, mister? Pretend and make off like you didn't know a thing—and even take an interest in the house, all of a sudden! That's what beats me. You should run to the delicatessen and the butcher and make telephone calls and help me clean the walls—ah, I'll never undertake such a job again!—and all the time you should be planning your little surprise! What did you do it for? Well, I ask you. Did you think it would be fun? Did you want your poor father—"

"But I didn't, I didn't, I'm telling you! I had no idea she would—"

"Ah, what the man suffered. That his own son should play such a trick on him! But what do you know? You've got as much brains as a cat. Do you know what it means to be a father?"

She would not listen to me. I no longer tried to interrupt her. She was right, as usual, absolutely right in the impulse if not the content of her words. I did not know what it meant to be a father.

"Believe me, if you were a son of mine! . . ." She had reached the peak of her anger, had taken me by the sleeve and begun to shake me, her face, meanwhile, having turned bright red and her lips nearly white. There were tears in her eyes, but they were not only tears of exhausted rage; for in the rising of her anger I had felt her achieving an intensity of emotion far beyond the demands of the moment, an emotion unnecessarily large, overweighing the need of reproving me and of expressing sympathy for my father. She was no longer speaking merely as his loyal wife, but, for the first time, was striving to satisfy herself, and in doing so had grasped at the passion hitherto unavailable to her—the intensity of personal suffering of which she had always felt herself deprived because she was not a mother. While she was shouting and shaking me I sensed the rush of her love, and my own answered her as I wanted to embrace her, to become her son, feeling that not only she, but I, too, had been deprived.

"Well, what are you standing around for?" She had spent herself. "Go wash up and eat something. You're hungry, aren't you? You should see what you look like—feh, skin and bones. She wouldn't even feed you right, that aunt of yours. Ti, ti, ti, ti—" here she wrinkled up her nose, folded her arms, and shook her head from side to side in mimicry of Minna. (That Minna never made such gestures was quite immaterial to her.) "Wait, just a minute. It wouldn't hurt you to take a tub either."

"Right now? But it's late—"

"Never mind it's late. You're dirty, you smell—I bet you didn't take one in all this time. Aie, such pigs! Go ahead, go live with your piggish aunt and eat pigs and roll around in the mud and look green and skinny like a stick. I'll give you a pig that you'll have something to remember!"

Having said which, she went off to the bathroom, and I soon heard the water running in the tub.

My father looked in on me several times while I was eating, but each time went back into the front room. This was evidently to remind me that we should have a talk when I had finished; and yet it was not his eagerness for the talk, but rather his anxiety over it that impelled him to come to the kitchen. When he appeared at the door I would begin to bolt my food, as if to let him know that I would soon be with him; but I would immediately check myself for fear he would see how hungry I was. It was difficult to eat, although the food was excellent; in fact, after Minna's suppers, the brown gravy that drowned the vegetables, winked with eyelets of fat, seemed to convey the very essence, the warmth and the familiarity, of home. I trembled, anticipating the scene with my father. It was not until I had seen him again that I fully remembered my guilt; for it was then that I realized that the impulse which had made me return home—an impulse that seemed to me so praiseworthy, that I was sure he would consider it to my credit—would be entirely discounted. He had every right to take my homecoming for granted, since from his position it was the very smallest debt that I owed him, and not until it had been paid could one consider the actual issue of right and wrong. Thus my homecoming, which I imagined would wipe out my guilt, was the very thing that established it. And so I no longer knew quite where I stood, and even my hunger was complex and compromising, for insofar as I had wronged my father my appetite was gluttony, and yet not to eat would further have demonstrated my ingratitude.

I finished supper and waited for my father to appear at the door again, meanwhile looking about the kitchen and noticing, one might think for the first time, the minor details of the room, the chip in the black porcelain knob of the kitchen door, the grain of the linoleum, the rough silver paint on the radiator, as if by absorbing myself in the security of the inanimate I might safely enter into the sense of home. "I'd like to have a word with you," said my father. I rose, scraping the chair on the floor, and followed him into my room.

We took up our accustomed positions: he on the bed and I in the chair at my desk. Even now I was in some measure denying him—the bed was lower than the chair and not as comfortable to sit on, and I had not waited for him to be seated first. But he shook his head in melancholy irony when I offered to let him have my chair. He seemed to be saying, "That's the least of my grievances."

Except that we were both wearing pajamas—I had dressed for bed right after my bath—the scene was as usual, the light at my desk, my father sitting in partial shadow. He would lose feature and personality and, no longer himself, would become mere and absolute father, an image at the periphery, never clearly seen. I, sitting in the light, would owe both my discomfort and my advantage to him. The light of my desk lamp would be shining in my eyes, for I would have turned it to prevent its falling into his. And yet he would be sitting in the outer darkness of the life he had created and furnished for me.

"Well, what do you have to say for yourself?" There was harshness and finality in his voice, as if, intending to shut out all criticism, he were telling me that there was only one account to be given—mine—and that he was in no way involved.

"I've nothing to say."

"Nothing at all? So. Very nice."

This was the end of the first interchange, and a most satisfactory one insofar as it was to my interest to defend myself against my father. But I could not overcome a sense of disappointment in myself for having done so, and I realized that it was only the fact that I wanted to yield to him which made me fight against him. I shifted nervously in my chair, and further lowered the shade of the lamp, casting the light more directly into my eyes—but setting him in an even deeper shadow.

Father—either unwilling or incapable—still did not seize the advantage over me. By my stubbornness—which was at bottom no more than fear of honesty—I had laid myself open to reproach, and now I was so full of the sense of my guilt, that my father, with the very least assertion of his judgment, could have brought it pouring out of me. But the moment of weakness passed. For father did not press his advantage, but preferred rather to pity me. My embarrassment grew as he forced me to recognize his restraint. Why had he chosen to pity me? Was it that he abhorred weakness so much that he would on no account make use of it in others? This only made me the weaker.

At last he asked, "Why did you go away?"

"I was afraid," I replied at once, making an effort to be honest.

"You were afraid? Of what?"

I realized that I wanted him to pity me. Why did he allow me to evade him? "I was afraid," I repeated.

"Afraid!" he cried, finally with that sternness I had been fearing yet longing to encounter. "A big boy like you!" But there was a note of bitterness and mockery in his voice; he was still not allowing himself to use his full force. "What were you afraid of?"

"You would have thought I told her to come, that I had done it on purpose!" I cried. But the moment I had made my confession it no longer was a confession, having become an empty and meaningless thing, a further evasion, even if a sign of truth. All the same, once I had confessed, I resented having had to do so. For I should have preferred to have him accuse me of conspiring with Minna; then, though I had not done so, the charge, while false, would at least have been honest. But by attributing it to him, as a false suspicion, I had suppressed the possibility, if not the element, of truth that I felt it to contain. Had he forced me to accuse myself?

If I had ever feared him, it was because he was my moral superior, capable of an honesty so much greater than mine that I would always appear mean-spirited and unworthy of him. But now, believing he had deliberately turned my own devices against me and forced me to accuse myself, I suspected that our relationship had changed entirely in the few weeks I had been away, and that he could no longer afford his original honesty. He was a weaker man, no longer the impartial, disinterested, yet intimate judge who, if he restrained himself, did so only out of an inherent modesty in the recognition of his righteousness and the employment of his strength. Now, rather, he had cause to defend himself—he had begun to fear me for the same reasons that I had long feared him.

"No, my boy. Why do you bring that up? That never entered my mind. I thought no such thing."

"I was sure you did," I insisted, convinced now that he was lying either to spare me, or, more likely, to spare himself. "I was sure you were blaming me for it. You knew I'd been going to see her—you must have known she had found out about the party through me. And then when I left the house with her, that must have proved it to you!"

"But I tell you I had no such idea," he replied, somewhat disconcerted by my aggressiveness, which must have made him realize that I was eager to cover myself with guilt. He held back, speaking softly and trying to fathom my purpose. "I only felt very hurt that you left home—and that you went to live with her. I never held you responsible for what she did."

"But ma does!" I kept pressing the point. "She blames it all on me. She says I planned it, that I wanted it to happen. She doesn't even say that Minna made me do it, but that I figured it all out by myself. Didn't you hear her hollering at me?"

"I wasn't listening," he replied. But he had caught the implication—that my stepmother would never advance an opinion unless it reflected his mind. All my uneasiness had been transferred to him, and I now appeared the accuser.

He got up from the bed and walked about the room, stopping before the bookcase and looking at my books. He always seemed to regard them as strange and remote objects, symbols of myself, and thus related to him—it was with his money that I had bought them—and yet as alien and hostile as I myself had become. My father ran his hand along a row of the books, which were standing neatly aligned on the shelf, as if he meant thereby to say, "You haven't been at them for a long time."

"To tell you the truth . . . I've forgotten about the whole thing." He came toward me but stopped outside the circle of light. "All I know is that you're back. It was wrong of you to leave, so wrong—you have no idea what it did to me! . . . But now that you've come back, all I want is that you should . . . This is your home!" he cried, shaking his extended finger and emphasizing the words, not, however, with the anger I had expected him to direct against me, but in protest against the impalpable that had drawn me away from him. "This is your home and your family, and you're going to live here! If it's not good enough for you, I want to know the reason why and I'll make it good! Here you stay until you're old enough to go out into the world to establish your own home. I didn't bring you into the world to—to—to become a bum, do you hear me?—and if I've got the means to provide you with a home, there should be no reason on earth why it's not good enough for you!"

While he was speaking to me, his expression had lost some of its customary acuteness. From what I could see in the dim outer light, he had ceased to stare at me and was no longer intent on penetrating the disguise of my emotions. He had turned harder in his love, and was berating me now for my ultimate denial; and yet he had a look, not so much of anger, pride, or sorrow as of distraction, as if the suffering he had borne prevented his passing far enough beyond his own emotion to understand mine. For though he may have come upon my true failure as a son, still he could not see that I remained unrelenting in the very face of his discovery. In all truth, what did it matter to me, or how should it touch me, that he had bared, along with his sternest and therefore most actual love, that vision of himself, the father as provider and homemaker, that justified the hardships of his life and made them ideal necessities? Although I had heard him proclaim his creed of fatherhood many times—so often that the present occasion, despite his emotion, impressed me as nothing more than a recitation—I was still in no way dedicated to preserving his illusions. The truth was that I lived my own life and would continue to do so, without a thought for the gratifications necessary to his.

But this, he would never understand, did not bar me from loving him. He failed to see the direction my impulses took. Though he knew me to be selfish, and upbraided me for it, he could not grasp how deeply my selfishness depended on him and involved him, so that, while I was leading my own life, nothing I did was truly independent of his, if only because, to find pleasure in selfishness—I could not bear to be alone—I clung to him, needing the knowledge and the assurance of his nearness. My love was my guilt.

It was for this reason, though I understood my motive but dimly, that I refused to let him wave aside the subject of Minna, and returned to it, insistently telling a lie in which, however, I realized there was more truth than in any other statement I had ever made before my father. "But pa, it's a fact!" I cried. "I really did plan it! I did want to go and live with Minna. As long as I've known her I've wanted to. I arranged the whole thing with her because—because of the way you treated her!"

I sprang out of my chair and stood before him, both defying him and urging him to believe me. "It is so! I'm telling you the truth!" I shouted, taking him by the sleeve of his pajamas (how rarely there had been physical contact between us!) and feeling there need be no further proof of my sincerity than the fact that I had hurt him.

He looked at me sadly, as if to say, "Can't you understand that I don't demand an explanation? It is I who have to explain!" I realized then—without being aware of it, I had feared this most of all—that our guilt was doubled and shared, and I felt so much the greater a need to affirm my own.

But he pushed my arm away and saying, "I don't want to hear about her," quickly left the room.

My stepmother must have been standing at a discreet distance from the door—near enough to placate her curiosity, yet too far to hear what was said; and evidently she believed it had all ended happily, say with the exchange of my humble apology for my father's warm-hearted forgiveness, for I soon heard her feet padding by my door, then the creak of the telephone chair as she sat down upon it, and the sound of a nickel and my grandfather's number spoken to the operator.

My father and I both ran to the phone to stop her. "What are you calling for?" he cried. "You don't have to call anyone."

She indicated the coin box by way of saying that the nickel had already been dropped. Father yielded to this, as to a piece of superior wisdom. Stepmother, smiling broadly, winking at us and failing to understand our reluctance, announced, "Morris, he is here!"

I heard my grandfather's exclamation come shrilly through the receiver, then a series of hacking sounds, as of laughter, or coughing, or words rapidly shouted, if not all three. Stepmother, the receiver stuck to her ear, sat facing the wall, immensely enjoying his oration. She did not turn to look at us; this was what her heart needed.

"Here, he wants to talk to you," she said, beaming, and giving me the phone. She stopped short when she saw that we were frowning. "What's the matter? Isn't it—"

I took the phone from her and resigning myself, said hello to the old man.

"Oh—ho—ha—this is you? How do you do?" His voice set the metal plate of the receiver rattling. "How do you do, a fine how do you do! So you're home again? No more running around like a bandit? You've come home, you bandit you? Aie-ya! Do you know what I would do to you?" He was all questions, but would not wait for me to answer. "Schmeissen! Schmeissen!" he cried. "A spanking and another spanking, a good one. You haven't had a spanking in years. You need a spanking, but good! Here, I'm coming over and I'll give you one! I'll give you a spanking that you won't be able to see straight. You won't be able to catch your breath for weeks! Here, take off your pants, come on, unbutton—and now your underwear, don't be ashamed. Now lie down, lie down you devil, spread out, that's it, aie-ya—one!—ha!—two!—ah!—three!—oo-vah? That's the way, that's it, that does it, but good you bandit! One-two-three—now you'll know! Now you'll have something to remember!—"

My father took the phone away and replaced the receiver, gently, as if to avoid hurting the old man's feelings.

"What's matter? Harry, I'm sorry. Was it too late to call?" cried my stepmother in consternation, unable to believe that her good will had miscarried, or that the affair had not come to a happy close.

"I'll talk to you later, Bessie," said my father, and putting his hand on my shoulder, led me back into my room.

"Boy, there is something I should tell you," he began. "Maybe you know already. . . ." It was difficult for him to speak; he paused, hoping, perhaps, that it would not be necessary. "Do you know what really happened between your aunt and me?" he sighed.

"Yes, I know," I replied, myself anxious to avert his discomfiture; but added, at once, "I mean, I don't really know. . . . I'm not sure, I mean." For I would hardly have prevented him from debasing himself if I indicated that I already knew what he had to confess.

He sensed my embarrassment. "You'll understand better when you grow up. . . . I just want to clear away any misunderstanding you may have now. . . ."

He stood near me; his expression, I was sure, was the same as my own when I feared him—when I stood ashamed in his presence. My father looked at me pleadingly, rather bewildered by the transformation that was taking place, the necessity he felt himself under to confess. He was still hoping, perhaps unconsciously, that I would stop him.

"Please, you don't have to tell me. Please, I really don't want to know about Minna." But I was aware of my deceit, persisting even to this moment. For while I honestly wanted to spare him the embarrassment, I nevertheless wanted him to commit himself, and, accordingly, I was not preventing him from talking.

"You heard what she said," went on father, "that night at the party. . . ." He paused, on the verge of an absolute commitment, still balancing alternatives. "Well, maybe she exaggerated a little," he smiled self-consciously, as if to make the truth seem less than the truth; "she was drunk, she wanted to make trouble . . .

"I don't know why I'm telling you this. But I don't want you to think that I'm hiding anything from you." He had taken fresh courage; I felt myself shrinking from our intimacy. "I know we've both hidden a lot from each other. It isn't right, Bernard. . . . It shouldn't be like that. We should have absolute trust in each other. You shouldn't ever be afraid to come to me. If there's anything you need, if there's anything you want to say, or to confide in me . . . We should be absolutely open with each other."

"No, please, pa, don't talk about her." I did not want to hear more. I was trembling inwardly and there were tears in my eyes. I knew now that I had reached the point of honesty with him. And yet in that very moment I could feel the beginning of a sense of disappointment—he had, after all, avoided talking about Minna.

"All right," replied my father, as if only to please me, "I won't say any more." He moved away and sat back on the bed. He was silent for a moment, and I saw that he was breathing very slowly; it seemed to me that he was carefully expelling—and concealing—a sigh of relief. "But tell me," he brought out suddenly, "how does she live? Does she have a decent life?"

"Yes . . . she has, " I faltered, my disappointment growing in me. "She wasn't really drunk that night . . . just excited."

He smiled. "It's all right, I understand. You know, you seem to have changed, you seem to understand certain things better. . . ." He yawned briefly; I saw by his wrist watch that it was after midnight. The house and the neighborhood were quiet. In the pauses of our talk there were now empty stretches of time. I felt that he wanted to end the conversation. "Well, tell me, do you still plan to see her? I want you to know I have no objection. . . ."

"No. I won't see her any more," I answered, resenting his generosity.

"Not on my account," insisted father. "Don't say that because you think I want you to."

"I'm saying it because *I* want to. I won't see her any more."

"Well, and Willy? Is she going to marry him?"

"No. They're breaking up."

"Ah-ha!" he cried, slapping his thigh in satisfaction. "I could have told you that in the first place. I knew that man would never settle down."

The vestige of an old loyalty to Minna had not permitted me to mention her marriage to Mason. I was shocked to see how lightly my father had let himself off and regained his pride, adding the final self-esteem of a boast. And I had wanted to throw off my pride, even as he had appeared to be discarding his. It was too late now.

"Well, don't be so down-hearted," said my father, rising and running his hand over my head. The caress seemed an expression of gratitude for the lightness of his ordeal. "Cheer up and let's forget about it. . . . Of course, this won't go any farther . . ., I mean, we won't talk about it to anyone. . . ."

I showed my disappointment.

"What's the matter?" he asked, drawing himself up against any further encroachment on his pride.

Was this my father, the man who never spared himself, who shamed the world by the struggle he conducted with his conscience? "But I don't understand!" I objected. "How can you—"

"Ah, child, enough," he interrupted me with a final pat on the head. "We've had enough of this. I think you need a good night's rest. You look all worn out." And turning back at the door he remarked with a smile—was it mockery, or paternal pride in the exploits of a son?—"And no wonder, the way you've been running around. Now get to bed. You'll have plenty of time to knock around later!"

And was this what it all came to? I lay in bed, unable to sleep, regretting my homecoming and my interview with my father, which had established nothing. I might as well never have left, or never come back.

Was this childishness? Was it this which my father, and apparently the whole world with him, considered childish? I had wanted to make an absolute commitment of the truth I had discovered about myself. Our lives contain a secret, hidden from us. It is no more than the recognition of our failing; but to find it is all of courage, and to speak of it, the whole of truth. If this was an error of childishness, I was proud to be a child.

I felt myself suspended over the unmade declaration, the postponed scene of final understanding. I had been ready to follow my father into the peril of intimacy where we speak clearly and know one another all too well. I had been prepared to reveal all that I had grasped about myself, to confess all my guilt, my inability to be honest and clear.

Now, I thought, it was too late. I had put off declaring myself, only to have my father deprive me of my last opportunity. From now on I was bound to accept him without question—and if without fear, also without the knowledge that there lay some truth between us into which we both might enter. My only hope had been to confess that I did not love him, to admit I had never known what love was or what it meant to love, and by that confession to create it. Now it was too late. Now there would only be life as it came and the excuses one made to himself for accepting it.

PART III

In Our Own Days

1920-1965

There are thus far only fleeting intimations of what the second generation born after 1920 will be like. In the forty-five years since that date, a great Depression, a second and more disastrous world war, and the painful readjustments to a peace punctuated by sporadic conflicts around the world transformed the United States. None of these conditions were conducive to large-scale foreign immigration. Furthermore, internal economic changes reduced the demand for unskilled labor. As a result, the number of entries was far lower than in any preceding period. The chief exceptions have been the refugees from Hitler's persecution in the 1930's, from the Displaced Persons camps in the 1940's, and from the Hungarian and Cuban revolutions of the 1950's. But even those unfortunate victims have not been numerous enough to keep the ranks of the second generation from thinning out.

The writers born since 1920 are just now reaching the prime of their creative careers; it still remains to be seen on what issues they will speak. Harry Barba (No. 30) and Vance Bourjaily (No. 31) deal with the theme of ethnic identification that had already evoked earlier responses. Richard Bankowsky (No. 32) touches on the quest for American success, David Shaber (No. 33) on generational conflicts, and Charles Bacas (No. 34) on the questions of identity and alienation. To that extent, the themes of their predecessors continue to occupy them. But there is no reason to doubt that as they mature these children of the uprooted will discover and explore the distinctive features of their own situation, just as others did in the past.

No more in the present than in the past has the second generation been an element apart from other Americans, distinct in a world of its own. Its marginality was an issue only in the years when American society left men of every sort isolated. More generally, the character of the second generation was shaped by the period in which it lived, and its preoccupations were with the central problems of the nation whatever they were at any given era. The sons and daughters of the immigrants were Americans, perhaps one of the more exposed portions of their society, and therefore particularly sensitive to its strains, but still fully a part of it.

30. HARRY BARBA

*The Picnic**

Harry Barba was born in June, 1922, in Bristol, Connecticut, the son of Armenian parents. He studied at Bates College, at Harvard, and at the University of Iowa, where he also taught creative writing. His novel treats the life of Armenian-Americans in the United States. He has also been involved in editing the magazine Ararat.

In Ford and Chevrolet sedans, in Dodge and Plymouth coupés, in half-ton trucks advertising Bagdasar's Rug Mart, Ohan's Oriental Pastries, and Sultan Babajohn's Grocery Mart, and in solitary Packards and Buicks, members of the Bulbul family followed the highways across the borders of Connecticut, Massachusetts, and New Hampshire into Vermont. Undaunted by the clouds gathering in a lowering sky, they converged on the web of dirt and macadam roads that led into the village settled in the green hills in the northwest corner of the state. Stopping frequently, they took out the letters of invitation and consulted the directions printed in Sonny Zar's spidery hand. No matter what the difficulties of the winding route, no matter how often they had to backtrack, their dark faces pressed forward to the early morning grayness. They were making the trip with gusto and anticipation, singing as they went. For it was no more than once in a decade that they would attend a wedding celebration such as this one.

A long black Packard sedan reached the outskirts of Barstowe first. The car held a group of five men who sat with their

* Harry Barba, *For the Grape Season* (New York, 1960), pp. 136–47, 154–63.

eyes quietly on the road. Piled on the floor at their feet were several musical instruments. Every now and again one of the men would pull a pint bottle of white liquor from his coat, unscrew the top, and tip the bottle to his mouth. Then he would pass the bottle on to the next man.

It was, yes, Bachelor Bedros' wedding day and they, the best *oud, dembeque, zurna,* and tambourine Makers of Music in New England, were finally to be given a chance to show what they could do at a wedding celebration that would really be a celebration.

"Hoi! Huzzah!" the driver of the Packard sedan called out as he took his turn at the bottle. The men grinned. They knew the *raki* was beginning to have its effects.

Above Barstowe the clouds were piled high in the sky like a dark reversed image of the hills. But the July 4th sun sailed free to seep through the broken window of the parsonage cellar.

"This—this," Bachelor Bedros made a strong effort to dislodge the barrel of wine from its stand. "This barrel has a hogshead will of its own!" He spoke to Gamba and Vassily Varan, who were helping him.

He was still wearing the suit in which he had been married to the widow an hour before by the pastor of the Sloecum church. When Bachelor Bedros and the widow had gone to Elizabeth Gadson for help in making arrangements for the wedding and the celebrations that would follow, the churchwoman herself suggested July 4th as the date for the wedding, and as the place, the grape-arbor meadow, the scene of the traditional Independence Day baseball game between Barstowe and Sloecum. When Sarah had said, "July 4th? The meadow? But why?" Elizabeth Gadson had smiled quietly and said, "Maybe we'll finally be able to bring the two groups together," and she had looked at Bachelor Bedros wisely. An hour later Bachelor Bedros got Sonny Zar to hand-print two special invitations, one to the Barstowe parish and the second to the Sloecum parish. He put the invitations in the mail slot in

Leonard Lunch's grocery store, sucked his underlip, and hoped.

And now the ceremony at the church was over and the celebration was ahead of them, and there had been no indication that anyone from the two parishes except Enos Morrill, A. D., perhaps Eugene Gadson, and certainly Elizabeth Gadson would join them in the festivities. Bachelor Bedros was not even sure the minister who had married them would have so much as a glass of wine at the bridal table.

"Bachelor Bedros, today's bridegroom," Gamba tapped the second of the three barrels. "The other vintage barrel will also be for a special occasion." He smiled knowingly at Vassily Varan.

Finally, they got the barrel into the stairway leading up to the trap door. At the trap door they stopped. Breathing hard, Gamba shook his head as he measured the narrow opening with his eyes.

The men hefted the barrel. It would not budge.

"We'll have to go all the way down and up the other stairway to the parsonage," Melope Priest muttered.

Bachelor Bedros pressed the barrel one way, then the other. But it was no use.

"It's stuck now," he said, standing back. "Look out." He herded the two men down the stairway. Behind them, below the barrel, he stopped. Bending at his waist, he gave the barrel a measured look.

"Hey, what are you about to do?" Gamba cried.

With a shout, Bachelor Bedros ran back up the five steps, like a water buffalo. Shouting, bellowing, he threw himself against the barrel. There was a great crash as the frame of the trap door burst into splinters.

But now the barrel was through the door. And Bachelor Bedros lay on the ground next to it. Gamba and Vassily Varan reached the door and looked out at him.

"Do not worry about the door—just a door!" Bachelor Bedros picked himself up. "You saw with your own eyes how it would not go through!"

As Pooshy Kat and Salla Mother unloaded boxes of food, Beluse looked over toward the women at the far side of the field, as though gazing into another, distant world.

"Right near the grape vines is best," she said over her shoulder to the two women. "If they want to join us, they'll join us. God knows we have enough food for a hundred."

Out in the green map of the meadow, some of the Yengee men were pitching horseshoes and running foot races.

"Thatta way, Daddy Hy!" a youth's voice threaded across the meadow to a tall man who was pitching balls to him. Every now and then, one of the older men would go off to one side, lift a jug from behind a tree, and tip it to his mouth.

As Beluse turned to help Pooshy Kat and Salla Mother, Gene Gadson came toward them. Beluse saw that Lalice's eyes were fixed on Gene as he approached.

"The lamb! The lamb!" Pooshy Kat shouted suddenly. "It is loose!" Out in the tall grass, a lamb frisked with the children after it. Yapping wildly, the three Belmountain farm dogs joined in the chase across the meadow, through the group of men pitching horseshoes and running races, and then back. In the far meadow, the picnickers paused to look on.

"Everything's ready, just waiting for our men—" Pooshy Kat interrupted herself with a gasp. "Look! Lookit Ando!"

Bouncing into view, the men sat tall in the front seat of a Roadmaster, like a captain and his navigators in the helm of a ship, while in the rear seat, Ando, the cabinboy, stradled the barrel of wine. He was shouting and waving his arms frantically.

"He is a cowboy and Indian!" Pooshy Kat giggled.

Hopping from his perch, Ando took a place beside the men and lifted with them as they carried the barrel down the hillside, through the meadow, and into the shade of the vineyard.

Bachelor Bedros looked out into the meadow where the children and dogs were chasing the lamb. He picked up a sharp, long-bladed knife from a box and tested it with his thumb. He took heavy twine from his pocket, put the knife into his belt, removed his suit jacket, and rolled up his sleeves. Then, he went out into the meadow after the lamb.

None of the men made a move.

Nervously, Vassily Varan said, "I think he'll want to do it alone." Gamba and Melope Priest pretended to be busy lighting cigarettes. Quickly Ando ran into the meadow after Bachelor Bedros.

"What is that crazy boy up to now?" Beluse said.

At the big man's side, Ando paced in step.

The lamb stood still in the tall grass, watching the man and boy approach. The pink skin of its muzzle vibrated and its slender legs shook.

At a signal from Bachelor Bedros, Ando circled about to the left. Bachelor Bedros waited and then began to move. Ando advanced. The man and boy moved in toward each other with the lamb between them. The lamb walked about nervously. Step by step, the man and boy advanced.

The lamb started to bleat again.

Within steps of their quarry, Bachelor Bedros waved Ando off. He kneeled, clucked and reached out to the lamb.

"Nice lambie," he crooned. "Nice *shish kebob!*" He moved forward a little on his knees. The lamb's bleating was soft now.

With a shout, Bachelor Bedros swooped upon it. When he straightened, he had the lamb bleating and kicking in his arms. Ando came rushing to him, took the heavy twine and tied the lamb's four feet together.

Some of the children ran part way out into the meadow. Vassily Varan, Melope Priest, and Gamba, huddled together, watched the scene out of the corners of their eyes. Gamba watched Ando for the most part.

"There, there!" Bachelor Bedros crooned to the lamb. "Is that a way for a nice little thing like yourself to act? You should be proud—soon you'll be delicious *shish kebob* in our watering mouths."

Bad Blavos and Meester Vaspos left their brothers and sisters and ran out to Bedros.

Kneeling and easing the lamb to the ground, Bachelor Bedros put his hands softly to its throat. He brought a knife within a fraction of an inch of the exposed skin.

He looked up at Ando for just a split second. In the next second, he plunged the knife with a single, direct, clean movement. Blood pumped from the severed artery like a small bubbling sand spring.

"Right now!" Vassily Varan forced a great smile. "Right now is the time to open the barrel of wine into our glasses!"

From the slaying of the lamb to the opening of the barrel of wine and the roasting of the *shish kebob,* Bachelor Bedros captained the festivities by himself. He let the visiting celebrants stand about and watch him at the fire, but that was all. He accepted no help nor heeded any advice, except that given by Ando, who had proved himself in the meadow.

A. D. and Enos Morrill had crossed from the other side with Elizabeth Gadson, and they looked on with interest. They stood among the crowd of Armenians at the fire, who were speaking all at once:

"Too long, Bachelor Bedros! The meat is cooking too long!"

"The spits, countryman, they are too close to the fire!"

"The chunks of meat should be cut smaller!"

"The spits should be cut longer!"

Bachelor Bedros studiously ignored them.

"The women, let them move among the guests," he boomed. "And the men—well, let them sit on their haunches in the shade of the vines eating and drinking and telling each other old land stories."

"*Shish kebob?* Is that *shish kebob?*" Enos Morrill asked.

"*Shashlick. Shish kebob* is *shashlick,*" A. D. said.

Bachelor Bedros beamed at the two men patiently.

"Why sure! Why not? Sure *shish kebob!* As for *shashlick* or *shishlick,* what you call it—I know nothing about that. I know *shish kebob* long before I hear about *shashlick.*" He grinned.

From a stone he took his glass of wine, sipped from it, and handed the glass to Ando. The youth took it and drank from it eagerly. Bachelor Bedros laughed.

"See! See! What is your boy scouting compared to this?" He handed him the glass a second time. Then he handed him a piece of the roasted meat on its spit. The meat was crisp and simmering. Ando took a drink of the wine, swallowed the meat, and took another drink of wine with a flourish of his hand, imitating Bachelor Bedros. Bachelor Bedros laughed wildly. As he laughed, his eyes traveled among his countrymen until they lighted on his bride. Yes, yes, he was the captain of that day!

He let his glance go over her hips. She was wearing a new dress, sheer and summery, which she had received two days before from a mail-order house. The dress made her hips seem even more supple.

Yes, sure, the big captain of that day!

Again, Bachelor Bedros reached for the glass of wine. He picked up a log, shoved it into the fire, and used it like a poker.

"Bedros *Aper,*" Meester Vaspos' soprano waul came from behind. Without turning, Bachelor Bedros pictured the boy's mouth working as he spoke, like a scavenging bird's, quick and sharp. "Once in Boston, in a restaurant, I saw a machine. On this machine such things—chickens, steaks, and even a lamb are roasted so much easier. You should get such a machine for today, Bedros *Aper.*"

Ignoring him, Bachelor Bedros relaxed with the sense of joy he had in being at the fire, turning the spit, watching the meat sputter and grow brown. There was almost nothing like being the big cook. If only the remainder of the picnickers from the other side would come over the wide expanse and join them. The celebrants had taken the first step. Now it was up to the picnickers to take the next. Worriedly, he eyed the two dozen fowls, killed and plucked the day before, now waiting to be skewered and put on the fire next to the roasting lamb.

"How much you planning on barbecuing?" Enos Morrill asked as though reading Bachelor Bedros' thoughts.

"Enough—for more than a hundred," Bachelor Bedros looked over his shoulder to the far side of the meadow, and then back to A. D. "If only your people would be so kind—"

A. D.'s eyes took in the waiting chickens and the roasting lamb, and then looked across the green-blue meadow. More men had joined the youths throwing and catching the baseball with Daddy Hy. Daddy Hy rubbed the ball in his big-jointed hands. Every now and again he wound up and pitched.

Aside from A. D. himself, Enos Morrill, and Elizabeth Gadson, only the Reverend Adam Hawley had come over from the far side. And even the pastor stayed only long enough to toast the bride and groom with a little wine, taste the roasting lamb and wish them all happiness. But many of the picnickers were looking across the meadow and watching the exotic wedding celebration.

A. D.'s eyes studied the group of men throwing the baseball back and forth.

"Yah, Morrill!" Daddy Hy paused with the ball swallowed in his hand as he called in a voice like that of a drunken crow. "You playing ball? Or gonna smoke pipes with them'uns the rest of the day?"

Enos put his glass of wine down on the rock and looked hard at the flat-boned captain of the Sloecum team. And then his eyes came back to rest on Bachelor Bedros.

"Heard all sorts of tales about you," Enos said. "Ever play baseball?"

"Baseball?" Bachelor Bedros returned the look dubiously.

"No matter," Enos sounded disappointed, yet he went on. "Us Barstowe ones usually lose anyway. One more poor player won't make no difference."

Bachelor Bedros looked across the meadow to the men throwing the ball back and forth.

"In a half hour we're having our annual 4th of July game with Sloecum," Enos said. "Be pleased if you see fit to join us." He looked straight at Bachelor Bedros. The big man hesitated.

Then he stopped turning the spits. His face lit up, he cut a cube of meat from the roasting lamb, and handed it to Enos with a wily smile. Enos raised his glass and sipped it thoughtfully, even as he munched the meat.

Abruptly Bachelor Bedros rose and went to the barrel of

wine. Grasping it, an end in each hand, he tried to lift it. Unsuccessful, he muttered under his breath, "Still full. The celebration is not yet really ripe." He picked up two empty milk bottles, filled them with wine at the spigot, put the bottles under his arms and returned to the fire. To Enos and A. D., he said, "I have my ammunition. Let's go!" The three men walked out into the meadow where the teams were warming up.

Overhead, more and more of the storm clouds gathered one upon the other, sending great tents of shadow floating slowly across the expanse of grass and hills. Yet for the moment no one seemed to give them much thought.

"Avak Vadis—from New Wessex—twenty-five dollars!" Camba Nohan's voice came over the applause and shouts of approval. He stood as tall and as dignified as he could on a box at the western end of the grape arbor beside the long table that had been set for the feast. His black mop of hair, standing up almost straight now, looked like a bishop's miter. Faces turned to his voice and then returned to the bountiful celebration spread. A handful of the guests turned about and watched what was happening out in the meadow.

A group of Sloecum men were waiting at home plate with bats in hands. His shoes and shirt off, his trousers rolled up over his knees, Bachelor Bedros ran out into the far field with the Barstowe players. He had a large glove in one hand and called out senseless phrases to his teammates as he went by them. Under his arms, he carried the two milk bottles of wine.

Every now and again, Bachelor Bedros would put one of the bottles to his mouth and take a long drink. Satisfied, he would hand the bottle around to his teammates. He gave the second bottle to a member of the Sloecum team who drank and then passed the bottle on to someone on his team.

Dark eyes among the celebrants followed Bachelor Bedros with wonder. What a way for a three hours' bridegroom to be acting! Yet there must be some reason for it that made sense at least to Bachelor Bedros himself! If not, well—it was his own wedding day, wasn't it? If he wanted to make it his funeral also, it was his own doing.

As for them, they had the greater part of the celebration ahead. For the moment, however, there was this business of collecting the money gifts to the bride and groom.

Vassily Varan was helping Gamba collect and record the gifts. He paused, looking out into the meadow, hopeful that some real excitement would be generated in that direction. But at once the Sloecum batters had begun to hit the ball. He had heard about the annual baseball rivalry between Sloecum and Barstowe, a rivalry that had much more than baseball to it, he understood. He laughed and shook his head.

He had his work to do. Moving with a long stride, he walked to the next guest. Yes, his work must be done with finesse and sophistication, to be appreciated and admired by all his countrymen.

As he approached his next victim, he placed a few large bills on top of the pad on which he was recording the gifts. His eyes and face were ready and challenging.

When he was leaving Avak Vadis, he had heard the man say to his wife, "That's Vassily Varan. You know, Vassily Varan, best friend of Bachelor Bedros!"

"Oh," the woman said, "That's Bachelor Bedros' friend." She looked at him admiringly.

To demonstrate the size of his friendship, Vassily Varan decided he would get at least ten or fifteen dollars from everyone, even from the tightwads like Melope Priest, his next victim. Yes, ten or fifteen dollars, even from Melope Priest who was a pinch-penny even though he had no family but Salla Mother to provide for.

"Melope Priest, *Baroon*—my countryman, relative, a real sport," Vassily Varan lowered his face close to Melope Priest's. Melope looked up quickly. He seemed completely sober, unaffected by the celebration.

"Ah, Vassily Varan, you must be after something from me."

"No, no, I assure you, *Baroon*, I want nothing from you. It is you who will take something from me and from the bride and bridegroom—a feeling of good pleasure and pride by making them a good money gift." Vassily Varan's voice was soft, ingratiating, even a little soothing.

"Do not call me *Baroon*—I give five dollars. I never give more than five dollars." He drew his eyes away from Vassily Varan, stood up, and reached for his wallet out of sight as his fingers hunted for a bill.

"Every man has his level of self-respect. If five dollars is your level—" Vassily Varan's voice sounded a little resigned, yet also a little pitying. "But I want you to know that you are the only one on the list who has the courage to put himself on that level. The rest all gave ten and fifteen dollars, three twenty-fives, two thirties. The rest is all ten and fifteen."

"How's that? No five dollars?" Melope looked outraged. "Are they all rich? Are they out of their heads? How can they with the mills closing down as they have been?"

"No five dollars," Vassily Varan persisted. "But suit yourself —pay on the level of your self-respect." Surely he was doing a job that was superb, Vassily Varan thought. Bachelor Bedros would have to be grateful when he heard about it.

Melope's eyes searched Vassily Varan's face. Finally, he reached into the wallet and extracted five one-dollar bills and added them to the first five.

"All right! All right!" he sounded resigned. "But remember, I made my contribution." He bent over Vassily Varan and watched him write the information on the pad, "Melope Priest Bulbul—and woman, Salla Mother—ten dollars." Melope wasn't satisfied until he saw every letter go down, together with the amount. Briefly, his eyes inspected the long list of sums. There were five or six five-dollar listings that he could see at a glance.

He caught Vassily Varan by the hand.

"Hey, you tricked me!" Melope's voice was loud and self-righteous.

Vassily Varan looked sagely at Melope and patted him on the shoulder. As he left, he said, "No five dollars from people on your level, family member—all ten and fifteen dollars." He moved down the line to the next guest.

Out in the meadow, the Barstowe players were trying to keep the ball game from turning into a rout. Shouts and clapping came from the picnickers gathered on the far side of the field. Even some of the wedding guests, looking on from the table under the arbor, joined in the clapping whenever someone, no matter who, won applause.

Vassily Varan paused to watch the game. As his thumb relaxed on the roll of bills, one of the greenbacks floated to the ground. Vassily Varan watched it out of the corner of his eye, and then with a deft sweep of his long arm and fingers, he scooped up the bill and put it back in the pack from which it fell. He mumbled a few words of prayer, just loud enough for his neighbors to hear, "The Lord God is also good to us—a ten-dollar money gift for Bachelor Bedros and the bride. It is a sign!" He gave a meaningful look at the ten-dollar bill, waved it so all could see, and walked to his next victim. Laughter and gibing calls followed him down the table.

"Mourad Toulian—and family—from Yonkers—thirty-five dollars," Gamba Nohan's voice was big and assertive. There was joy in his voice and something hortatory. Applause came and eyes turned. The hubbub rose and then subsided. Vassily Varan paused to catch the next name Gamba would call in the wake of the applause.

"Mikaiel Mimoz and family—from Hartford—" Gamba's voice paused and then triumphantly, "*fifty* dollars!" The applause thundered, shouts of approval came after it, *Yellah* Mikaiel Mimoz—*Gaitzes* Mimoz! *Mussallah!*" Over the applause came Gamba's voice again, now ringing with happy irony, "And sympathetic regards to the *virgin* bride!"

Laughter, laughter—hysterical shrieks of delight from women who poked their men in the ribs. Did you hear? Regards of sympathy to the—the—oh, precious joy! That Mimoz was still a delightful, rascally joker!

"Simon Sultan—" Gamba's voice went on.

Vassily Varan decided his fists were full enough for the moment. He decided to deposit the money and the list with Gamba, and go watch the ball game. . . .

Still dressed in her harem costume, Pooshy Kat ogled Melope Priest and took him by the arm. She pulled him to his feet and pushed him out into the meadow to the line.

"Oah!" she scolded him. "You have grieved for your children long enough." She reached into the cleft between her breasts and drew out a long orange, purple, and green tissue of silk.

"Here, you'll need this," she said, as she pushed him into the head position of the line of dancers. "But don't forget to return it to its place." She winked at him. Slowly, under Melope's unsure leadership, the borrowed handkerchief twirling awkwardly, the dance line unwound, curling in and out through the meadow grass like a giant human snake. Slowly the Makers of Music increased the vigor of their playing.

One group after another took up the rhythm of the dance with their clapping hands. Two by two, they joined the sinuous dance line.

Most of the Barstowe and Sloecum picnickers stood to one side and looked on. Concerned about the unexpected turn of the ball game, some of the Sloecum men stood in one corner of the meadow with a group of the Barstowe men and a few of the Armenians. The game had generated excitement and needed to be discussed. As wine and hard cider flowed, the Barstowe players began to smile and make extravagant gestures, as though reliving the moment of Bachelor Bedros' magnificent home run ball. The faces of the Sloecum men seemed to become paler, almost bloodless; those of the Barstowe men, ruddy and glowing. The celebrants somehow looked even more dark-skinned, almost purplish, just as if the color of the grape were actually rubbed into their skin.

"That home run was nothing," one of the Barstowe men said. He was a small man with the look of an overripe crab apple, his eyes almost closed from the hard cider and wine he had drunk. "Heard tell this man Bachelor Bedros once hit a ball so mightily, a passing bird hopped a free ride all the way to its nest in the county's highest hill tree." He smiled into his glass.

"He says the truth," one of the celebrants said. "I know. It was I who was there to see it." He grinned to his countrymen and was about to continue but decided against it. The Sloecum men stared blankly, looking from the small man to the rest of the celebrants. Then one of them put a jug to his mouth and took an overlong pull at it. It was more than a minute before he passed the jug to a Sloecum neighbor.

The late afternoon sun was hardly visible, except where it sieved through a thin break in the gathered clouds.

Following Bad Blavos' lead, the Nohan boys ran about the meadow in their underwear. All the girls except Artivick, the oldest, undressed down to their bloomers and chased after their brothers.

"*Yellah!* What *kepf!*" Bad Blavos clucked his lips like Bachelor Bedros as he emptied the glasses left standing by the picnickers. "What fun!" Little wine moustaches grew on his lips and chin.

"Bad Blavos," Hartune the poet called, "why are you drinking that wine? Do you think it will make you big like Bedros *Aper?*"

Bad Blavos continued to empty the glasses, his eyes gleaming.

"Bad Blavos," said Meester Vaspos, "that wine, is it making you happy like that?"

"I think it is the wine making you happy like that," Hartune said. He picked up one of the glasses and tasted it. Then he emptied it. He picked up another glass.

Meester Vaspos and Haic followed suit. All four began to drink as though they were in a race, until they were grinning and giggling.

The identical twins, Samson and Samuel, as well as the girls, began to drink too. Hartune gestured with his hands and recited the one poem he knew in English, in a loud, singsong voice—

> "Thirty days hath September,
> April, June, and November. . . ."

Bad Blavos swung his arms out, hitting the girls with his fists.

The girls giggled.

"Hoii!" Bad Blavos shouted. He shook his arms and danced about among his brothers and sisters.

Hartune inflated his chest and recited his poem, this time mixing Tatar, Armenian, and Assyrian words with English.

Meester Vaspos agitated his mouth as though about to deliver a speech just as his hero Sonny Zar might.

Bad Blavos grabbed one of the picnic knives and ran yelling into the meadow after the three farm dogs that were glutted on scraps and drowsing under a tree. Bad Blavos cornered the smallest of the dogs and advanced slowly with the knife raised.

A foot from the cowering, panting dog, the boy stopped.

"The pond!" he cried in a fit of excitement. He dropped the knife, took the whining dog in his arms and started running toward the woods.

Behind him his brothers and sisters, yelling like wild Indians, rushed through the woods, across a small meadow, and down to the swimming pool.

At the pond, they stripped and ran after Bad Blavos into the water. When they had waded so far in that the water was up to the chest of the smallest girl, they stopped and formed a circle.

Bad Blavos raised the dog in his arms. And then, yelling wildly, with a shaking of his head, he threw the dog headfirst into the water.

When the dog came up, she clawed wildly with her front paws, moving only inches in the water. Her eyes wide, she swam around in the circle of children.

Bad Blavos picked her up again, lifted her high and heaved her back in, headfirst.

The dancers formed a wide circle, clapping their hands as the Makers of Music took up a new tune. Again the purling of the clarinet-*zurna,* the squinging of the violin, the plinging of the *oud,* and the pulsing of the *dembeque* and tambourine.

The meadow, the hillside and the hills beyond resounded again.

In the center of the circle, Bachelor Bedros threw out his legs, shook his torso and head in time to the music, the clapping, and the calls of his countrymen. The fingers of his left hand snapped in time, while his right hand flourished a large silk handkerchief. His head was thrown back, carried lightly, and his eyes glowed.

"Oophf!" he cried.

"Hurray for Bachelor Bedros!" The countrymen clapped him on.

In the circle, clapping uncertainly, the bride watched the man she had married a few hours before. Every now and again Beluse or Pooshy Kat shouted their good feelings to her. Once she grinned back at them, a little uneasily, and then watched her groom.

Bachelor Bedros hardly moved, yet the rhythms pulsed subtly in his muscles. Mostly he simply turned about, but every now and again he stamped, gestured, and hopped. As he danced his gestures and his turns grew broader.

The countrymen took up the beat with their feet, snapped their fingers and swayed as the instrumentalists carried the rhythms.

Bachelor Bedros swung about wildly. Color rose in his dusky face, sweat ran from his forehead down his face, from his neck down his bare chest and back. Gamba ran to him with a glass of wine and held it up to his mouth while he, still moving about, emptied it slowly.

"*Yellah,* Bachelor Bedros!"

"Hurray for Bachelor Bedros!"

A troubling excitement stirring within her, the bride looked about in the circle to Beluse's flushed face.

"The bride! We want to see the bride dance!" Beluse called.

"The bride! The bride!" The clapping hands and stamping feet became insistent.

The bride looked from face to face in the circle. She was caught. Wherever she turned, she was met by the same urgent smiles. Looking outside the circle to the picnickers, she met hard stares. Even Elizabeth Gadson gave her no help. In the circle itself, hands pushed her from behind until she was out in the center.

Bachelor Bedros smiled knowingly as he advanced upon his bride with his pulsing rhythms. The clapping in the circle crescendoed while those outside still looked on glumly.

As they sat on the hillock overlooking the celebration, Gene turned to Lalice again and again as if to speak, but remained silent. During the past three weeks as Gene avoided her, Lalice had felt herself wanting more and more to reach out to him. During those weeks, when she had brought sandwiches and wine to her father and his countrymen in the vineyards, she had watched Gene working off to one side by himself. Mutely he would look up from his work. He was trimming the excess leaves and tendrils from the luxuriant vines to let the bunches of green fruit through to ripen. He watched her as he worked, but said nothing.

Through the entire first half of the wedding celebration, they said scarcely more than a word or two to each other. On the hillock now, as the dance circle unfolded in the meadow below them, Lalice turned in response to Gene's glance. Each time she found herself saying something about the celebration.

Then she saw her brothers and sisters catch the dog and carry it into the woods.

"They're going to do something to that little dog!" Lalice sprang to her feet.

With a glance at Gene, she ran down the knoll, through the meadow. Gene rose and ran hesitantly after her. They ran past the dancers, the cluster of onlookers, through the meadow and into the small woods. On the other side, in another meadow of tall grass, they stopped and looked across the tips of the grass to the pond.

The Nohan children stood in a circle and yelled and splashed. Gene and Lalice ran hurriedly through the grass.

"Bad Blavos! Haic! What are you doing to that little dog?"

Lalice called. But the children went on yelling and splashing water.

Gene watched a moment and then spurted ahead of Lalice. At the water's edge, he stopped. He could see nothing of the dog. The circle was a tight one. One of the boys bent to the water, picked something up and threw it in the water with a great splash.

Without removing her shoes and stockings, Lalice ran past Gene to the circle. Gene followed her quickly.

Hartune was the first to see them.

"What fun! What fun we are having! With the dog, Lalice! You and that man take off your clothes and get in the circle with us!"

Lalice broke through the circle. And there was the dog, face wet and eyes straining, swimming about frantically, looking for help. Tears brimmed in Lalice's eyes.

"That—poor little dog!" she sobbed.

Quickly Gene broke through the circle and picked the dog up. It went on paddling, its feet striking his chest, ripping his shirt. Gene pressed the animal soothingly. He and Lalice waded out to the grass bank. For seconds the children just watched them. Finally Meester Vaspos spoke.

"Hey, Lalice, what are you and that man doing, spoiling our fun?"

"We want the dog back!" Bad Blavos cried out.

"Fun spoilers!" Haic the fighter yelled. All the children shouted now.

Gene wrapped the dog in his shirt and placed it gently on the grass. Sitting on the grass next to him, Lalice patted the dog's head as Gene rubbed its body with the shirt.

The children came out of the water and stood at a distance, watching. Then the girls got dressed and started off across the meadow toward the woods. Bad Blavos walked up to Lalice and Gene. Standing over them, he made a face and then turned and ran.

"Hey, Lalice!" Meester Vaspos was among the last to leave. "We're going back. Aren't you and that man coming?" Haic picked up a stone and handed it to Meester Vaspos. Meester

Vaspos looked at it and handed it to Bad Blavos. Bad Blavos flung the stone. It went wide of its mark.

Neither Lalice nor Gene looked up as the three boys turned and ran through the woods. Yet they knew when they were finally alone, with the dog panting, its heart pounding hard, between them.

As she lifted her eyes to his face, from the distance came the hollow, fervid thumping of the *dembeque*. Really hearing it for the first time that afternoon, she felt her breath come quick. Gene reached out to her, put his hand tentatively over hers. His face was flushed.

"Lalice—I—"

She let her head fall against his chest, feeling her own pulse beating in her throat. Between them, the dog stirred and scampered free.

"On the other side of the hill," he said, "there's a place—overlooking Secret Lake." She felt his arm go avidly about her waist.

"Oh, Gene! Gene!" She buried her face hard against the flat of his chest. She could feel his little hairs on her lips.

Gene's hand tightened on her quivering waist. Slowly he began to walk her toward the miniature mountain overlooking the lake. Behind her, came the whomping of the *dembeque*, vague and distant, yet rising.

As he advanced upon his bride, Bachelor Bedros sensed her emotion. He expected that she might be a little afraid, but he had not anticipated this. She was trembling.

Yet she was not a girl. Why should she be afraid of the many ways of the world?

When he was almost upon her, he knew he had to do it differently.

He made an effort to change the tone of his dancing, so that his movements became more graceful and easy. Slowly her face relaxed. Still she did not move.

He moved slowly. Softly, he clacked his fingers together. Softly, on the pulsing strains of the clarinet and the weeping of the violin and the *oud*, and with the pulsing of the *dembeque*, his body floated like a caressing wind about her. He moved slowly and softly round and round. He circled her and moved in, and then away from her, and then in to her again.

Finally, he was next to her, actually touching her with his hands. His face was on a level with hers and his eyes held hers fastened.

Slowly, erratically, her body started to move.

The clapping in the circle became vigorous and now those standing outside looked on with interest.

Touching her lightly with his arms, he led her about until he was carrying her along. And she was dancing, swinging with him rhythmically.

As they danced, the clapping hands, the throbbing of the *dembeque,* and the plaintive sweep of the *zurna,* the violin, and the *oud* rose. The circle of celebrants called out:

"Hooray for Bedros Bulbul, no longer the bachelor!"

"Hooray for Bedros and Meeses Bulbul!"

"Hurray for Bedros and Sarey Bulbul!"

And, yes, those outside of the circle were clapping and calling out too.

The meadow became tumultuous with joy.

Seconds later, however, Bachelor Bedros turned about with a startled gasp as someone from behind the circle shouted wildly, "They're fighting!"

"Fighting?" Eyes ripped from the excitement of the circle and turned to the group of men at the far side of the meadow. "Who?" Noisy with angry talk only a few minutes before, the group was now a mass of jumbled torsos, thrusting legs, and wildly aimed fists. Through the sounds of the music, the sound of fists meeting flesh came sickening clear. The music died abruptly and the clapping stopped.

"Oh, my poor, lost God! They're fighting!" The tumult turned from joy and exultation to astounded incomprehension and fear. Was it possible? The ballplayers were attacking one another. Men ran from the circle to the fighters in an attempt to separate the tangled mass, only to be drawn themselves into the fray.

With the realization of what was happening, Bachelor Bedros left his bride abruptly and pushed his way through the throng of celebrants and picnickers to the fight. He grabbed a pair by the scruff of the neck, shaking them. Behind him, Enos Morrill, Vassily Varan, and Daddy Hy plunged into the thickest part of the mass, pulling men off each other. Bachelor Bedros roared and shook men at arms' length, trying to startle them to their senses by the force of his person. Vassily Varan pulled men to their feet and tried to reason through their thick clouds of drunken anger, only to find himself shaken off, shoved, and once even struck in the face.

The two who had started the fight, Leonard Lunch and a Sloccum youth, grappled at the bottom of the pile of men.

Bachelor Bedros, Vassily Varan, Enos Morrill, and Daddy Hy tore into the group again and again. But to no avail. The fight spread. Now even some of the merrymakers were swept into the fray, and more of the Barstowe people, still more of the Sloecums. Until the tangled mass became a churning mob.

Mothers went scurrying off in search of their children Old men and old women looked about the meadow with startled wonder. How had it happened? Something about the way tho game was won, the way the home run ball had been sent cannoning through the air across the road to the second field. What had happened to the men that they should fight about such a senseless thing?

And suddenly lightning split the sky and thunder crashed deafeningly. Big splashes of rain flopped down. Again the attention of the on-lookers was diverted, this time to the sky, and they really noticed the roiling clouds for the first time that afternoon. A bolt of lightning crackled across the westerly hills. But the struggling men were unaware of anything but their own wild fury.

Picnickers outside the fighting mob broke in groups and scattered across the meadow to their baskets and picnic boxes.

Gathering their things together, families felt their way

through the darkening meadow to parked cars and distant cottages.

As awareness of the rising storm reached the fighters gradually, the men began to break free, stare about wildly, and then, comprehending, go hobbling and limping after their families. Some of them staggered. Dry curses sounded, as feet tripped and shins knocked. The vehicles filled with Sloecumites and Barstowites. Motors sputtered; there were a great many near scrapings of fenders. Finally, only the wedding guests were left amidst their wounded, with the scattered baskets, plates, and remains of the feast. Some of the men sat heavily on the ground where they had fallen in the fight, and had to be helped to their feet.

It was fully a half hour before they had gathered their things together and were ready to make their long return trips to Springfield, to Worcester, to Hartford, and to Boston, to say their goodbyes to their countrymen.

"The night be with you! See you next time—next time someone decides to get married!"

"The light be with you! See you next time Bachelor Bedros decides to get married, you mean. It is only at a marriage of Bachelor Bedros that we can expect another celebration like this!" Smiles through bruised mouths.

Laughter and more laughter echoing dimly through the gathering storm.

"Give my regards to everyone—to everyone in Hartford, to everyone in Springfield, and if you see anyone, to everyone in Wooster, everyone in New Wessex, in Boston everyone—if you see anyone!"

"The night be with you!"

"The light be with you!"

31. VANCE BOURJAILY

*The Fractional Man**

Vance Bourjaily was born in Cleveland on September 17, 1922. His father was a native of Lebanon, a Catholic Arab, who came to the United States and went on to a successful career as editor and publisher. Bourjaily lived in Cleveland, New Haven, and Bangor and was a student in Bowdoin College when the war broke out. He enlisted in the American Field Service and then entered the army from which he was demobilized in 1946. A year later he completed his studies at Bowdoin. He has written four novels and numerous stories and has taught in the writers' workshop of the State University of Iowa.

Now I must invent a scene, and knowing that you already know quite a lot. You know that mine was not the kind of family which preserved as anecdote or legend such a matter as how it got named.

I must invent my grandmother, too—invent her as a young woman, that is, for as I knew her she was always old, big and square as a monument, with a strong, swarthy face and a brooding, noncommittal forehead; the pain she knew showed only in her eyes.

I will remove the pain, for the purpose of my scene, and make her pretty. There is evidence for the prettiness in a photograph I saw once, but do not have.

She is twenty, the year is 1901, and the child whose hand she holds is my father, at five, for she married at fourteen a man whom she has left behind in Lebanon. She walked barefoot

* Vance Bourjaily, *Confessions of a Spent Youth* (New York, 1960), pp. 237–40, 258–73.

across mountains holding this child by the hand, worked in Beirut to save passage money, and now she is on the famous island, almost in New York, so that what she knew of girl's pain, in the bad marriage arranged by her parents and in the hard work it took to get here, is canceled now in the near realization of the immigrant's dream . . . opportunity, plenty, gold, all those words.

And liberty, for the land she has left is a province of the Turks.

I think I will put a heavy suitcase in my grandmother's other hand, as she stands with her child by the desk of some official. The suitcase is foreshadowing. She will spend many years carrying just such a dull, heavy, flat-sided bag from door to door in these United States, selling in broken English to the housewives of Lawrence, Massachusetts, and Syracuse, New York, the linens and laces which Syrian and Lebanese merchants, relatives, have consigned to her; she will be putting her child through private school. But she doesn't know about that other suitcase now, of course; she wants to get by the official and on to the opportunity, the plenty, and the gold.

The official asks her name. She is pretty and he is roguish. I rather hate him because he takes advantage, in my scene, of the fact that her hands are so completely engaged, beckoning her around to the side of the desk where he can pat her hip as he talks to her. She knows no English at all yet, and of course he knows no Arabic, this immigration official; he knows that her eyes are brown and her cheeks red. He has a mustache and sideburns since the year is 1901.

"Name? Name? What is your name?" He shows her a place on the form, and she says a word which is not intelligible to him. It is barely intelligible even to me, though it is our name in Arabic.

The official does not understand; when she writes it for him, in Arabic characters, putting down the suitcase (the child's hand can never be released), it makes him laugh. He pats her hip again.

Now a comic character enters the scene. He steps up to the

desk, a fellow immigrant who has learned some English; he is a small man, with a small, funny hat on, and he means to be helpful. He repeats the unintelligible name.

"What?" says the official.

"Means quince," says the comic character. "Like fruit. Quince."

"Quince? Quincy." The official guesses, and laughs again. He is not a bad fellow, in spite of my dislike for the liberties he has taken with my grandmother's hip, and it is his job, in this good-natured era to get immigrants in, not keep them out. "Quincy." He writes it down, smiling.

Twenty-one years later I was born, and named, and it is time to explain the initials now—U. S. D. The first two are *Ulysses Snow*, my mother's father, a farmer whose people arrived in Ohio from New England; then *Davids*, Welsh, her mother's maiden name and coming from a wave of immigration not so much earlier than that which brought my father and my grandmother.

Ulysses Snow Davids Quincy—the fractions of my heritage are in it: a quarter of what is more or less colonial American of which my mother tried to teach me to be proud. A quarter Welsh, of which no one ever said anything much. Half Lebanese, the largest fraction, pretty well concealed by my unintending godfather, the sideburned Ellis Island man.

I was brought up not so much to conceal as to ignore that fraction; it was not particularly a secret, rather something which my father dismissed. He was busy being an American, a successful one which I guess means a good one, or used to. He spoke Arabic with his mother only when they quarrelled; for normal conversation he wanted her to speak English, and he sent her to night school in her late forties, where she was supposed to learn to read and write it.

I remember her bringing her reader to me, when I was ten or twelve, for help with the one-syllable words: *cat, can, John see the cat. . . .*

It wasn't until eight years afterwards that I could imagine what it cost her in pride, coming to a child for help, what profundity of dislocation it indicated. When a limb is dislocated it is painful; when a life is dislocated it produces the look I have described in my grandmother's eyes.

I myself was twenty, just the age at which she'd left it, when I finally found myself in Lebanon, at my grandmother's starting point, and once, just before the Corps left Syria, I tried going home, if that word can be used, to the mountain town that she grew up in, my father's birthplace. But I did not make this visit during the first three months in Baalbek; by the time I made it, I had been to El Tahog, Egypt, taken the driver-mechanic's course in Palestine, and was back in Baalbek once again.

It did not occur to me until much later—just now, even, as I write of it—that in going to my father's birthplace, I solved the riddle of my grandmother's eyes; always self-concerned, youth asks the idiot question, "What about me? What about me?"

I deserved no particular answer to that and I got none, except perhaps the negative answer that the fractions of my heritage were merely that, fractions, adding up to no Englishman, Welshman, or Arab, so that for me, as for many, there is no heritage. Each of us is a fresh, a slightly different combination, with only his shaving mirror to tell him with what face he looks back at the face of the earth.

As a child I didn't care much; my interest as I went through school was precisely academic. In Geography the Lebanese were grouped with Syrians. In History the modern Syrians were not to be confused with Assyrians, who were ancient. In Arithmetic the Phoenicians had had something to do with numbers. I noted with interest Solomon's preference for Lebanese cedars, Zenobia made a noble footnote, but we seemed to be on the wrong sides in the Crusades, if we were on any side at all—mostly we were a supine little prize on the invasion route. My identification with such bits was extremely remote.

There was a time, though, when it seemed to me to matter what I was, and as I approached the Near East, it began to seem to me I might find out. . . .

Perhaps I had better explain now, if I can, why, in the first three months at Baalbek, I had not tried to make the thirty-mile trip to Kabb Elias, my father's town. To do it, I will have to go back to the first journey across Palestine up to Syria, by train, when we were freshly arrived in the Middle East and knew nothing about it:

. . . On the morning of the second day, the train passes the Sea of Galilee and we cross the Syrian border. I manage to take over center stage from Stork Berger who had the best claim to identification with Palestine, and am allowed two minutes to analyse my quite imperfectly realized sensations. I say something like:

"Well, I don't know as much as I should about this country, and I keep looking for some sort of borderline recognition, one of those mystical, I-saw-this-landscape-once-before-in-a-dream feelings, but I guess I haven't got it. Still, I'm kind of moved just by the idea of being here, and maybe when it's really Lebanon and not just Syria it'll be more so, but I don't really feel much like one of those boys in the long white dusters . . ."

"Let's try you," Eddie suggests, and he and Stork catch me and wrap a towel around my head.

"Of course you're an Arab," they insist, but Stork looks just as convincing when we put the towel on him. Even Bingo does, seized as he comes in unwarily from the lavatory.

The train is going slowly now, uphill, so slowly that we can open the door on the side of our cubicle, step out onto the ground, and walk along beside it. Eddie and I start to trot; we begin to pass the cars ahead, and to catch up with the cab of the engine. It seems very funny to be running alongside, waving at the engineer and the fireman. Perhaps, with our American sense of competitiveness about the performance of the machine with which we are connected, we expect them to be annoyed. They aren't at all.

The engineer motions for us to jump up, come into the cab, the fireman moves to the top of the iron steps and holds out a hand to help, and in we go.

We are allowed to test the throttle, toot the whistle, shovel a little coal into the fire; they have heard there were Americans in the train, and wonder if we know their relatives in America, and I say:

"Ana ibn Arab," I am an Arab's son. The enthusiasm is tremendous, they laugh and pat me on the back and cry, "Shu ismak? Shu ismak?" What is your name? And when I say it, the Arabic word for quince, I am nearly hurled out of the cab by the fireman's rush to embrace me, for it is his name too, though if we are related it is impossible to discover just how.

Nevertheless, though it is barely ten o'clock in the morning, he seizes his lunch box and makes Eddie and me eat every bite and wash it down with wine.

Now we are in Baalbek . . . I have cousins here, as everywhere. In Baalbek, the most closely related cousin is a barber, who keeps me in his chair for an hour sometimes, shaving and shampooing and massaging, waving other customers away, talking and talking, probably aware that I understand little of what he says; he will not let me pay. This is embarrassing, for he is not prosperous, yet he will know of it in minutes if I step into another shop; I urge my friends to patronize him, but they object, reasonably enough, that if they go there with me, they have to wait too long.

One day he gives me a silver ring, with a green cedar tree enameled on its surface; I take it to be a kind of national emblem, and wear it around for a day or two, until an older hand advises me that it is the symbol of the local Falangist, the pro-fascist, party. I stop wearing the ring, of course, but it does not really turn me against the barber who seems a simple, rather nice man, with, I believe, a naïve urge to protest his condition. But it is another instance, like the time I had to eat the fireman's lunch, of how one cannot claim relationship with people without being, in turn, claimed. This was the sort of thing which kept me from Kabb Elias.

When I got back to Baalbek from Palestine, I drove an ambulance for a while, making almost daily runs across the Bekaa Valley, up through a pass in the coastal mountains and across, down the other side to Beirut and the sea. At the inland foot of this mountain drive was a town called Chtaura, where I generally stopped for lunch. Each time, as I started on my way again, I noticed a narrow dirt road, off to the left, just outside of town, with a marker pointing down it which read "Kabb Elias, 8 km." That was the place, of course, but I was still reluctant to make the visit; I was not prepared for it. My Arabic was too shaky, I hadn't listened closely enough to my grandmother's accounts of who still lived here, who immigrated to what continent, how we were all related; I was diffident about their using up the food and time which my visit would cost them if I went, and I feared involvement.

The barber, however, urged me on: "They would rather see you than your father, even," he said. And finally after several months, knowing that I would leave the country soon, thinking that it would mean a great deal to my grandmother when I returned to the States to tell about it, I prepared to go, feeling more dutiful than festive.

I got a weekend pass, and arranged to borrow a light truck. Somewhat melodramatically, I left written directions with Eddie of where I was to be and when to expect me back, not knowing who I might meet there, but knowing that this would be not one of the civilized valley towns but a mountain village. I drove to Chtaura, ate an unnecessary early lunch which I invested with a sort of Last Supper atmosphere, and took the left turn.

The road was paved only for a hundred yards or so; then its surface became dirt, and there were wagon tracks in it. By the time I had driven slowly on another hundred yards, and Chtaura was out of sight behind me, there was no sign left of any of the colonizers who had ruled here—French, Turks, Arabs, Romans, Babylonians, Etruscans—the ground covered them. It was fertile ground, fertile in fruits and grains. Endlessly fertile in people who had grown here and would always grow here, and perhaps leave, as they had always left, not like their cousins, the Jews, who had left all at once, but individually and by dozens every generation, to become laborers, merchants, and sometimes professors in whatever worlds were new, but always somehow leaving seed, roots, for new generations in the fertile ground behind.

The road followed the base of the mountain, not climbing much, and I supposed the path had always gone so, from Kabb Elias to Chtaura, before turning up to the pass. There were no people on the road that noon, but suddenly I had a vivid image of my grandmother going along it fifty years before, barefoot and leading her child, going to Beirut to emigrate. There were trees and clumps of bushes along the road, and I could suppose her hiding in one of them, a hand over the child's mouth to keep him still, as a patrol of Turkish soldiers went by, or horsemen from her husband's family in pursuit. Thinking of horsemen, I remembered a story she had told me, of a band of strapping brothers concealed on the slopes above this road to throw sharp stones at the horses of the armed Turkish tax collectors and then run back, by mountain paths, to the towns, where resistance might be continued with silent clubs or knives should a collector be unwary in one of the dark streets. I didn't disbelieve the story yet it was hard, even here, to picture my gentle Uncle Dahir, one of the brothers, in so fierce a role; he was a shrewd, sweet-tempered old man, a buyer of teddy bears he couldn't afford, eater of prodigious dinners, encourager of little boys showing off, an indulgent man. Perhaps he had fought Turks—it was easier, though, to see him as a character in another story, one of his own; he and my grandmother had been taken as small children twenty miles to Zahle, surely along this road, on foot and with a mule carrying gifts of produce, to make a visit to another branch of the family in strawberry season. It was the strawberries which the old man remembered most—his first, they must have been—and I could now believe that he and my grandmother had indeed kicked this dust, felt it between their toes, as they followed that mule. But as for myself, in my foreign uniform, with my garrison Arabic, was I not more to be identified with the Turkish exploiters than with the children on their way to strawberries, the warring brothers, the young woman in flight? For this was an occupied country; the British whom I served had won it from the Vichy French in the first small victory of the war and now administered it, and I was of them.

With these uneasy thoughts, I came abruptly into the town itself.

Although I drove along what was apparently the main street the town was all above me on the right, built on the slope. On the left was a stream, and here and there a building was built out over its bank. I went slowly down the street, attracting a good deal of quiet attention in my Army truck, and I tried to make myself small in the obscurity of its cab as I looked around.

On the mountainside, which rose up so directly from the street, the houses were of wood, stone, and stucco, and they were built in a series of terraces so close together that the roof of one house was like the front yard of the house behind it. Dirt paths wound up between the houses, and I could imagine that the same paths must spread laterally along the terraces. The street I drove on was cobblestoned, and one or two short streets, similarly paved, went off to the right, among the houses, but they did not go very far. The whole town of Kabb Elias wasn't more than five-hundred yards long, and within the five-hundred yards I probably saw two men, five women, ten children. Yet I had the feeling that there were many more who saw me.

The women wore unshaped, ankle length dresses; their heads were covered, but their faces were not for this was a Christian not a Moslem village. The two men I saw wore trousers, shirts, sheepskin vests, and the children were dressed in shifts of what looked like toweling. There were mules and dogs and chickens around, in normal proportion; the only abnormality was me.

Where was I to start, who was I to ask?

I reached the far end of town and turned the truck around; I started driving slowly back as I had come, town rising on my left now, stream on my right, and I felt very strongly that I should keep on that way, throw the truck into high gear, roar through and out to Chtaura, turn left and up over the mountain and down to Beirut where I could spend a fine weekend in the French part of the city, brushing against other soldiers who spoke my language, finding the security of isolation among similar numbers which is the emotional mainstay of occupying troops.

In this mood, I had almost reached the end of town I'd entered at when I noticed, on the stream side of the street, a rather large building, which was set out over the bank. It had a porch, open on three sides except for lattice work screening on which grape vines were trained, and through the interstices I could see several empty tables with chairs at them. A restaurant. I could deal with this. I stopped my truck, pulling off the road just past the place, got out, locked it, and went into the building. First there was a large, cool room, without furniture or people in it, but full of bottles. I crossed it, and went out on the other side, onto the porch. A man, and a boy of about eighteen, were sitting at one of the tables.

They were looking towards the door watching me come in, and they did not turn their eyes away. I did. One of them, the man, rose, smiling without warmth as I sat down at an empty table, and came over. He was stout, swarthy, past middle age. The boy, who sat very still watching me, was of the same coloring but slim, with wild eyes and matted black hair. They both wore nondescript European peasant sort of clothing, but the boy, whose pants fit tightly and whose upper garment was more blouse than shirt, had a certain dash to his appearance.

The man came too close, much closer than a waiter generally does, and said: "All right?"

"Have you a glass of wine?" I asked, in Arabic.

He shook his head and continued standing there, looking down at me. Finally he said: "We make Arac here."

"May I have a glass? And some ice?" I have mentioned before that it was not legal to sell Arac, which runs 120-proof, to troops; the man hesitated. Then he nodded and went out of the room. The boy and I sat there in silence. I would glance at him and glance away; he never took his wild eyes off me. I was nervous again; perhaps they took me for an agent trying to get evidence on them for the Arac sale. Such fantasies were always occurring to me in those days; they made life more interesting and more trying, and sometimes, as in Tel Aviv, they came excessively true.

This one was sharp enough to convince me that I'd better declare myself, after all.

The older man came back with a bottle of Arac and a pitcher full of shaved ice and put them down in front of me.

"Is there . . . anyone named Quince left around in Kabb Elias?" I asked tentatively.

He laughed, and flung out his arm in a gesture which might have been meant to include the whole population of the town. "Quinces," he said. "I'm a Quince. He's a Quince," pointing at the boy who did not seem pleased to be identified. "Everybody."

"I am the son of Michel, grandson of Terkman and Faris," I said carefully. I had hardly finished the sentence before I was lifted out of my seat by a crushing hug, and the boy, leaping up and overturning his chair, rushed to seize me, too, the unexplained unease I had seen in his face wiped away by an intense and radiant smile.

They shouted and pummelled me, and the boy cried: "Why have you been so long?"

The man said: "We heard you were in Syria, in Baalbek. When I saw the truck go through just now, I thought it might be you. I sent for Joseph, look, your cousin. Do you know where you are this minute?"

"No," I admitted.

"In the Arac factory of Joseph's father, your uncle George."

"Elias is in the fields," Joseph said. "He will come."

I must have looked confused, because the man explained: "Joseph's brother, your other cousin."

"And Uncle George?" I asked.

He was dead, hadn't I heard? The war of course; important news could be lost in it. Died in Africa, where he had gone to keep a store, left by a brother who died of the same fever before him. I should have known it actually; both deaths had taken place before the war and were known to my grandmother, whose nephews they were.

We sat down, and I looked again at Joseph. Perhaps if I hadn't been so edgy, I'd have recognized him before, for he was not unlike that other second cousin, Saloom, from Detroit, whom I'd impersonated. Joseph was slimmer, though, and at the same time stronger, I would guess, and even in its cordiality, his face never lost its look of wildness.

I was not surprised, as we sat talking, to hear that Joseph was lying low here in the village; he had killed a man.

"With a knife," the factory manager said. "Tell your cousin."

Joseph shrugged; the topic seemed to make him moody.

"A year ago," said the older man. "In a quarrel. Both had knives. Joseph was seventeen, and the man bigger and older."

"We were drunk," Joseph said. Then he smiled: "I have been in jail. Only last week I came back here, meaning to say good-by and go to Palestine."

"Only a year in jail?" I asked.

"There was no trial. No witnesses would come to the French court and they had to let me go."

"But they would like to arrest him again," the manager said. "And the relatives of the man he killed . . ."

"Can't you get away from here?"

"Nafi said no," Joseph said. "I came to say good-by, and get some money but Nafi said to stay here."

"He is safe here," the manager said. "More safe."

I was trying to decide whether to ask who Nafi was—from the way they said the name, it was assumed that I would know—but before I could decide Joseph's brother, Elias, came in.

He was a year younger and much stockier, a successful farmer already and would be married soon. We greeted, and he sat by Joseph, declining Arac but picking up a piece of quartered cucumber which had just been brought to the table and eating it with great satisfaction. He wore the sheepskin vest and a small, round hat, and looking at the two brothers together, I could not help but think of Cain and Abel.

More food came, cool things: slices of tomato, flat loaves of bread, soft goat's milk cheese with olive oil and mint leaves on it; chickpea, eggplant, and sesame spreads, with garlic, parsley, pomegranate seeds. I knew them all, as the first courses at elaborate Near East meals; drinking, is not separated from eating in Lebanon, and it goes on almost always at a table.

A small boy came in, not long after Elias, and his presence seemed to be a signal that we were to move. I got the truck out of sight, running it into one of the cobblestoned cul-de-sacs, and behind the orthodox church. The churchman himself came out to see what was going on, helped us heave a tarpaulin over the vehicle, and took us into the rectory for cups of sweet black coffee.

It was he who told me a story to set aside my immigration scene of how we got our English name: taking out a huge, gold-crusted volume of family records, he showed me a name, in Arabic characters I couldn't read, which went back to the eleventh century. It was the name of a court official, the orthodox priest said, a commoner but one who was conspicuously able and loyal to the feudal king; he could not be rewarded with a title which included land, so he and his heirs were given the right to a perpetual share in the quince harvest . . . eleventh century. The small boy was back again, looking more imperative. Elias said something to the priest, and I heard the name Nafi again; the priest nodded, and I went with my two cousins up the hill.

We went first to the house of their mother, George's widow, where I understood I was to stay, and I was greeted with great ceremony. The widow was spare and strong, looked to be just under forty but since she managed her late husband's property, she had already come into an importance women did not ordinarily achieve until much later in their lives. Nevertheless, she stood aside for us to enter.

"Nafi will not meet him until sunset," was the first thing she said, after our greetings were finished. Joseph said something in protest, but Elias hushed him.

The room we stood in, in the cool stone house, was carpeted

but had no furniture whatsoever except for benches along the walls. As we stood talking, though, three young girls came in, carrying a light table which they set in the center of the room; they went out, and came in again with chairs. I looked at the girls, because they were pretty, and because I understood that they too were my second cousins, daughters of the house, but they did not meet my eyes nor were we introduced. Some other men came in now and joined us at the table. George's widow and her daughters disappeared into the kitchen—I knew it was the kitchen from the marvelous smells of cooking which came in whenever the door was opened. Suddenly I realized that, ready or not, I was going to eat again.

That afternoon I learned what a day of feasting meant. Men came and went, sat with us, talked, sampled a course or two and took their leave, while Joseph, Elias and I ate, lightly but steadily, with Arac to accompany the food, the entire afternoon. It seems impossible, looking back, but every plate that was set before me was different, and they were all irresistible.

I remember much about the food, and only the general drift of the conversation—it was of crops and emigrations, families, crimes, feats of strength or poetry; stories were told I didn't understand, men laughed and I laughed with them. Somehow the fellowship was as complete as if I had understood, as we ate along together, dishes of lamb and eggplant, rice, wheat, poultry, okra. The other men were served by the young girls; each dish that came to me was brought by George's widow herself.

Most of the men were old; I think Joseph and Elias may have been the only young males in the town, Joseph because someone called Nafi had said he must stay a time, Elias, oddly enough, by choice. He said, several times, that he would not leave Kabb Elias, that the orchards which he tended were good, and he did not think there would be better ones in Africa or South America. At first I thought it must be the older men, then, who ran the town, but as the afternoon went on I began to realize from the conversation that, in spite of their apparently subservient position, women ruled here. But they came to it gradually; as soon as they were out of childhood, they disappeared into the kitchens and the granaries, where they worked hard, threshing and cleaning and learning the very intricate and important art of how to cook. At thirteen or fourteen, they were married, if a man could be found, by arrangement. They were lovely little creatures, with pale olive skins, round faces, and enormous eyes. They would work and bear children for a number of years, walking behind their husbands, carrying loads of wood and water, working long hours. They would get stout and deep-breasted—a spare woman, like George's widow, would be rare.

Once a woman is past child-bearing, she begins to come to power. Her place is still the kitchen, but she imposes her will from there on her entire immediate family. As she grows older, and has had charge of the growing up of three generations, down to great-grandchildren, her power grows, her word becomes absolute. They are wonderful to look at, these powerful old women, broad-shouldered, heavy-breasted, carrying their weight with the graceless dignity of mountains, their faces strong and beautiful as the remote, weather-worn cliffs above the tree line.

I had seen these women now and then, in the Lebanese and Syrian villages I drove through; now, as sunset came and with it the hour at which I was to be taken up to Nafi, I realized that I was to meet one, and I knew that I had to ask who she was.

Joseph and Elias looked at me with more than surprise: then Elias said, "Our grandmother. Your grandmother's sister. She is waiting for us now." I had not known that any of my grandmother's sisters had stayed behind.

We left the house heavy with food and began to climb; in a hundred yards, I was exhausted. Fifty more, and I had to rest. Then we resumed and it seemed to me we climbed forever, between the old houses, up the narrow paths. Nafi's was the highest house of all; half the village, I learned, made this climb each day, either to take Nafi food and water or to ask advice, to carry gifts or seek judgments.

When we arrived she was sitting on a heavy wooden bench, set against the southwest wall of her house in a kind of alcove, for there were short, low wings reaching out on either side of her, one towards the mountain and the sunset, the other back down the hill, towards the town. On the roof of the upper wing four girls were silhouetted against the sky, wearing dark, biblical robes and grinding wheat on flat stones. A silent goat was tethered to a pear tree.

Joseph, Elias and I stopped chattering as we came around the lower wing, and thus when I saw Nafi for the first time it was to the accompaniment of the ageless sound of stone against grain.

I do not know how many years she had outlived her husband; I do not know how many years it may have been since she had been out of her own yard, down to town, for it was plain that her weight by now was too great to have allowed such an expedition. It was plain that her legs could not bear such weight unaided, for there were stout canes resting against the bench on either side of her. Yet she did not seem fat, for she had that physical serenity which is, in the appearance of the old, what glowing health is in the appearance of the young.

There she sat, spread out on her bench, the mountainous old woman at peace, allowing her equal, the sun, a last respectful look at her as it set. I remember wondering how the Semites, which my people are, had ever hit upon the notion that God was male.

Then she stirred, saw us, and welcomed me with human excitement. She chided me (I think), for not having come much sooner, but in such a way that I knew I was forgiven; I knew what she said mostly from the tone of the words, for her Arabic had an inflection all its own, which I could only penetrate at times. I was a little in awe of Nafi at first, but she motioned for me to sit beside her on the bench, and put me at ease, asking simple questions about myself, my brothers, the immediate family. My older brother had been married in New York a few months earlier, and she wanted to hear all I had learned, in family letters, about the wedding.

She dismissed Joseph and Elias, but not before each had consulted her about a problem. Joseph wanted to go back to the village of the man he'd killed the year before, to see what people were saying there; Nafi laughed at him. He asked, then, if he mightn't make a journey to Zahle, where the fight had taken place, and Nafi said:

"Stay here, and help your brother with the fruit. When it is harvested, go with him to Zahle when he sells it."

Elias said: "The problem of the boundary with Nahum; he is still not satisfied." And Nafi replied that he should bring Nahum, and they would all speak of it together, but not before Sunday next, for it was a time of year when men should not lose hours of work in argument. They withdrew, and I thought: There is nothing oracular about her, no soothsayer's riddles. When she spoke it was brief, it was practical, and, from the conduct of my cousins, it was binding.

We sat together quietly after they had gone; then Nafi reached behind her on the bench, saying, "I have something to show you. Who are these?"

It was a studio photograph, forty years old, of two dark, pretty girls in white dresses, one sitting, the other standing behind with her hand on the first one's shoulder. I studied it for a moment without recognition; then my eye caught the photographer's signature, on the flap opposite the picture, and with it: "Lawrence, Massachusetts, 1903." Nafi's sisters then, my grandmother and my great aunt Rinjus, but I had to ask which was which. She smiled, and told me, and I think now that seeing Nafi and that photograph together is the only true sight I shall ever have of the woman my grandmother was born to be. Nafi is dead now; my grandmother is too, and where the photograph may be I do not know.

We sat together for half an hour, Aunt Nafi and I, while the sun went down. Men came; Joseph and Elias returned. They talked and she listened, benignly, putting in a word from time to time; yet I felt, and I know that she did too, that it was she and I who were together, understanding not so much one another's words, or thoughts, or even feelings. What Nafi and I understood together was something at once more savage and more noble, and I can only explain it by going around it: no two dogs of the same litter know for long that they are brothers; to a grown tomcat his mother is only a female, and to a cockerel his father merely the strongest competitor for corn and hens. What Nafi and I understood was something she had known all her life and which I learned then and knew for a little while afterwards: that we were of one family and, should the world be against either of us, as perhaps it was, each could count upon the other.

Two more things which I shall not forget happened in Kabb Elias. The first took place at ten o'clock or so that night, when they showed me to my room, back at the house of George's widow. I was pretty groggy from the day of feasting when I sat down on the bed, on what I think must have been a feather mattress. I was untying my shoes when a knock came at the door.

"Come in," I said.

The door opened and in came, in procession, the three girls, the daughters of the house, all in their early teens. The first carried a basin of steaming suds, the second a towel and the third, the eldest, a basin of clear warm water, smelling of rose essence and with five petals floating on the surface.

Gravely, without a trace of self-consciousness, the eldest knelt at my feet while her sisters stood back. Pushing my hands away, she began, gently, to unlace my shoes. I felt embarrassed; I looked up to catch the eye of one of the others. Both had their eyes correctly turned down though I thought the very youngest might be smiling.

The eldest now removed my shoes and handed them to one of her sisters. She gave my heavy army socks to the other, drew the hot suds over, and began to bathe my feet. It was all done in complete silence; I composed my face and gave in to the enchantment.

After she had washed my feet carefully, the girl rinsed them in the rose water, and dried them off. Then she stood up, the three bowed to me and filed out, taking the shoes and socks along.

In the morning I found the shoes and socks by the bed, as I

might have left them myself were I a neat man. The shoes were inexpertly shined. But the socks, which had, the night before, been of coarse grey Australian wool were as nearly beautiful as such a pair of socks can be. Not only had they been washed and dried—someone must have sat up drying them by a fire—but they had been reshaped, and mended, and finally combed, somehow, with such delicacy that each fibre seemed to stand out, erect and soft as cashmere.

The other thing that I shall not forget is my good-bys. I said them to Joseph and Elias in the orchard, among the fruit trees where we had eaten lunch outdoors, and then they went on with their work, thinning the fruit, saying they would come down to the truck to say good-by again when I was ready to drive off.

I said good-by to George's widow at her house, over a final cup of thick, sweet coffee. She said that Nafi was expecting me. I hooked my musette bag over my shoulder, wondering what I could do or say to thank her and knew there was only one thing: I promised to come again. But I knew it was not a promise likely to be kept. The rumors that my unit would be pulled out of Lebanon and Syria any day had been too frequent lately to be discounted. She may have heard them too, for when I promised she was not as effusive as I had expected; she only smiled and bowed, turning her eyes away. I left then, and climbed the hill to Nafi's by myself, aware that my musette bag was heavier than it had been when I'd come, heavier, I was to find, with delicacies packed among the clothes—pistachio and pine nuts, sweets, small cakes, and fruit.

When I reached Nafi's the great old woman was sitting on her solid sunny bench, just as I had left her the day before. There was no one working on the roof this time, but the goat was still tethered as he had been. She greeted me with a few ceremonial words, and I sat comfortably by her. But the depth of communion was gone for me, now; I was conscious already of my watch, thinking of my friends at camp, wondering if there were new rumors yet of leaving.

As we sat, thinking our separate thoughts, for it seemed to

me that form required I should not take my leave until dismissed, a woman and a young girl appeared around the back of the house, daughter following mother with her face not covered but cast down so as to be almost hidden. They approached us; Nafi greeted them. I started to rise but my aunt restrained me. She and the woman began to speak, too quickly for me to follow; I hardly tried. Something, I gathered, about a pasture. I looked at the girl instead—a brown-eyed one, of course, about thirteen. Then I let my eyes look up into the mountains, and thought about something else.

Nafi dismissed the woman; she and her daughter bowed to me, and I smiled and bid them go with God. As they left, around the west wing, another little group appeared from behind the eastern one—as if they had been waiting to replace the first pair. This was a mother and two daughters—one twelve, perhaps. One fourteen. Again, there was quick conversation between the lady and my aunt, and again I paid it little heed. This time sheep seemed to be involved. As before, the conversation built to a certain intensity, and ended with a series of courtesies.

It wasn't until they had left and a third mother and daughter pair—respectful, dressed more freshly, I noticed, than if they had come from work—it wasn't until this third pair came into our little court that I began to divine what was in progress. This time I tried to listen. The talk concerned a house, a mule, an orchard, and—I was right.

Nafi, as calmly as if there were no war, which brought me here, no America, no Army, no difference at all between me and Joseph and Elias, was bargaining to arrange for me the most advantageous possible marriage.

When I tell this story, I generally describe it as having been more of a dilemma than it really was, allowing my hearer to forget that Nafi was too wise to have been more than tentative, discounting the probability that she was doing this more as a wishful ceremony than a real negotiation. I show myself as the victim of a deeply cultural misunderstanding, soluble only by a quick-witted *tour de force*.

("As soon as I realized what was up," I am apt to say. "I whipped out my wallet, got out the picture of a girl whose name I don't even remember, and stammered 'arusi, arusi' which is Arabic for 'fiancée.' We weren't engaged of course; I was just lucky I had her picture . . .")

There are several lies here: I remember the girl's name perfectly well. She was Jeannie Childress, of course, and we were more engaged, as you know, than my way of telling it admits. But those are permissible lies, the kind men tell to give point to a story which do not really change the truth of what happened.

The real lie is that I acted with such decision, that my American nature rejected so summarily the suggestion that I might be Joseph or Elias, Cain or Abel, as well here as in my own land. For an instant—hardly more than that—there crossed my mind the notion, sentimental if you like, that I might accept, might stay, or if not stay return. That I might take them all—the goats, the fruit trees, the brown-eyed child; the sheepskin vest, the hoe, the wooden plow, and the stone house.

That I might do so and so bury the restlessness of one generation and the struggle of the next which had culminated in making me a fractional man on the face of the earth, and different from Nafi and Joseph and Elias—incomprehensible to them and unhappily so, uselessly complicated and discontent as they were simple and steadfast and proud.

32. RICHARD BANKOWSKY

*No More Roses in the Lunch Pail**

Richard Bankowsky was born in New Jersey in 1928, the son of Polish parents. He studied writing at Yale under Robert Penn Warren and, after two years of army service in Korea, taught and wrote at the University of Iowa. The selection that follows comes from his first novel.

GLORY BE TO THE FATHER AND TO THE SON AND TO THE HOLY GHOST . . . But really it is no great wonder, no great wonder that Pyotr should have allowed old Stanislaw the few extra days to wait for his Stella to get here, no great wonder he did not let them rush him into the ground after the three days named for the wake so he could put in some windows right away and move in the new tenants and begin making his investment pay; for he will lose nothing by his charity; the new tenants will pay for it. And besides, it pleases him to think of himself as a generous man so long as it does not take anything out of his pockets; pleases him to be able to do something for his poor dead friend Stanislaw, whom (if he has said it once, he has said it a hundred times) he has always loved like a brother; saying, "Jozef, is it not true I always loved old Stanislaw like a brother? Is it not true, Jozef? How is it you can ask why I would allow him the few extra days to wait for the coming of his little Stella? How can you ask it, Jozef? Surely it is little enough I can do. You know I loved him like a brother, Jozef"; blowing his nose into his apron, his eyes wet behind the spectacles, weeping, truly weeping; but not so much for poor dead Stanislaw, whom surely I must know he

* Richard Bankowsky, *A Glass Rose* (New York, 1958), pp. 25–47.

loved like a brother and whom he will never see again, as at the thought of how beautifully generous he was to allow old Stanislaw the few extra days; just sitting there across the street in front of his store, sitting on an empty soda case (why should he have a bench built when an empty soda case costs nothing?), sitting there in his blood-stained apron, saying, "I know it is foolish of me. I know it is bad business to be sentimental. But you know how I am, Jozef. It is little I can do. Besides, it will not be more than a day or two. It is not possible that she will be longer than a day or two, is it, Jozef?" all the time looking out across the quiet street at the house in which old Stanislaw, whom he loved like a brother, was lying—the house he had bought right out from under poor dead Stanislaw, who if he were alive would rather have died than sell it to him—the house he says he bought, not so much because he wanted another house, since he already owned three, but simply because he would do old Stanislaw a favor, since they would need the money from the selling of the house to bury him properly. "For who but a brother would buy such a house, Jozef? Anyone can see it is a bad investment at any price. No porch even, not a single picket on the fence. Why, just to put in new windows will cost plenty. And you know as well as I, those chicken coops are good for nothing but to bring rats. Truly, I am losing money on this house, Jozef. But you know how I am. It is bad business to be sentimental; but for Stanislaw . . . Ah, I cannot help myself. Truly, I can not."

And who can say he does not believe it? Who can say that his charity is not the one thing he really and sincerely believes in, that his peculiar kind of generosity is not for him a most beautiful and touching thing; so beautiful that when he thinks of it he can only weep, perhaps even actually believing that he has really made a bad investment and out of pure generosity, and in a few years after the house has paid for itself twice over will say and perhaps even believe that it is only a case of God's rewarding him for his unselfishness? For even now, sitting here before the casket of the man he is sure he always loved like a brother, so that you can hear his sniffling even over the saying of the rosary, he probably weeps not only because Stanislaw's Stella has come at last and tomorrow morning Stanislaw will be decently in the ground and he can begin getting things ready for the new tenants; but because God has been generous and has rewarded his own generosity by not allowing Stella to stay away any longer than she did. If I were to ask him now, "Why is it you weep, Pyotr?" I know what he would say. "Jozef," he would say, "I cannot help myself. Truly, I am a foolish sentimentalist. I am not hard like you, Jozef. Surely you could not have loved him as I did or you would weep too. When I think that now that Stella has come, tomorrow it will be all over and we will never see Stanislaw again, I cannot bear it. Truly, Jozef, I cannot. I almost wish that she had stayed away another day so we could have him with us a little longer. It is so little I have done for him, Jozef."

Ah, Pyotr, perhaps you are right. Perhaps I am hard. Perhaps I too should weep in public like a woman. But she is a woman, Pyotr, and not once has she shed a tear. Perhaps she is afraid the paint will run—so hard-faced. What do you think, Pyotr? Perhaps you should go up to this hard-faced Stella and tell her why you weep. Tell her how her father was a fool but how you loved him like a brother. Show her how you have forgiven his foolishness, how though he has sinned against all that you know is right and sensible, all that you know is good in the eyes of God, since He has been generous to you, how you have forgiven all, how all your laughing and all your insults were only your way of trying to lead him out of his foolish ways. Show her how now that he is gone you are all tears; and make her weep also. Ask her to forgive as you have forgiven. Take an umbrella and walk with her out into the yard; show her the chicken coops; let her smell them up close in the rain. Then ask her; ask this girl, this painted one, this Stella, whom we have both known since she was born and whom now we can hardly recognize, this Stella who has changed so much in less than a year. Ask her as she stands under the dripping umbrella with the cigarette in her mouth and all the paint on her eyes and her yellow hair short under the hat with the rag flowers. Take her right up to the coops, Pyotr, and tell her how for three thousand dollars you have bought them—them and the house for three thousand dollars—the house in which her poor foolish father, the man you loved as a brother, still lies, the house you have bought even before they had time to take his body out of it and put it decently underground. Tell her to smell what you have bought; tell her to smell it good, and then ask her. Ask her if in the dark she can remember. Ask her to remember very hard way back there before the chicken coops, before the strike, before it all began to happen like it did. Ask her if she can still remember—standing there under the umbrella in the stink of the chicken coops—if she can still remember those lazy Sunday mornings after Mass and how it used to smell then.

Ask her to remember that, Pyotr; and make her weep. Make her weep to remember; or if that is not possible for her, make her weep not to remember. If sadness will not touch her, Pyotr, perhaps joy will. Perhaps like you, Pyotr, she can weep only when she is happy; then make her happy, Pyotr. Make her happy to think that even after only a year she is already done with remembering. Or if still remembering, probably remembering only not to remember, remembering to forget, to forget the garden that was there long before the chicken coops, long before she left, before the strike and the thing in the house, long before she was even capable of remembering, long before she was even a seed in her good mother's belly—the garden that was already as good as planted that day long ago (How long is it? Do you remember, Pyotr, how long? Do you remember any of it, Pyotr?), that day long ago when Stanislaw and Rozalja picked the seeds out of the garden in the old country.

It was the beginning of the fall. (Do you remember that fall, Pyotr? You and I, remember?) The sun was not yet an hour below the trees and already the moon was cold in the sky. We were young then (How young were we? How young we were), and still I could feel it, the air biting my face, and my hands like an old man's cold on the reins—the wagon rattling and the dust like fog on the road. For it had been hot that day (Pyotr, do you remember?), and the roads were dry and we even talked about how it comes so suddenly, how when we left the town not two hours before, it was still warm with the sun there just above the trees, and how now there in the wagon on the road to Old Machek's place we could feel it coming, biting, rising in the twilight like the cold moon; talked of how it would be good to miss the long, freezing winter, how in America it would never be so cold, and how in the big cities, Old Lipinski had said, the streets were cleaned and snowless even before you got out of bed in the morning. How excited we were, how young. And when you reined in the horse in front of Machek's fence—the old dog yelping up out from under the porch around the horse's hoofs—and we saw them there in the garden—the two of them working there together like two old married ones, like they had been married three years instead of three days—both of us so young, so excited, laughing, calling to the old married couple; both of them laughing too, the white pillowcases in their hands full of seeds and bulbs, Stanislaw holding his up, laughing, saying, "Do you have room in the wagon for a garden, my friends?"—poor, foolish Stanislaw, we thought, he is still drunk, he has still not recovered from his wedding.

And later, in the house, as they packed the pillowcases into the trunk, how we joked; you, Pyotr, asking if flowers were good to eat, saying, "What good are flowers if you cannot eat them, Stanislaw? You cannot live on flowers in America. Flowers are only for the dead, Stanislaw. For funerals you need flowers. Better you should sell your seed and your trunk too and take money with you to America like me and Jozef, Stanislaw": but Stanislaw only smiling, sitting on the trunk, and his Rozalja snapping the locks shut, saying, "It is not Stanislaw's idea, my brother": and Stanislaw just smiling, looking down at the trunk, saying, "Yes, of course you are right, Pyotr; but they do not use much room, and seeds are very light": and then Old Machek rocking in his chair by the fire smoking his long pipe, spitting into the straw on the floor, his hand stroking the old dog lying beside the rocking chair, his old eyes bright in the light of the fire and under the heavy brows, spitting and saying, "No, Pyotr, it is not Stanislaw's idea": and then the joking gone, and the laughing gone, and the dog jumping up and snuffling over to young Pawel, who sat in the straw sharpening the scythe and who did not look up once through all of it: and only Old Machek there, rocking and puffing the long pipe, looking into the fire, speaking like for the first time in his life he would make a speech, saying something about how he could not allow a son who would leave him in his old age, leave him and the land he was born on, leave him and the land, with only a sixteen-year-old boy to help him care for it; how he could not allow him to leave without giving him something; how he would not give him his consent or his best wishes, and could not even wish such a son luck, but how a father must still be a father even if his son has ceased being a son; how a father must give his son something. "He could take the house if he wished it, or the barn, or even the cow if he could carry it. Only, he must take something. Ah, but such a son, what do you think? He says to me, 'Tata, I want nothing, only your good wishes, only that, nothing more.' And so he would go without taking anything. Because he has stopped being a son, he would make me stop being a father. And so he would take nothing because he has no room for anything—only his clothes and his Rozalja's clothes and his money. He wants nothing but his Tata's good wishes; but I cannot give him that. Yet he must take something, and since he is very clever and his wife always liked my flowers anyway, he takes the seed, for it is light and uses little room and it will satisfy his old stupid father who cannot understand all this leaving for this America, who cannot understand what is so much better than here, who cannot understand any of it. The seed he will take and later, on the boat, he can dump it into the ocean. But he must take something."

And that was the last of it. He had said it, and that was the last of it. He had spoken more in one breath that evening than we had ever heard him speak at one time in all the years we had known him, since we were boys and would drive out there with Tata on those lazy summer Sundays (do you remember?), riding out of the town, both of us on the front seat with Tata, our bony knees high and hot under the sun, or taking turns riding up on the horse's back, and Mama on her rocking chair in the wagon bed with all the wine jugs and the baskets, maybe sewing on something, and little Rozalja, her feet dangling off the back, watching the long dust road winding out behind her, and the dog yelping, and Stanislaw and Old Machek and his good wife with the baby Pawel to her breast all in the shade on the porch waiting; and then later under the trees in the garden, the drinking and the talking, and Mama and Pani Machek bringing the cold wine, and Rozalja with the baby, and you and I and Stanislaw in the barns or chasing the pigs and them squealing, and Tata talking always talking, and Old Machek always quiet just listening, once in a while saying something and then listening again and Tata talking about how it was better in town, easier money and less work, but how he was glad to have Old Machek's farm on Sunday.

How fast it all went. How soon it was all over—Pani Machek, Tata, and Mama, all gone in three short summers; then seeing them only at Mass on Sunday, the three of them—Old Machek, his hair going but still black, the heavy eyebrows and mustache black and thick over the long pipe, and Stanislaw and young Pawel sitting in the pew beside him; and later Stanislaw coming to court Rozalja in the Count's carriage, looking so grand in the livery, holding the great stamping horses. And then what, Pyotr, what then? A wedding, and you giving the white-veiled Rozalja to Stanislaw; the church almost empty, because why should anybody go to a wedding without a reception, but Stanislaw not caring, and Rozalja not caring (since the money that would pay for a three-day reception would come in handy in America), and only some drinking back at the house, just the four of us and the witnesses, and all of us drunk and nobody caring, for in three days we would be on our way to America. Only Old Machek cared, not talking, not understanding any of it, saying how he would not ever be able to face his friends again after allowing a son to get married like that without even a reception, like he got married every day, like it was nothing very important, like nothing was very important, only to go to America where there were jobs and money to be made, and only that was important. He could never understand any of it, Old Machek, and there was just no talking to him. For even after we lifted the trunk into the wagon bed, and Stanislaw and Rozalja went to say good-by, he just sat there not speaking, lighting the twisted straw in the fire and holding it to his pipe, puffing with all the smoke blue around his amost bald head—the mustache still black over the long pipe and the brows heavy—not even looking up when Rozalja kissed his cheek, and stiffening with Stanislaw's hand on his shoulder; and young Pawel too, just like him, scraping the stone on the scythe, not looking up, not even allowing Rozalja to kiss him; and Rozalja crying, and Stanislaw helping her into the wagon bed and the weathered wagon rattling and the sound of the scraping and the old dog howling in the lighted doorway, and after a while only the crying and the wagon rattling and the road long and cold under the moon.

How sad it all seemed. How sentimental to think on it now. Is it that which makes you weep, Pyotr? What do you think on as you sit there weeping? What, Pyotr? You could always weep so easily. You wept then too (Remember, my brother? Remember how we talked on that long ride?)—the wagon clattering on the cold road, and Rozalja and Stanislaw sitting against the trunk in the wagon bed behind us holding each other for the warm, and all of us talking so sentimental, just remembering the good things, and you weeping as much as Rozalja. Only, you wept for different reasons; she for what we were leaving, and you out of joy of leaving it, or perhaps at the thought of how generous you were to have given Rozalja such a good dowry even though Tata left it to her to begin with. But it was you who said you would miss the "old lady summer" with the webs covering all the trees, silver in the moonlight. And it was you who said you would miss the violets, how you could smell them everywhere in the spring and how Lipinski had said there was no "old lady summer" in America and only very sickly violets with no smell and so few of them. However, it does not seem to me that you have missed either of these things too greatly, Pyotr. It was just the night, perhaps, and the leaving; because we were all shamefully sentimental, talking only of the good things and closing our eyes to all the bad that made us decide to leave in the first place—the Austrian occupation and the threat of being forced to serve in the army that was not even our own, that was overrunning our country and raping our women and eating our bread and providing no jobs and . . . all the rest. Old Machek had said those things were not important, that they were terrible but would pass if only the young ones would not run from it but stay and fight it or just endure it—anything but run from it. But we knew it was all hopeless, that the young ones would soon be old ones and still Old Machek would go on saying, "It will pass. It will pass." We were not going to wait. No, we were not going to serve in any Austrian Army, and we were not going to work all our lives for Austrians; we were going to go to America and get rich, and we were going to take our sister with us and her husband and not leave anything behind except a few hundred old friends who would be dead soon anyway, and an old butcher shop in a town that was really too small to make any real money in, and of course an old man and a sixteen-year-old boy sitting before a fire in an old run-down farmhouse who were nothing to us anyway except that our sister happened to marry that boy's brother and that old man's son.

But we did not talk about those things that night. We did not even let ourselves think that it was because of most of those very things that we were leaving at night with the moon cold in the sky and the fog hanging like smoke over the road. We had the papers, and Old Niemotka knew his job, and they were good papers and would pass us as they had the others. Niemotka would be pleased to hear of our passing and he would not worry because he was old, and before they would find him out with all their military efficiency he would have already sent half the young ones of the town across the ocean, and in America they would thank him and pray for him and he was old and it was prayers he needed now, prayers and the pleasure of fooling them, and perhaps that even more than the prayers. At dawn we would be in Lublin and there was nothing to worry about until then, and so we just sat there on the sagging and broken-springed seat with only the rattling of the wagon and the creaking of the unoiled and weathered wheels and the steady sleepy sound of the horse's hoofs on the dirt road and the slap once in a while of the reins on the broad slick back and maybe the single note of some foolish night bird left behind with the autumn moon and the coming snow.

All night you talked—you and Stanislaw—and the wagon would jolt and I would snap awake, and the circle of your cigar would glow orange like a pigeon's eye. And I would listen for a while, watching the circle glow and fade and glow again as you talked—talking about all kinds of things, talking about how Old Machek was not young any more and was settled in his ways and could not be expected to understand the ways of the young, and Stanislaw sitting there in the wagon bed against the old and battered trunk, his arm around the sleeping, shawl-wrapped Rozalja, answering in whispers like it was not important whether he was heard or not, like talking to himself almost, saying how perhaps there was something in what Old Machek had said, that all this leaving for America might be useless, that perhaps it would not be any different there, that we were running away from the foreigners who lived among us and going to live among foreigners, that "at least here it is they who are the foreigners, the intruders," as Old Machek had said, "at least here what you have, though it is not much, is at least yours. There, nothing will be yours, and you will lose even that which you take away with you—lose yourselves, and what is worse, your children"; Stanislaw's voice running down with the horse's hoofs, like a heartbeat running down, slower and steadily slower, and then the quick easy slap of the reins and the heartbeat picking up again and Stanislaw's voice with it, only to begin running down again, talking, whispering his father's curse as though he had memorized it or was memorizing it like you do a catechism lesson or something, like he had to learn it in order to pass some test he was afraid to fail, whispering, about how it was a sin for a son to leave his home and his father like that and how some day Stanislaw would pay for his sin, how some day he would wake up in the new land and find that he had lost everything, even his children, and that he hoped Rozalja would not give Stanislaw any sons to do to him as he had done to his father.

Do you remember that, Pyotr? No, why should you? As you said, those were just the foolish words of a useless and bitter and spiteful old man, and better forgotten as soon as heard; saying how Stanislaw knew as well as you that Old Machek was a fool, an old fool with dried-up ideas who could see no further than the front gate of his worthless and rotting farm, an old fool who made as poor a farmer as he would have made a priest if he had stuck it out instead of giving up all those years in the seminary just to come home and take over a farm which his older brothers did not even want—did not even want in hard times when even a farm like that was something; an old fool who should have gone on and become a priest at least, since surely he was good for nothing else, had proved he was good for nothing else, not even to run a farm, to run a farm that at least made some money, for at least as a priest he could have preached his nonsense and made money too, since that is the first thing they teach them in the seminary—how to make money; and Stanislaw not speaking, just sitting there with the sleeping Rozalja on his shoulder, not even smoking, asleep too perhaps, for all we could tell in the dark; and you talking anyway, not to anybody perhaps, not to Stanislaw or to me either—though I was listening, watching the orange circle of the cigar glow and fade and glow again—your voice low now above the slap of the reins and the hoofs picking up, saying how at least you could have admired him if he had become a priest, since nobody could say that you did not admire and even envy priests, for surely priests are the wisest of men and the most practical, for nobody knows the value of a dollar like a priest does, "Why is it any priest can make a good farmer or a good administrator? Why are they always the best politicians? Not so much because they know all about faith, hope, and charity—all very fine sentiments, and nobody admires them and tries to live by them more than I do—but because they know that all faith and all hope and all charity are just manure without the dollar."

Manure. If that wind does not change they might as well have the wake out in the coops. Somebody must have opened one of the kitchen windows, because it is even worse now; it is enough to wake the dead. But he does not seem to mind. It means nothing to you, eh, Stanislaw? You do not have to smell it, not any more. You look quite content lying there. Yes, they have done a good job with your face, old one. This young fellow knows his business; he has made you look quite well, Stanislaw, quite fine. He does good work, and he is very helpful and respectful for such a young fellow. It is good to see such a young fellow so respectful. It is not even his job to be here tonight, to sit here through the saying of the rosary. Why, he has even brought some beer and two bottles of whiskey. A nice boy, Stanislaw, very polite. He has done much to make it easier for your daughters, and for Rozalja too—though there is little anyone can do for Rozalja, the way she sits there not understanding any of it, mumbling like that with the bowl of glass flowers in her lap—mumbling, smiling sometimes, weeping sometimes. She too will be gone tomorrow, Stanislaw. They have made all the plans and the car from the sanatorium will be here for her in the evening. It will be like two funerals in one day, my friend. Perhaps they should have at least waited until Monday, but you know they must get back to Dupont to work, and anyway, she will not mind. It is all very easy for her now, Stanislaw; no need to worry about her. She smiles at everything. She weeps too, yes; but when you talk to her, she smiles and smiles and gives you the bowl of flowers to smell like they were real. She will be all right. They will all be all right, Stanislaw.

Only perhaps . . . I do not know about Stella. She has changed so much, I do not even know her. Why, she will not say more than two words to me, and I am her godfather; she could at least talk a little to her godfather. But she is so far away. It is as though she is thinking of something far away, like maybe how it used to be—only there are no tears, Stanislaw. I cannot understand it. Perhaps she still thinks of the other thing —whatever it was. But we never talked of it while you were alive, and now it does not matter. Still, she worries me—the way she is painted . . . And she does not look healthy, even with all the paint. Though she could not be called skinny; she is plenty woman; but something . . . And this man with her, this pink-faced one who looks like in all his life he has never needed to shave once . . . Even when they drove up in the car . . . Pyotr and I were sitting in front of the store on the soda cases as always when we saw this wonderful car come driving up with its horn making music at the boys playing in the street. It was no wonder we did not recognize her sitting there in that big black hat with the rag flowers on the brim and the cigarette in her mouth and her face hidden behind the sunglasses, and with that man sitting next to her pushing on that wonderful horn that plays music. Even while he was in the car, we could tell that he was not one of our kind—sitting there behind the wheel in that yellow Panama hat and his face so round and pink. He does not speak much, either. All he seems to do is follow Stella around and give her cigarettes and light them for her and then follow her around some more. Neither of them talks very much. But he, of course, does not understand Polish, and he looks like he thinks every time we say something we are talking about him. Yet he looks like a good man, the way he follows her around and watches over her. And he must be very rich to own such a car and to live in New York.

Whoever thought little Stella would grow up to live in a place like New York? Such a big unbelievable place. Remember when we first saw it, Stanislaw? Standing there at the rail, the four of us waiting with all the others to get our first look at it, Rozalja's shawl blowing in the morning cold, the white gulls screaming and hanging in the air around the boat and falling and slanting and screeching so loud that Pyotr had to say it twice, "Look, you can see it now! Look now!" pointing, and through the cold haze the statue standing on the water and later the points of the buildings and all of it so large and unbelievable, and all the shouting and singing all over the boat, and Pyotr with tears in his eyes and his nose going in his nose rag, and everybody so happy—until we got there. For it was very bad on the docks, with the men pushing and cursing and telling us what to do and where to go and none of us understanding a word of it and not knowing where to go or what to do and sleeping as much as twenty in one little room, men, women and children, and practically nothing to eat for days—all of it so terrible and unbelievable until the day we dragged the old trunk up the seven flights of stairs to the room in the tenement in Prescott and put it down on the bare wood floor and just sat down on the window sills catching our breath and watched Rozalja take out the pots and pans and underwear and the Sunday suit and dress and the overalls and aprons, and dump the seeds out of the pillowcases into the empty trunk and put the pillowcases on the bed and lock the trunk and push it into the middle of the floor away from the wood stove and put a tablecloth on it. And then, though we had no chairs and most of the dishes were cracked from the long trip, we had our first real meal since we had left the old country and it was home at last.

Those were good days. (I am beginning to talk like Pyotr now. All I need is a few tears. Forgive me, my friend!) But they *were* good days—hard, but good too. Not as easy as we had expected; but not so bad as it might have been. And when you and Rozalja and the baby Helcha finally moved into Anderson and took the house here across from Pyotr's store, it was not so bad at all, was it, my friend? (I am still of the opinion that Pyotr made himself some money on that bargain he got for you.) Not so bad at all, what with the garden . . . How did it happen, that garden? It was early spring, you had not yet been living in the house a year. A Sunday it was—a good Sunday, warm and bright like all Sundays should be after a long week in the factory—and Pyotr and his good wife and myself were coming home from Mass all dressed up like Sunday, when we saw you there across the street in your yard in your work clothes—the scythe flashing in the sun like a looking glass—and we went over, me with my pipe in my mouth and Pyotr with his cigar, and just leaned over the fence like two big sports in our Sunday clothes, watching. You did not even see us at first, working there like that with your shirt wet on your back; did not see us until Pyotr spat into the weeds, saying, "Hey, Stanislaw, what is it you do? They cannot work you very hard in the factory": and you, turning, that smile big under the mustache and behind the smoking pipe, leaning on the scythe wiping the sweat out of your cap, not speaking, just smiling, and your breath going hard: Pyotr saying, "Do you not know today is Sunday? You should be in church, Stanislaw. What kind of Catholic works on Sunday?" and you going over to the faucet on the side of the house and putting your head under it and drinking some and wiping your mustache with your cap, saying finally, "A friend would not ask so many questions and bring a working man some beer," saying this and wetting your cap in the rain barrel and putting it back on your head, saying, "But truly, this is not work, my friends. After the factory, this is play, eh, Jozef?"

"For a man like Pyotr, who sits in a store all day and talks to women, this is work, Stanislaw."

"A man who cleans his yard on Sunday instead of going to church is no Catholic."

"But I am not cleaning my yard. And besides, I do not sleep like you, Pyotr. I was in church praying for your lazy soul while it was still lying in bed dreaming about the women you talk to all day."

And even Pyotr laughed, fingering his cigar, saying, "At least I do not work on Sunday."

"But I am not working. I am playing. I am making myself a garden. I have the seed in the trunk and it would be a sin just to throw it out, and besides, a garden will be nice."

"Truly, Stanislaw, I would rather see you working on a Sunday than playing around with such foolishness. Come, give it up, my friend. Let us get some beer and sit on your porch and play some dominoes."

"Dominoes? It will take me all day just to finish with these weeds. If I did not know better, I would think that the Hollanders were growing them, they are so thick."

"The Hollanders had better things to do than plant gardens, my friend. Besides, they said the town was going to the devil anyway with all of us Polacks moving in from across the river, so why should they bother about weeds? They could not wait to move out. And you should be thankful, Stanislaw; how else do you think I could get you such a good bargain on such a fine house? Pah! But it is too hot even to watch somebody else work. Goodby, Stanislaw. If you are serious about this foolish garden, however, I advise you to get yourself some new seed. After five years, that in the trunk is worthless."

But it was not worthless, not even after five years, and by the middle of that summer, the garden was already beginning to be something. Of course, it was not yet the garden it was later to be—a few snowball bushes and violets and sickly rosebushes hardly tall enough to reach past the first rungs of their trellises—but the grass was fine, and some of the transplanted crab-apple trees were already providing shade. So that even in that first summer, even Pyotr, who lubricated his cigar and laughed, enjoyed sitting there under the trees on those Sunday afternoons playing dominoes and drinking beer—his little pig eyes bead-bright behind the spectacles—laughing and saying, "Truly, Stanislaw, this is the sickliest garden I have ever seen. The first truly hot day and all those little roses will give up the ghost. And surely this is the smellingest garden ever. People ask me, 'Pyotr, what is your friend Stanislaw raising in that garden, roses or manure?' Which is it, Stanislaw? Truly, I cannot decide which is worse, playing dominoes across the street in front of my store and being eaten alive by flies around the empty soda cases, or playing here and being poisoned by the stink from your manure garden." And he would laugh and maybe place a four next to a five, and somebody would say, "It is too bad that your eyes are not as sharp as your nose, Pan

Pyotr." And he would lift the spectacles up onto his forehead and look, saying, "Oh, forgive me gentlemen," and he would take the four back and go fishing in the pile for a five, all the time talking very fast, saying, "The stink makes my eyes water so, I can hardly see to play correctly. Surely, Stanislaw, this garden of yours is a joke. Perhaps Old Machek was good for nothing else, but at least he could always plant a flower garden that was at least a flower garden and smelled like one. You should write to your old father, Stanislaw, and ask him how to plant a garden that smells like a garden. You can bet he has some flower garden this summer. He probably has nothing to eat, but you can bet he has some garden."

Only Old Machek had no garden that summer. There was no longer even an Old Machek that summer. For that was the summer the letter came from Old Lipinski (do you remember, Stanislaw?)—the letter in the big brown envelope with the Austrian stamps; the letter in the big careful hand of Old Lipinski, every letter precise, perfectly formed, so flowery that it looked like the old brown pages of some Bible copied by a monk in the days of King Ladislas; the letter written by Old Lipinski, who had gone back to Poland because while in America he could think of nothing but going back, and who once he was back in Poland could think of nothing, dream of nothing but America—Old Lipinski, who must have spent a month composing his letters to his good friend Pyotr in America, to whom he wrote religiously four times a year, the letters coming regularly every spring, summer, fall, and winter, in the same neat, precise, flowery hand on the same brown paper with the Austrian letterhead and the Austrian stamps; the letters telling about the old friends, about the births and deaths and marriages, and about Old Machek, who would not write himself and who, whenever Old Lipinski would ask him why not, would just show him the unopened letters, saying, "Some foolish one keeps sending me letters. But my eyes are too old to read. And besides, I know no one in America"; Old Machek, whose farm was running down since young Pawel was taken into the Austrian Army, and who just sat and drank and worked a little on the farm, just enough to keep himself in food; Old Machek, who luckily had found himself a friend in the Old Count Resniski, a friend for his old age to sit and drink and talk with through the long lonely nights on the farm—the Old Count, who would drive the twenty miles in his paintless and broken-down carriage behind the one remaining half-dead horse just to sit and get drunk and talk with Old Machek, their old voices singing and rattling far into the quiet country nights. The letters came every spring, summer, fall, and winter, and Pyotr would read them. And then, that one summer, the first summer of the garden, he brought the letter into the garden that evening after work, and all of us sat there holding the lighted cattails against the mosquitoes, and Pyotr held up the letter to the bug-swirled lamp, saying, "It is bad news this time, Stanislaw," and began to read.

It all happened that spring (do you remember?). In fact, as Lipinski said, it happened a few days after he had mailed his spring letter and that was why we did not hear of it until almost three months after it had happened. Why they did it we could never understand; and how it happened exactly not even Old Lipinski knew, and he worked at the Stockade. From previous letters, we knew that Old Niemotka had been arrested and was being held in the Stockade. And we all knew that Old Machek was never any friend of Niemotka's and indeed cursed him many times for making the papers which were responsible for sending the young ones like ourselves away. So none of us could understand why he would do such a foolish thing. It was not as though the Austrians were going to harm Old Niemotka. For, as Lipinski had said, they fed the old man well and indeed even liked him, for he was always such a pleasant and funny old man. And Old Niemotka himself did not mind being in the Stockade, for he was old and it was difficult to make a living and in the Stockade they took care of him and he could make jokes to their faces about how long he had fooled them. So we could never understand why when Pawel came home on leave from the border, he and the Count and Old Machek would go riding up like that in the Count's broken-down carriage with the broken-down horse which they should have known would drop dead in a gallop; go riding up to the Stockade in the middle of the night when everyone but the sentries was asleep, and somehow get into the Stockade by stabbing one sentry and shooting another with the rifle of the stabbed sentry, and get Old Niemotka out into the carriage even before the sleeping soldiers could get into their trousers, and go riding away with the horse at a gallop and Pawel still in his Austrian uniform using the whip on him, and the horse galloping and then just rolling over and dropping dead before they could even get more than a hundred yards from the gate—the carriage turning over and the old ones rolling out with the pitchforks and the scythe, and Pawel popping at the oncoming soldiers with the borrowed rifle as they came running out of the gate in their underwear tops and trousers, and the old ones shouting and swinging the scythe and the pitchforks for a few minutes until they were all dead and bloody in the street with a couple of half-dressed soldiers lying bloody beside them.

No, we could never understand any of it. All we knew was that they were all gone, and that it had been a complete waste, and that we would never be able to understand any of it. For no one ever understood Old Machek or his ways, except maybe Pawel and the Count and perhaps even Old Niemotka in his own way (for they were really not very different from each other no matter how much they said they hated each other), and of course you, Stanislaw. Perhaps you understood, or understand now, lying there in your coffin. Perhaps you understand why they would get so drunk and do such a foolish thing, to even burn down the farm and what was left of the Count's estate, saving nothing but some jugs of cider and an old scythe and some pitchforks. Perhaps you understood from the very beginning, my friend, though you said nothing. For when Pyotr finished reading and we all just sat for a while understanding none of it and only being able to say how sorry we all were, you did not speak. And after we had crossed ourselves before the Virgin and were going, we could see your face in the growing twilight and we just left you there in the garden in that first summer with the night coming fast.

So that was the first summer, Stanislaw (do you remember?), the first summer here in Anderson. How long ago it all seems. That was a spring and summer of endings and beginnings—the end of living in the tenements across the river, and the beginning of life in Anderson; the end of Old Machek and Pawel and the farm in the old country, and the beginning of the garden. It was a small beginning, just a small garden that first summer with more manure in it than flowers. But there was the next summer and the next and the next, with everything going well and easily, with the work good at the factory and steady and the garden progressing each year with more flowers and more trees until it was really something of beauty in the town. And in those early days (do you remember, Stanislaw?), whenever any of us of the town spoke of flowers, we would also have to speak of Stanislaw; and one could hardly speak of or to you, my friend, without speaking also of your garden. Truly, it was something of beauty in the town. Those were the days when many of us who worked in the worsted mills in Prescott could hardly wait for the week to be over so we might come back from church on Sunday morning and sit with the wives under the big crab-apple and cherry trees there in the garden—Rozalja and Pyotr's good wife bringing the beer and wine from the kitchen, and the little ones playing hide-and-seek or cowboys and Indians or whatever it is children play; the men talking about all kinds of things, about the work at the factory or the old times in the old country; the women telling of their dreams, and Rozalja telling them what their dreams meant; and maybe Pyotr telling some of the scandalous tales about the people of the town which he would hear from the ladies in the store. It was good there in the shade, talking and drinking, and when the night would come, we would kneel before the white statue of the Virgin that Rozalja had stood on the rock among the roses, and cross ourselves before going home to our beds. And after the peaceful Sundays in the garden, the next day at the factory would not be so bad. And anyway, every day you would bring your garden to work with you in your lunch pail.

Do you remember that first day, Stanislaw? It was in the second summer, do you remember? We were all sitting beside our machines after the whistle had blown—opening our lunch pails and shouting to each other as usual—when you opened your lunch pail and there, along with the hard-roll sandwiches and the sour pickle, was the rose. You got all red in the face, my friend, laughing and holding it up for all of us to see, saying, "By golly, my Rozalja plays jokes on her husband. A rose in my lunch pail—why, it is almost indecent." And how we all laughed and joked about a man bringing a rose to work with him in his lunch pail. And how you blushed, Stanislaw. And though the rose was a little withered from being in the lunch pail all morning, it pleased us very much, and we all laughed and joked and passed it around the entire department—some of the crazier ones dancing around with it like it was a woman, and smelling it and pretending to almost faint from the fragrance, saying how romantic this Stanislaw fellow is to bring a rose to work with him, a rose from his wife, a rose from Rozalja, saying, "Truly, this Stanislaw must have made his Rozalja very happy in bed last night if she sends him a rose this morning." And everybody joking and asking what this Stanislaw's secret was, for after more than five years of marriage and children such romantic foolishness was indeed indecent. And you could do nothing but blush, Stanislaw, trying to take the rose away from the jokers. But of course they would have none of that—one of them filling a soda bottle with water and putting the rose in it and setting it up on top of your machine just as the whistle blew and the machines began going again; and through the rest of the day, all over the department, the men shouting and laughing and joking about working in the prettiest department in the entire factory, and saying how even at the farthest end of the room, they could smell the fragrance, even over the stink of the wool and the greasy machines, and how they could not even be sure any more whether they were working in a factory or a garden.

For almost a whole week, it went on like that every time you took the rose out of the lunch pail—the laughing, the joking.

But soon it became an accepted thing to see the rose in the soda bottle on top of the machine; and even in the winters, we had the garden there in the factory with us. Perhaps it was not always a rose, but there would always be some kind of flower which Rozalja would cut from the plants that grew in the small greenhouse you had built behind the house, and which she would pack along with the hard-roll sandwiches and the pickle in the lunch pail. And it was good to be able to think of the gray snow in the courtyard and then look above the crashing machines and see the green soda bottle with the flower sticking up out of it.

But like all things, even that had to come to an end, eh, Stanislaw? And after the coming of little Stella, there were no more roses in the lunch pail. And then the strike was there, and soon there was no longer even a garden—only the flowers steaming and rotting under the sun and the toppled crab-apple and cherry trees, their stumps sticking up all over what used to be a garden. And now, not even Stanislaw; and just nothing left of it, nothing left even to remind us of it—nothing except maybe the stink of the chicken coops to remind us not so much of what was, or even what is, as what can never be—not in this world, anyway. For it is the same old story over and over again, eh, Stanislaw? And it happens to all of us, only in different ways—a little joy, a little sorrow, and the hope for maybe just a little glory. And so many different things happen, in so many different ways, in so many different places; and still it is always the same story and it always ends the same way. You would think that by this time some of us would begin to understand it, eh, my friend? But we never do. Pah, it does not even pay to think about it. What I need is another drink. I did not think this praying would take so long; I am beginning to get sober. I think I will get extra drunk tonight, Stanislaw. I will drink to you, my friend, and then I will sleep the sleep of the dead. Tomorrow morning, I will throw a flower into your grave and maybe a handful of earth, and try to remember again how it was in the beginning . . . IS NOW AND EVER SHALL BE, WORLD WITHOUT END. AMEN.

33. DAVID SHABER

*Escape from Mother**

David Shaber was born in Cleveland, Ohio, in 1929. He studied at Western Reserve and at Yale and taught at Smith College, before coming to New York to write and to work in the theater.

O I'll sing you a song of my Father's eyes, blue, child-blue, and baby-bright. What he will try to do when he reads this story about Laurence Sattenstein is keep them open, but when it gets past this part where I talk about him into the part where I start talking about Laurence I doubt that he'll have much luck.

My Father's eyes are his worst enemy. He regards them mysteriously, as creatures with minds of their own, two organisms which have consented to live within his head but who take orders from no one, Mister. They cry when they want to, which is often, and close when they want to, which is every time he starts to read. But try and catch him at it. 'Dad . . . Dad!'—and he starts back to wakefulness—'What are you doing?' 'I'm reading, I was just reading.' And he yawns. My father is the world's greatest authority at reading through his eyelids. 'It's a terrible thing, you know,' he says ruefully, shaking his head and blinking. 'The minute I sit down to read I can't keep my eyes open.' Well, blink, blink away and blink again if you must, Father, but this time please make a special effort to stay with it. Because this is written not so much to amuse as to edify, and who knows? You might do yourself a favor.

* David Shaber, "A Nous la liberté," *Transatlantic Review* (Spring, 1960).

It ought to be an eye-opener for the Sattensteins too. I'm thinking of Mrs. Sattenstein in particular, though I can't imagine where she would see this. *I'm* certainly not going to send her a copy. But after what her Laurence did that afternoon I wouldn't be surprised if Mrs. Sattenstein turned around one day and discovered she needed consolation as badly as my Mother and Father seem to now.

How I ever slipped through my parents' fingers none of us will ever know. They spent (and still spend, for all I know) hours trying to figure it out. The only way you can be somewhere in our house and not know there is a conversation going on somewhere else in the house is to step into the stall shower and turn on the water. And so I could hear them that summer while I sat uneasily upstairs over my scribbles on the sway-backed bridge table. I was fed each day as usual by my Mother, a woman determined that even failures should live out their days with stomachs digesting oatmeal and scrambled eggs for breakfast. I would take the second cup of coffee up to my room for the day's work while she stood at the stove, the picture of snappy unconcern. (My Mother's idea of shrewd parental psychology is not to let on that she's alive in front of me.) Then in the evening I would hear her downstairs talking to my Father while he ate his dinner. Unconcern? For every minute I was upstairs wasting my substance on literature and other idiocies there were two minutes of anxiety below. The ratio mounted in geometric progression until at the end of each day I could hear a life-time of heartache rising and falling in the sonorous mumble coming up from the breakfast nook. While me, I was supposed to know nothing about it, of course.

I wish I could remember how many times I leaned against my bedroom door so that the latch would not click when I opened it, and crept to the head of the stairs, putting one foot ahead of the other in elephantine slow motion, teetering, holding my breath at each faintly creaking floorboard under the gray pile carpeting (everything in our house was a bland, smooth gray except for the knotty pine wallpaper in my bedroom and the monogrammed green awnings over the windows

—it was *that* year); and I would stand in the gloom of the little upstairs hall and listen to my Father's wandering voice and my Mother's fervent interjection importuning him to do what I didn't know, except that it boded no good for me at my bridge table. In the occasional moments when the voices fell silent I knew they were sitting in the yellow light under the fixture made up to look like twin brass oil lamps, my Father holding his cup of tea in both hands, the two of them staring, recounting, considering, trying to recollect where they had gone wrong, whose fault, whose fault, enough to figure something to *do* later, right now whose fault was it, how had they been too indulgent with me, how had they been too weak. And when they looked through the breakfast-nook window at the Sattensteins next door, that didn't help much, either.

Mrs. Sattenstein had named her four dark-haired, sallow-skinned, petulant-lipped Ashkenazics as though they were a brigade of Scottish knights: Keith, Stuart, Bruce and finally, Laurence with a *u*. With four boys in the house the Socratic Method was a luxury she could ill afford, I suppose, and Mrs. Sattenstein ruled her four with a lightning rod of iron and a voice banded with steel and ribbed with thunder. A voice, such a voice, *quelle voix, questa voce,* a voice to clean sewers in any language, a voice to dig pavements, a voice to sunder the Red Sea. The window over my bridge table faced on the Sattenstein's house next door, and I lived that summer right in the throat of the klaxon, so to speak. Yet Mrs. S. always took me by surprise, and I would drop my pen in spastic despair when she gathered in the brood for supper, shattering the summer evening with at least one more syllable to each name than there was in the Pronunciation Guide of *What To Name Your Child:* Kee-yeeth! Stoo-oo-ERT! Broo-oose! and Lawr-err-RENSS! with a *u*. And I would look up just in time to see Mrs. S. on her front steps, an enormous stub-headed woman in a blue cotton sundress as big as a small tent, turn and with her beefy arms lolling down at her sides shuffle like an ape back into their house, slamming the screen door behind her. Though my parents winced when Mrs. Sattenstein let go with her pipes, still they would nod at each other in approval. There, there was someone who knew who was boss and who wasn't. For a change, they thought, a woman who didn't let her kids get away with murder or anything else.

The two older boys, Keith and Stuart, at seventeen and fifteen were already firmly set on paths of righteousness with full-time summer jobs. Once I saw Keith struggling through a mistake at the drug store luncheonette where he was clerk; I never knew into what dungeon Mrs. S. had stuck Stuart to learn to become a man. Bruce, third down the line at twelve, was enjoying his last summer of freedom and wise enough to stay out of his mother's way. Only Laurence, who had achieved the wintry age of five, only Laurence was left around the house through the length of the summer days. Only Laurence. And Mrs. Sattenstein knew how to take care of *him*, she did.

Sitting at my bridge table I could see only Mrs. Sattenstein's bedroom, our windows facing each other across our driveway like the lens-holes of two box cameras; but if I leaned forward over the table and stuck my head right up against the window-screen I could see the Sattenstein front lawn to my left and to my right their backyard. So I had plenty of opportunity that summer to watch Laurence.

To be perfectly honest he was not the kind of a child you could take to your heart. Did David Copperfield walk around with a mouthful of tin and rubber-bands? And Laurence scuffled his feet which drove me wild in the first place. He had great solemn saucer eyes that were always shifting and never gave you a straight look, one of those dark little boys with a guarded expression on his mouse face and the face on a skinny, runty body. Just a born Nasty, a Whiner, a Cry-Baby, a Fibber, corrupt at five. No, a David Copperfield he wasn't.

But slowly as the summer passed I couldn't help wondering what he was getting out of life. If there were anything Laurence wanted to do, it was only a matter of moments before he was told it wasn't allowed. He couldn't dig perfectly good holes in the yard, he couldn't swing on the garage door, he couldn't even walk the way he wanted to: 'Lawr-RENSS! WILL you pick up your FEET?' Before I knew it I found myself rooting for him: Scuffle that foot, scuffle that foot. I'm with you, Buddy. I began to look for the sight of him loping around the yard, clapping his hands to and fro, taking each new adventure as it came. Being left alone in the shadow of an Olympian woman like Momma was now no bowl of strawberries and cream, with or without a *u*. But Laurence was never daunted, and I wondered what kept him going.

He certainly got nothing from his father. I didn't see much of Mr. Harry Sattenstein, and from what I could gather, Laurence didn't either. What Mr. Sattenstein did for a living was to make a living. It was the only thing he had time or interest for, as far as I could see. The means of support for the Sattensteins stood on view in the backyard every afternoon, a battered two-and-a-half ton Chevy stake truck with Sattenstein's Fresh Produce in faded white letters on the doors. It was rumored that Mr. S. got up at three in the morning to go to work, which put him one step from God as far as my parents were concerned. I never saw him leave, no matter what varied time of day or night my summer star finally set. But every afternoon at three he would come racketing into the backyard with that truck, and from then on Mrs. Sattenstein's voice would sound the call: 'Be QUIET. Your Father's aSLEEP.' In his few waking moments at home, Mr. Sattenstein moved through the house at appointed times like a king through a captured province, accepting tribute.

I used to try to imagine him on vacation with his family. The table at the lake hotel or midway cafeteria would be heaving with his sons and his wife everywhere among and over them, threatening, pulling them up to the table, cutting swiss steak, buttering bread, slapping hands. Mr. Sattenstein would be sitting silently, majestic, removed, a visitor among strangers. He went on vacations—who doesn't?—but I'll bet he was uneasy from the instant he left. By the third day he must've already been itching to be back among the ice-fresh smells of lettuce in the chilly morning that was still night, missing the heavy voices in the gray half-light, the feel of the damp wood crates sliding under his fingers.

I don't mind admitting he fascinated me, did Harry Sattenstein. Though inclined to flesh and stomach he was a big man, a presence over six feet tall and stone bald. If his wife was the shrill treble he was the mushy bass, with a voice that got lost somewhere between his thick lips and his gummy cigar, barely emerging beyond a grunt or a growl. He didn't have much of a vocabulary, but Laurence adored him.

Oh, how Laurence would try to please that man. Sometimes late in the summer afternoons or on a hot Sunday morning when the papers on the bridge table were sticking to my wrists, I would look out through my window and see Mr. Sattenstein cutting his grass, trudging along behind the lawnmower in a pair of trousers rolled up to the knee and an old torn undershirt. The sweat ran off his bald pate into his eyes, and he would stop every five minutes or so, taking the cigar from his mouth, and wipe his face with his undershirt before putting the cigar back into its corner in his mouth and starting off again. Laurence would follow alongside his father, swinging his arms to and fro in that rolling adventurous step. At the end of every swathe he would scramble to empty the cuttings from the catcher, carrying them to a bushel basket that stood in the drive. Each trip Laurence spilled half of the cuttings and Mr. Sattenstein, over at the mower, squinting against the sun and the perspiration in his eyes, would call, 'Luhrenss, don't spill the grass. What are you doing there with the grass?' Finally, exasperated with the waiting and the loose cuttings all over the drive he would grab the catcher from the boy, eager to finish the damn job and get out of the sun. And Laurence would cry and his father would ignore him, or give him a crack to have something to cry about, all right, if he wanted to cry. And Mrs. Sattenstein, who was watching from the back porch, would call, 'HArry, It's SUNday.' With Laurence standing tearfully at a distance Mr. S. would finish one-two-three. Then he would go in to take his nap. He slept, I think, even more than my own father, which made him practically a victim of the tsetse fly.

Every session on the lawn ended with the same song and dance. Mr. S. would go in and sleep and Laurence would stand and cry. One Sunday, after five or ten minutes of dismal wailing alone, Laurence pulled himself together and ran into the garage. In a moment, still gasping with the end of his tears, he came out carrying the catcher. It was bigger than he was; he had to hold it with both hands and then he couldn't see where he was going. After knocking over two clothes-props and crashing into the front fender of the Chevy he finally made it onto the lawn, where he dropped the catcher and began to drag it behind him. Every two or three feet he stopped, bent to pick up a lose handful of grass and dropped it carefully into the catcher. He wandered over most of the lawn this way, now and again looking balefully at the house. What all that proved I could never understand. But Laurence seemed to have fulfilled some secret agreement with himself and strode out of the yard, arms swinging, undismayed once again, ready for the next adventure.

And if his father ignored him it was better at that than what Laurence was dealt from the hands of his brothers. The big three of course excluded him from their backyard sports, snatching the basketball from him if he chanced to get his hands on it, begrudging him even his three strikes at bat in First-Bounce-or Fly. On those rare occasions when one of them did include him in something Laurence never seemed to realize he was only being used. And nine times out of ten, used hard.

The Sattenstein back porch was set into a corner at the rear of the house, a railed platform opening off the kitchen and connected with the backyard by a short flight of steps. The twelve-year-old Bruce and a pudgy sneak from somewhere down the street named Sheldon had cooked up a war game in which they barricaded the porch by up-ending a large plastic wading pool (property of Laurence, of course) and laying it over the steps. Then each snapped a long stalk from one of the overgrown backyard shrubs, the name of which I don't know. (I'm a true product of Cleveland Heights. The world of nature consists for me of creeping bent, burberry and rhododendron; period.) When they stripped the leaves from the stalk they had themselves a cunning combination weapon about four-and-a-half feet long, stiff enough to be a sword, pliant enough to be a whip, and painful as hell. One of them would defend the porch and the other would attack, and then they would switch places. But after a brief time it became apparent that something was missing; obviously what they really needed was a common victim they could both go after. Who else but Laurence?

It was nothing to lure him into the yard; he was thrilled to be invited. They handed him a sword-whip, stuck him on the porch behind the wading pool, and amid enough home-made bugle calls for the charge at Balaclava, fell to. Laurence shut his eyes, ducked his head behind the wading pool and stuck out his sword. He poked at them, they poked at him, and they both poked again. Then Laurence made the mistake of raising his head and one of the sword-whips pinked him a stinger on the cheek. 'I kuh-WIT!' Laurence screamed. Throwing his sword at them, he kicked over the wading pool and clumped off the porch. The other two pursued him in a circle about the yard, apologizing earnestly like the little hypocrites they were. Before he knew what had happened Laurence was back behind the wading pool, now with two swords as a bonus, and they were at him again. The next time he got nicked I could hear it clear up to my room. In all, Laurence kuh-WIT four times that afternoon. And four times he was sucked back again, never once catching on that he was no more than live bait for the hook.

Laurence was not even allowed into the unspoken cabal against Momma by which his three older brothers had managed to survive, and he had to cope with her by himself. Exactly what went on inside that house I couldn't say for sure, but it was obvious that he lived on borrowed time between disasters. 'Lawr-err-RENSS! Keep your FEET offa that

COUCH! What did I TELL you?' Followed by the smack of a hand, the bull's-eye of a wail, the scamper of terrified feet. The holy of holies was Mrs. Sattenstein's bedroom. In her window directly across from mine there were curtains of dotted swiss swagged with sashes of the same material, and on the window sill I could see bits and pieces of china figurines and one elaborate Dresden girl alighting from a tinted porcelain coach, all the last little fragments Mrs. Sattenstein had shored against her salvation. When it came to this final sanctuary there was no question of teaching Laurence respect or any other gentle virtue; it was kill or be killed. 'I'm gonna MURDER you. Get outta that BEDROOM.'

Once I saw Mrs. S. sitting on their front steps for a moment by herself. Her fat hands were plumped into her lap. The loose flesh sagging along her arms shone damply, and even from that distance I could see the beaded line of moist hair on her upper lip. Looking at her like that, an enormous, steaming woman, exhausted from raising four kids, and realizing the race Laurence must have run her, it was hard to know who to side with. How was Mrs. S. to know that her youngest was any different from her first three? How was she to know that Laurence was keeping score, totting up each insult to his infant *hubris*, waiting only for the day of rebellion? I doubt if he knew it himself. And that's why after what Laurence did I'm glad that these poor words and Mrs. Sattenstein are in the same world, where chance might confront one with the other. After all, it may not have been altogether her fault. But if you roller-skate on ice does it make any difference whether you get pushed or fall of your own accord? Ice is ice, and either way it's looking for trouble. Ask Mrs. Sattenstein.

What Laurence did, of course, was to lock her out of the house.

I almost missed the whole thing. Sitting upstairs that hot July afternoon I first heard an ominous rattle at the Sattenstein front door, and Mrs. S.'s voice in its native pitch at the top of her lungs: 'Law-RENSS. Laurence, are you in there? What did you do to this door?' At my table I batted not an eye; the sun had risen and set on her screams all summer. So it was nothing to me when she shook the door again as though to tear it from its hinges and bellowed, 'Laurence are you listening? If you know what's good for you youbettercomehereandopenthis-doorrightNOW.' A few more fruitless rattles, silence. I heard her waddling up their drive and next she was at the back door, wrenching the knob fiercely. 'All right,' she screamed. 'ALL RIGHT. This isn't funny any more. Laurence, I can see you in there. I can SEE you, Lawr-RENSS.' Inside the house now I heard the scamper of feet. What finally caught my eye though, was a flicker, a ripple of shadow across the way. I put down my pen and looked up to see Laurence staring at me through the window of his mother's bedroom.

I leaned forward and looked to my right. Mrs. Sattenstein, wearing another bust of the groceries crammed into her arms, was still trying the back door. 'Boy, you think this is funny, you'll see how funny this is. When I get in that house you're gonna see my hands FLY.' It must've been that that did it. I looked back to Laurence. Our eyes met and locked across the drive. We stared at each other, two spirits in communion, he behind his window and I behind mine; and I knew Mrs. Sattenstein wasn't going to get him to come and open that door. Whether or not he had planned it all along I don't know, but I looked at those great dark saucers of his and knew that for a moment at least, Laurence was his own man.

Mrs. Sattenstein must have sensed it, too. '. . . Laurence?' she called tentatively, and then in a voice I had never heard her use before, not even to her husband, 'Laurence, Laurence Baby, Mother's arms are full of packages, and she can't get in. Please, Sweetheart,' she crooned, 'Open the door. Laurence, my arms are full of PACKAGES.' I saw Laurence back away from the window upstairs. Oh no, I thought, oh no, he's not going to fall for that, is he? and leaned forward anxiously.

But when I focused my eyes on the shadowy interior across the drive I saw that Laurence had only withdrawn to the middle of the room. Now he began to run in tight circles right where he was, not looking to left or right, his face intent and serious. He didn't touch any of the objects d'art, not even to ruffling the bedspread. I leave it to Talmudic Scholars and Sarah Lawrence girls (with a *w*) to applaud the spiritual integrity of his rebellion; all I knew was that he was running around in his mother's room and I was scared to death for him.

Down below, Mrs. S. was on the move again. She had remembered the door from the porch to the kitchen. Clambering onto the porch and almost breaking her neck on the wading pool across the steps, she leaned against the door. Nothing. She tried again. This time it gave with the sound of crashing milk bottles. The last barricade had fallen. For a wild moment I wished the bottles had been full of corrosive sublimate. 'Now,' Mrs. Sattenstein said, stepping into the kitchen and shuffling through the bottles. 'Now. NOW. Now you're gonna see. Now you're gonna find out.' Upstairs, Laurence was still running in the dizzy little circles when I saw Mrs. Sattenstein explode into the room, grab his shoulder. 'Now,' she said, 'NOW,' and yanked him off the floor like a hooked Flounder. Mercifully, I closed my eyes.

Mind you, Father I make no predictions. My intuition is lousy, and for all I know Laurence may turn out to be as staunch and sensible as oak. But if ever in the years ahead when the boys are grown and gone, if ever then Laurence is the one who gives Mrs. Sattenstein cause to sit in the breakfast nook with Harry over his supper tea, pondering in the yellow light where they went wrong with him, I could tell them. I could tell them of the moment when their son's eyes met mine through the window and I had the flash, they're going to lose that one. They're going to lose that boy. So don't tell me. No matter how properly Laurence may appear to have turned out I have that instant's glance from those great dark saucers to tell me different.

And if you want to know the truth, Father dear, sometimes I look at your own tired baby-blues, and I wonder about you, too.

34. CHARLES BACAS

*What Remains of Life**

Charles Bacas was born in Weymouth, Massachusetts, in 1939. His father was a Greek, a native of the Epirus who had lived through the disturbed times of the Balkan and world wars and who came to the United States in 1919. He worked in various American cities before settling in Brockton, Massachusetts, where he found a cluster of fellow countrymen from his village. He returned to his native place briefly and was married there; but the province was by now Albanian. Upon his return to America he settled in Weymouth, where his son was born and raised.

It was at the beginning of the dinner rush when Spiro brought Jimmy in. Peter heard the back door slam, but it was only a small sound under the noise of the thrashing exhaust fan and the whirring of the old dishwashing machine, and he didn't pay any attention to it. That summer he had been working for Spiro since June, and by then (it was mid-July) he was used to hearing that door slam just about this time every night. It was Spiro coming back from his late afternoon nap right on time to help out with the dinner rush.

The back door of Spiro's restaurant, the Cape Fish Net in Hyannis, was the kind that had to be slammed. It led into the alley behind the restaurant and was in a brick wall where the rain water had been splashing down from the roof and running all over it for more than thirty years. It was warped and

* Charles Bacas, "The Lost Days," *Massachusetts Review,* V (Spring, 1964), pp. 497–521.

scarred and fit unevenly in its jamb. To make the latch catch and hold it well, it needed what everybody soon enough learned to give it: a good hard slam. So when Peter heard it that night he assumed it was Spiro, and that was all.

He didn't even bother to look up. He was keeping his thoughts on what he was doing. It was a Friday night and the rush out front was large and hectic.

The waitresses were swooping in through the swinging door behind him carrying large oval trays of dirty dishes and momentarily letting in the sound of talking, eating customers out front. As the door swung shut behind them they would sigh, or remark something out of their busyness into the hot, thick air of the food-smelling kitchen. Instantly, they dropped their trays down onto the stainless steel counter that Peter worked at and walked quickly across to the pick-up board calling out an order, or getting a clean tray to pick up a ready one.

Peter went through the trays quickly, hovering his bony, young hands over them like scavenging birds, taking up the silverware and the napkins. He put the silverware into a wire mesh basket and stuffed the napkins into a laundry bag that hung from a nail on the wall. Next he tipped up one end of the tray and slid the dishes clatteringly onto the counter top. He wiped the tray clean with a sponge, spun around and set it into a rack and spun again back to his dishes.

In the center of the counter there was a hole, and on the floor beneath it a corrugated aluminum garbage barrel. A thick rubber gasket about an inch high fit into the hole. Peter picked up the dinner plates one by one and banged them down on the rubber gasket to loosen the garbage and slime and then wiped it off through the hole with his hand. He did that with all the other plates too. Afterwards, he stacked the dirty dinner plates, salad bowls, butter plates, bread plates, dessert plates, and vegetable nappies into high piles according to size. Then he poured out the remaining contents of the coffee cups and water glasses onto the counter. There was a slight left incline to it and all liquids swirled down to a drain at the end. He stacked the coffee cups and saucers too, and pushed the glasses into one corner against the spattered stainless steel shield wall that ran up two feet from the counter.

By now his hands were sticky from having handled slimy pieces of lettuce, ravaged fish bones and the hollow shells of lobsters. He turned on the faucet that poured onto the counter top and rinsed his hands.

After that the job was easier. He stacked the plates up on end into one of the wooden racks that fitted in the machine. He interleafed them, packing in as many as he could and piling little ones on top. Then he slid the dish rack into the machine, pulled down the door, and started it up with a lever on the front. Four minutes later the dishes came out the other side clean and steaming hot. He gingerly pulled them out of the rack, his fingers never quite used to the heat, stacked them again, and carried them over to the shelf suspended on the cook's work bench.

So he was working like this, steadily and hard at his counter, and he didn't notice that Spiro had come up and was standing behind him, seconds after his door-slamming entrance. He was chanting a song in his mind, sometimes humming it nasally to the throb of all the noises around him. Spiro patted him on the back. When he turned around he could see the top of Jimmy's bowed head over Spiro's shoulder.

"This is Jimmy," Spiro said, "he'll be working with us from now on. He's starting right now, so show him how to do everything and tell him where everything goes."

Jimmy stepped from behind Spiro and extended his hand to Peter. Peter wiped his hand on his apron and they shook hands. Peter told Jimmy his name and Jimmy told him his again. Spiro just stood there for a moment and Jimmy looked down at the floor. Jimmy knew Peter would be looking him over, studying his face and his body in the precise moment of first meeting, to see what he could find out about him. The way Jimmy stood, his head bowed, his eyes straight down on the floor, it seemed to Peter that this must have been happening to him all day.

Jimmy was forty-five years old. He was thin and round shouldered and had a washed-out Irish face. His skin was chalky white, as if the blood had turned to water behind it long ago. He might have been handsome once. He had a hard formed nose and a huge jaw that descended like the head of a falling sledge hammer. But he was all in shambles. His frozen, pale blue eyes seemed to be melting down his cheeks.

"Okay?" Spiro asked, clapping Jimmy on his bony shoulder. "You'll get along all right," he assured him.

"Yah. Yah," Jimmy said, nodding with a bob of his head and a slight bend of his shoulders.

"Teach him good!" Spiro said to Peter with a smile. Jimmy was the third man Spiro had brought in for Peter to train so far that summer. A college kid had quit after two days and a young local kid hadn't lasted a week.

"Sure, Spiro," Peter said.

Spiro turned and walked out through the swinging door into the dining room. Jimmy looked after him a second through the port hole window in the door.

"Nice guy," he said to Peter.

"Yah, Spiro's a good guy," Peter said.

Peter was still looking at him in that studying way. Jimmy was a bum, a derelict. Peter had seen men like him walking in the shadows of walls in his home town, in the railroad district, in factory neighborhoods, in the back streets of the downtown section. Jimmy was an alcoholic. There was a redness to his large-pored nose and thin, blue veins showed on its hard shape. There were gray wattles on his throat just below his ear lobes and a dry boil on his forehead. Peter had seen men like him sitting in the rocking chairs on the long porch of the Salvation Army Men's Service Center in his home town. Now one of them had a name: Jimmy.

Peter stopped his work long enough to show Jimmy around the kitchen and tell him what to do. He didn't have it in his heart to be aloof and abrupt with him. Peter wasn't five years beyond the age when it had been something dangerous and funny to taunt a man like this, if they had come upon him in gangs on the street. But he did show him around badly anyway. He was tense about being interrupted in the rush and he was very involved and rigid concerning the way he went about doing the job. Aside from swinging a pick for his home town highway department, washing dishes was the second job Peter had ever conquered for a week's pay.

Peter paced up and down the five square feet of floor space where most of the job took place, talking quickly to this gloomy-looking man, a youth instructing, feeling strange about what he was doing, and stranger still about this bum called Jimmy.

He remembered bums from way back in the undeveloped tendencies of his childhood. He remembered them as men to be afraid of; as enemies. Before the days when he had stood in the safety of a gang and thrown out his part of the mocking taunts to men like this, he had walked down streets by his mother's hand and had seen these men through her eyes. They had pitched and lurched along sidewalks, they had stood staring out from dark doorways, and his mother had reached out and put a protective hand on his shoulder as they passed them. "Be careful," she had said before the faces of these men, in the secret cover of their second language of Greek. "When you are alone be careful of these men and stay away from them."

One time, when they had reached the safety of his mother's kitchen, where from a sanctified corner the hard eyes of Icons stared down off the wall, he had asked his mother why. And she, with the reckless need to express her pain to a child, had answered him by investing these men with terror. She had given them the inarticulate power of her own uprooted loneliness. It had seemed to him then that she had called them a plague; that they could infect you with the leprosy of their lives; that they could get close to you, breathe on you, touch you, and soon your fingers, your ears, your cheeks would drop off, too.

Peter finished with a final flurry of quick directions and pointings to where things were and Jimmy gave him a foggy look, as if he hadn't understood some of the words Peter had used.

"Did you get that all right?" Peter asked, going back to the counter that was now stacked five high with trays of dirty dishes.

"Well, not all of it kid, not all of it." His voice had a cheerful, palsy sound when he called Peter "kid." "I worked set-ups like this before though, and I'll pick it up in no time."

While he was talking he was unbuttoning his frayed white shirt. He slipped it off slowly, revealing the bony casing of his small body underneath his tee shirt. The tee shirt was murky white, lived in, with two small holes on the sagging belly part. On the back, up by the neck, was stenciled the name POWERS. Peter was reading the name as Jimmy turned sideways from him.

"I got this off a guy in the Navy," Jimmy said, reaching his hand back and covering the name. "My name is Donelly."

"Yah, I know," Peter said, "you just told me."

Jimmy walked over and hung up his shirt where he had put his jacket when he had come in. He shuffled over to the drawer in the cook's work bench where Peter had told him the aprons were. While he was putting it on and tying it behind himself he suffered a short spasm of twitches.

Jimmy came right over and went to work on the other side of the machine beside Peter. He pulled out the clean, hot dishes, stacked them, and hauled them to the cook. They worked together like this through the rest of the dinner rush.

Two and a half hours later, about quarter of ten, the rush was finally over. The swinging door only sighed open now and then, and trays of dirty dishes came in once every ten minutes. Peter stopped working, lit up a cigarette and asked Jimmy if he wanted anything to drink or eat.

"Can you do that?" Jimmy asked, feeling out the rules of the house.

"Sure," Peter said, "Spiro doesn't mind if you have a little snack right about now."

"I could do with a cup of coffee, kid."

Peter went out into the pantry off the dining room and drew Jimmy's coffee from a tall, stainless steel coffee maker. He put a handful of cracked ice in a glass and poured himself a cool ginger ale.

There was a small oval table and two camp chairs in a back corner of the kitchen. Peter brought the drinks back out and they sat down. Jimmy borrowed a cigarette from Peter and they smoked and sipped their drinks.

"You planning on going into the business?" Jimmy asked.

During the rush Spiro had been helping out sometimes by seconding the cook, Art. A few times Spiro had called over and asked Peter to go down to the walk-in refrigerator in the cellar to get something. Those times Spiro and Peter had talked back and forth in Greek.

"Hell no," Peter said, "what makes you say that!"

"Well, I just figured; you know."

"No," Peter said, "I'm just down here for the summer."

Jimmy sat back in the chair and held the warm cup in his two hands. Peter could tell he was making much of this comfort. Jimmy gulped down a few more swallows of coffee and then took a deep drag from his cigarette.

"What do you do," he asked, "regular I mean?"

"I'm going to school, college, next September."

"Oh."

"Out in Michigan."

"Oh."

"I'm no relation to Spiro. I'm just Greek."

"Yah, I know," Jimmy said. "I worked for a lot of Greeks."

Peter looked at him with a tired smile, thinking Jimmy had meant to make a joke about all the Greek restaurant owners there were. But Jimmy hadn't meant that at all. He had just meant what he said. He looked down and took another gulp of coffee.

"Where are you from?" Peter asked, disguising his curiosity.

"Boston's my original place," Jimmy said, "that's where I was born and all."

"You ever work on the Cape before?"

"No. This is my first time. I never been here before."

"Never?"

"Yah," Jimmy said.

"Where did you work?" Peter asked guiltily, touching on a bum's past. "Before, I mean."

"All over," Jimmy said.

"Like where?" Peter asked, pushing it on.

"Everywhere, almost. I been to Cleveland, Baltimore . . . Pittsburgh, Philadelphia. Spent some time in Albany. Lots of places. I come here from New Bedford."

"New Bedford?" Peter asked. The city didn't fit with the others Jimmy had mentioned. Perhaps because he knew New Bedford and not any of the other places.

"I was only there five days," Jimmy said and he grinned, or at least Peter thought he grinned, into his coffee. "The cops took me to the city limits this mornin' for vagrancy. So I stuck out my thumb, and here I am."

It seemed to Peter that Jimmy didn't mind talking about these things. They were just the facts of his life, Peter thought. The facts were all he had. A cup of coffee now and then and the places he had been to.

"How did you get the job? I didn't see you come in and ask or anything."

"Yah, funny thing about that. The guy that gave me a ride this mornin' told me about it. He's from here, Hyannis, and he said he knew this other guy who could maybe use a dish washer. I told him I never been here before, so he took me down to Spiro's house."

"You mean he hired you there?"

"Yah. I hung around out front of his house a couple of hours and he brought me in when you seen me."

"Oh."

"Can I have another one?" Jimmy asked, tapping Peter's pack of cigarettes on the table.

"Sure."

Peter stood and took up Jimmy's empty cup and his empty glass.

"You goin' back now?" Jimmy asked.

"That's all right," Peter said, "finish your butt."

He walked back to his counter with the cup and glass and left Jimmy at the table.

Jimmy was still at the table and Peter was just putting the last dish into a rack, when a waitress swooped in with a tray. It was Carol MacGowan, short, fat, with a round white face that had downy blond hairs on it. She had a short, blond pixie haircut.

There were five waitresses. Three of them were friends and classmates at a teachers' college in Worcester where they lived. They would be seniors next year. Amongst themselves, in the quiet off hours, they would sit in a back booth of the dining room talking about college and "Education." But there was one thing they all didn't want to happen in their lives. They didn't want to wind up teaching elementary school forever. They wanted to get married. All of them were openly on a manhunt that summer. They had a tough gloss to their lives. They flashed around with a wry attitude about the softness of their hopes, calling each other by their last names.

They were tough, they were working girls. They liked Peter. He was the "Kid." The kid who washed dishes at the restaurant where they worked, here on Cape Cod, where the sun tanned you all day on the beaches that were right down every street, here in Hyannis, where crowds of tourists roamed through the small town at night.

Carol dropped her tray onto Peter's counter and stuck one hand in her apron pocket, jingling her night's tips.

"Hey, hon," she said, "who's the new guy? Spiro never hired anyone like that before." Neither one of them could be too sure about that. "Before" went as far back as June of that summer; but that was all time, all the history of their lives.

"I don't know," he said, motioning with his head that Jimmy was sitting right over in the back corner. He slid the rack into the machine, slammed down the door and started it up. In the extra noise he leaned over to her.

"Who is he?" she whispered, and tweeked him in the ribs.

"Some bum, I guess," he said, and he side-stepped her hand.

"He looks like it," she said, making a sour face.

Another waitress swooped in and dropped her tray. She hurried over to the pick-up board.

"Hey, MacGowan," she called, "you going to bus that table or what?"

"I'm talking to my honey," Carol said, putting her arm around Peter where they stood so close, whispering.

"Come on, be *serious,*" the other waitress said harshly. She put the last dish of a ready order onto her tray and swooped out again.

"Don't mind her," Carol said, "she's having her 'troubles.'" Peter didn't know why it was, but every time one of the girls was having her monthly woman's trouble everyone who worked in the restaurant, including him, eventually got to know about it.

"Oh," he said.

"What about this new guy?"

"I don't know. He seems all right. He's kind of interesting in a way."

"He's a bum, huh."

"Yah."

"Well," she sang, and spun away from him picking up a clean tray and went out to bus that table.

Twenty minutes before closing time, Jimmy helped Peter haul out the full garbage can from under the counter. Jimmy took one handle and Peter took the other and they teetered heavily across the kitchen floor and out the back door. They put the barrel down in the alley with the others there.

The finished job called for a cigarette. Peter offered one to Jimmy, lit one up himself, and went to the mouth of the alley. He peered around the corner out to the busy Main Street of Hyannis. Headlights arced and flashed and tires hissed by. One of the summer movie houses had just let out a crowd of bermuda shorts and summer dresses, chino slacks and sport shirts.

"Have you got a place to stay?" Peter said to Jimmy, who was peering around behind him.

"Yah, the Grayson down here." The hotel was the closest thing to a flop house that Hyannis had. A mangy, two story hotel over a block of stores down by the old railway station. Peter wanted to ask him why he had picked that place, but he didn't bother.

A while later Peter was finishing with one of his last closing up jobs. He had carried a large tray of clean water glasses out to the dining room and was setting them on a shelf. There was no one in the dining room but the waitresses, chattering tiredly and leaning over their tables, setting up the silverware, menus, and sugar bowls for tomorrow. Peter put up his last glass and carried his tray over to the booth where Spiro was sitting.

Spiro's glasses were up in his hair and he was massaging his eyes with his fingertips. There was a pencil, a pile of the day's checks from the cash register, and a cup of coffee on the table in front of him. Spiro was about forty-five, fifty. He owned this restaurant and managed another one on the other side of town. He spent sixteen hours a day, all summer long, chasing back and forth between them in his new Oldsmobile. He was always contesting with workers, and salesmen, and customers, and delivery men. He was always tired. He lived on the coffee that was always by his elbow wherever he sat down.

Peter quietly slipped in on the booth bench opposite him. Spiro continued to massage his eyeballs with a slow, sticky motion and sound.

He was an Island Greek. He had come over from Samos with his mother and father when he was twelve. He had told Peter a story about his life there as a boy. About how he used to dive down underwater and swim under the keels of frieghters that were anchored in the bay at Samos. That was in the Twenties he had said, when he was ten. He had told Peter his bathing suit was made of an old piece of jersey and was as big as a jock strap.

"How's Jimmy?" he said, opening his watery eyes.

"Okay, I guess."

"Good. He's going to work mornings. He'll start about ten and stay through till nine o'clock to take the dinner rush with you. You keep coming in at three."

"Art doesn't think he'll last," Peter said, quoting the cook. "Because he's a bum and all."

"So?"

"That's just what Art said."

"If he quits we'll find somebody else."

"Okay," Peter said, standing up.

"Give me a glass of water," Spiro said to him in Greek.

Peter went into the pantry and got it. He set the glass down by Spiro, where he was double-checking the totals of the day's checks, and went back out to the kitchen.

Five minutes before midnight Jimmy and Peter were all through. Art the cook was tearing down his steam table, which was his last job of the night too. Peter walked over by the washroom door, near the cellar stairway, and pulled off his sweaty tee shirt. There in the kitchen help's washroom, he had a clean, fresh one that he brought with him every day.

He washed up and pulled on his clean tee shirt. He had stashed a bottle of shaving lotion in one corner of the floor, under a pile of dirty whites. He took it out and splashed his face. He wasn't thinking about Jimmy anymore. He was going to meet his girl.

Peter had a romance going with a girl named Laurie Dawson from Dayton, Ohio. She was a waitress at Spiro's other restaurant. She wasn't much to look at, kind of thin and plain, but she had a fantastic summer wardrobe. They both lived at the same rooming house, Mrs. Carpozzi's. Laurie had come out to the Cape with her older sister, who lived there too. Laurie's sister was in college.

Peter cupped his hand to his cheek and tried to smell his own face. He looked in the mirror and patted his hair into place with his hand.

He turned and walked out into the quiet kitchen. All the machines and the big oven had been turned off. In the high wall window the propeller of the exhaust fan was barely turning in the evening breeze. The only sound was the soft, steady humming of a refrigerator motor.

Jimmy had gone already. Art was standing behind his bench drinking a can of beer.

"See you later, Art," he called.

"Mmm," Art said, swallowing, and Peter banged out the back door.

The next night at work Art the cook and Jimmy exchanged war stories. The night before, Peter had noticed that Jimmy had a bracelet of blue numbers tattooed on his under wrist. While they were together in their second day as work mates, Peter asked Jimmy what it was.

"That's my Army serial number," Jimmy said.

"How come you've got it there?"

"That's in case I drop dead somewheres," Jimmy said coolly.

"What do you mean?"

"If I drop dead and they find me, they'll see this on my wrist and give me a military burial."

A minute later, when Peter was over by Art's bench, he told him that Jimmy had been in the Army and about the numbers on his wrist. Peter asked Art if it were true about the military burial.

"I don't know," Art said in his whispering voice. Art had been two years in Korea in the early Fifties as a sergeant in the Marines. He hadn't been a cook though. He had picked up the trade only five years ago. Art had been wounded in the back and had lost his hearing in one ear from a close shell explosion. That was why he whispered when he talked. It was like everybody else was whispering to him, and he whispered back.

Peter called Jimmy over and Jimmy showed Art the bracelet of numbers tattooed on his wrist.

"Sure," Jimmy said, "sure, they give ya a military burial. A sergeant of mine told me that before I got out."

"What was you in?" Art asked.

"Army," Jimmy said.

"Marines," Art said, pulling up the short sleeve of his cook's white shirt and revealing the big, blue Semper Fi tattoo on the muscle of his left arm.

"You were in Korea, huh?" Jimmy said, gauging Art's age.

Art nodded.

"Me," Jimmy said, "I was in the last one. Didn't see much action though. I got drafted near the end, right after I got out'a high school. I was in the quartermasters over in Naples a year and a half."

Peter had never had the courage to ask Art about Korea. He had wanted to ask something straight out, (something like tell me a war story, or, I'd be afraid, were you?) but Art wasn't the kind of person who took to questions like that. Art had simply told Peter that he had been to Korea, when Peter had asked about his tattoo. He had also briefly explained his deaf ear and asked Peter to talk loudly. But now seemed like a good time for Peter to ask.

"Did you see much action, Art?" he asked, leaning back on Art's work table and folding his arms for a story. Art checked his duplicate slips and saw that his orders were all right. He lit up a cigarette. He knew what Peter wanted to hear.

"Sure," he said, "plenty. I was two years in Korea. They sent me back to Pendleton on rotation after my first year. But I liked Japan, and I had two more years to go, so I signed up for Far Eastern again. I asked if they'd send me back to Japan. But . . . the mothers, they sent me back to Korea. I was two years there all together." He gave a wry smile. "That's when I got my ear like this," he said tapping his finger on the lobe of the deaf one. "I told you about that. It happened the second time."

"I never saw much in Italy; by the time I got there it was near the end," Jimmy said.

"Yah," Art said, cutting through Jimmy's speech and going on with what he knew Peter wanted to hear. But then he found that he felt like telling a story anyway. "I seen a lot of things. I seen our own guys killin' each other."

"What do you mean?" Peter said.

"I'll tell ya," Art said, blowing out some smoke and stepping back a second to his oven to check a piece of broiling swordfish. "The second time I went back I was promoted sergeant. Me and this corporal, this guy named Red, we was good buddies. Real asshole buddies, you know what I mean. We was out on this hill near Seoul after the second time we lost it. Night times me and Red would go around bringin' coffee to the guys in their holes. We had this big gallon coffee pot, you know. That gray enamel kind.

"Anyway, one night we had this new kid who was out on point. That's the first hole a couple of hundred yards up away from everybody. This kid had come to us two days before on rotation. Well, anyway, something happened that night and I couldn't go around with Red bringin' the coffee.

"It was okay bringin' the coffee around. It was cold as a witch's tit and we'd come up two o'clock in the morning. The guys were glad to have it. Only thing was, we'd scare the hell out of them comin' up on 'em at night like that. Lots of times we had rifles stickin' in our faces and guys callin' out to ask us who it was.

"Anyway, this night I couldn't go with Red; he brought the coffee around alone. He was kind of eager sometimes, you know, the kind of guy that doesn't be careful and follow the rules, and that night, this new kid up on point—it was his first time up there—he shot Red.

"They must have trained that kid good in Basic. He thought Red was a gook sneakin' up behind him, and he shot him sideways two hundred yards away in the dark." He paused, looking at Peter, dragged on his cigarette and looked down. He thought to himself and decided he had told it all. At least that was the way he felt about it.

"What do you mean by sideways?" Peter asked

"Sideways," Art said, swiping one hand down from his shoulder to his hip. "The kid put four M-1's through him in the dark, right down his side."

Carol MacGowan came in and called out an order. She tore the dupe slip out of her order book and slapped it down on the work bench. Art moved back to his oven and pots, and Jimmy and Peter went back to their dishes.

Jimmy was finished with work at nine that night. As yet, he hadn't taken his second meal of the two a day that Spiro allowed them. He was dressed in the same frayed white shirt and gabardine slacks he had worn the day before.

"You didn't eat yet, Jimmy!" Art called to him, when he saw him dressed to leave.

"I'm gonna eat now," Jimmy said.

"How about baked fillet of sole?" Art asked. The help always took whatever he offered them.

"Okay," Jimmy said.

He took the plate of brown, baked haddock sole, mashed potatoes and green peas, and sat down at the corner table in the kitchen, with a fork and a glass of water.

Peter was going down to the cellar to get something from the walk-in refrigerator and walked past Jimmy where he was eating, hunched over his food.

"How did you make out at the Grayson?" Peter asked.

"All right," Jimmy said. "It's okay. I guess I'll stay there for a while. It's only eight bucks a week. I guess I'll stay here too. This job ain't bad." He forked some mashed potatoes into his mouth and brought the fork down and cut off a piece of fish with the edge of it.

There was nothing for Peter to say, so he went on down the cellar steps, where he was going in the first place.

After work that night, after the war stories and the quiet way that Jimmy had set to working, Peter figured Jimmy would be with them for a while yet.

Peter thought that Jimmy might even be trying to reform himself out of his bumhood. At least the drinking part of it anyway. He sort of wished he could help Jimmy out in this. He imagined the lonely, factual struggle of Jimmy's slipping life and thought it would be good to help him. He sort of resolved to himself that he would do this.

He had no conception of himself as a good guy or a hero,

but after all, people were supposed to help other people. If he could, he would do his little bit with Jimmy and help him to change the agony of the life that he wore in his face. He might even change a little of the frightening world that Art had talked about in his war story. He wasn't quite in the world yet, but he could soften it up for himself before he entered it completely.

But that was only a dream he had, walking home from work that night, down the quiet streets of his usual route with the trees rustling overhead.

The next morning he talked about Jimmy to Laurie while they were lying on the beach. The confused thoughts he had about helping Jimmy didn't come out right though.

"So what does that prove," she said, squinting at him in the sun and adjusting the halter of her fancy bathing suit. "He's only a bum."

"No, I didn't mean that. I mean about helping guys like that. You know, they sort of suffer for everybody else." That was a thought that just came to him in desperation to explain

"Suffer for what?" Laurie said.

"For everything."

"What's everything?"

"You know," he whined out at her blockading question. "Like wars and crimes and sins."

"That's deep," she said. "What are you so excited about. He sounds like a bum to me. There's a lot of them in Dayton too."

"You mean you think he's just a bum and that's all!"

"Sure. A bum's a bum."

She was getting the upper hand. He thought of telling her about the fellow-feeling he had for Jimmy because they worked together. But he knew that she would point out that Jimmy was a professional dish washer and he was only doing it for the summer.

"Come on, let's swim," he said, rolling up onto his knees. He stood up off his towel.

"Wait!" she said, and reached back for her bathing cap.

When Peter walked into the unwelcoming blast of hot, stuffy kitchen air that afternoon, with the salt and the sun of the beach still on him, Art was razzing Jimmy about something.

"I'll ask *him,*" Jimmy said, clumping around towards Peter from behind the yellow wood cook's table. He stopped in front of Peter and hiked up his apron above his knees.

"Don't say nothin' now," he said to Art over his shoulder. "What do you think of them, kid?" he said pointing down to a new pair of shoes. Peter was sun blind from having walked into the dark kitchen a second ago, and he blinked and looked at them twice.

"They're not so bad," he said. They were very institutional looking shoes. Peter had seen the same kind sitting in the windows of Army & Navy stores.

"You see!" Jimmy called.

"Would you buy them yourself?" Art said to Peter, coming around from his table with a french knife in his hand. He pointed down to the shoes with the knife.

"Yes . . ., for work or something, maybe."

"What d'ya mean?" Jimmy said. "Them are dress up shoes too. The guy who sold 'em to me wouldn't lie," and he let the word "lie" hang in the air and unconvinced himself.

"See," Art said, and he gave a silent chuckle and walked back to his table, and the pots and pans that hung up over his head from a large, silver painted ceiling rack.

"They're nice shoes," Peter said softly to Jimmy. Art didn't hear that because of his deaf ear.

"They ain't worth a pint of whiskey," Art taunted, as he diced a green pepper on his bench. "Ask him how much he paid for them."

"Ten bucks," Jimmy said insecurely to Peter. "That's not bad, is it?" He held up one foot for Peter to get a closer look.

"You could buy two fifths for that much," Art said hearing that.

"I ain't drinkin' much these days," Jimmy answered with a tough edge to his voice.

"They're good shoes for working, Jimmy," Peter said, pulling his sweatshirt over his head.

"That's why I bought 'em. Spiro advanced me fifteen bucks on my week's pay. My other ones had holes in the bottoms. Did you notice that?"

"No," Peter said.

Jimmy walked away from him abruptly. He reached up on the shelf over the dishwashing machine where they kept odds and ends of broken cups and plates.

"Here," he said, coming back and handing Peter a pack of cigarettes, his brand.

"What's that for?"

"Them are for the ones I borrowed from you yesterday and the day before."

"You didn't have to do that, Jimmy."

"That's okay," he said, "I don't like to mooch." He picked up a basket of lobsters and trotted down the cellar steps with them.

Peter went over to the whites drawer and got out an apron. "They are kind of crummy shoes for ten bucks," he said to Art as he tied it on.

"That's what I told him," Art said.

"Look, he gave me these." Peter showed him the pack of cigarettes.

"I know," Art said, "the money went to his head."

"Your getting brrrowwnn-er and browner every day, hon," Carol said as she swished in behind Peter.

"Put that away, will you." She set a partly empty five pound bag of sugar on the table. In her other hand she had half a dinner roll palmed against her apron. She leaned over the steam table and dipped it into a can of beef gravy. She popped it into her mouth.

"Hey, fatty," Art whispered loudly, "get out of my kitchen."

"I am," she said, stuff-mouthed; she bumped her behind into the swinging door and went out.

Later that night, while Peter and Jimmy were eating their suppers together at the table in the kitchen, Peter talked to Jimmy about going to school out in Michigan the next year. Peter tried to make it Jimmy's kind of conversation, levelled low and simple, and the main point he made concerning his nervousness at starting college was that he had never been as far away as Michigan before.

"That's all right, kid," Jimmy said, "I been to a lot of places and they're all the same."

"I know, you told me all those cities."

"They're all the same. I'm thinkin' I'd like to settle down."

"Really?"

"Sure. There's no sense in going around so much as I do. I can find the same thing in one place as another. I like this town right here."

"It's kind of dead in the winter," Peter said.

"Oh, I wouldn't mind that. It would be all right so long as I could keep on workin' with Spiro here."

"Well . . . , he stays open in the winter. That might be a good idea, Jimmy." Peter was thinking now would be a good time for him to do his bit about the reformation of Jimmy's bumhood; even though the feeling had passed in him. "You could settle down here in Hyannis and be a regular . . . well, just like a regular person from the town."

"You think so, huh?"

"Sure," Peter said.

They bowed their heads and continued eating across from each other at the small, oval table. As he ate there, looking down at his food, aware of Jimmy, hearing the sound of Jimmy eating, almost smelling the smell of his body, Peter began thinking he was Jimmy. Not imagining it, but thinking it. He broke off a piece of roll and stuffed it in his mouth over some carrots and tasted it like Jimmy would taste it.

How did it feel to be eating, after all these years, in just another kitchen, in just another town. He swallowed Jimmy's mouthful of food; he swallowed it sickly, thinking it had been wet by Jimmy's saliva.

It became uncomfortably empty to be Jimmy, to be faced with washing dishes for Spiro the rest of his life. Jimmy's life had an iron chain around his stomach, pulling, tightening. A cold, empty fear of emptiness chilled through his veins. He tried to shake it off, to shake off the whole feeling of being Jimmy and it happened easily. It all happened unconsciously in him.

He had looked at Jimmy, thinking of how many generations it takes to make a bum like him, blowing about the country like a crumpled piece of newspaper. He had thought of his own self, born into this country for the first time, brought here in fact by his parents to be born here. In the deepness of himself he had felt a powerful strength, a right to disinherit all that he didn't want of this place. There was a promise and fitness of the things to come to him. There was Michigan this Fall, there was . . . , and who knew all the things to come.

He brought another forkful of carrot up to his mouth and went on eating like Peter, the person he was, and the person he was meant to be.

Two days later, Tuesday, was Peter's day off. It would have been Jimmy's fifth day of work at Spiro's. He was supposed to go in at Peter's time that day, three o'clock, and work Peter's shift through 'til midnight.

That day Peter went to the beach with Laurie early in the morning. The situation between them was somewhat nasty that morning. Both of them seemed to be repenting things. They were beginning to be very exclusive about themselves in this romance, having found that the other was not going to hold up a mirror to their own niceness. But they didn't talk much, tried not to bring it up, and just lay on their towels toasting in the sun. There wasn't much to do now but go through with the whole thing until Labor Day, when it would be all over.

Peter went up to the beach stand and bought cokes and hot dogs for their lunch and they stayed on the beach till three o'clock. Then they walked the two miles back to Mrs. Carpozzi's.

Laurie took a shower, combed her hair, put on some fine smelling perfume, and dressed in her waitress uniform to go to work. She was due at five o'clock. Peter offered to walk her down, as he usually did on his day off, but Laurie said he didn't have to and, owing to the situation, Peter didn't offer again.

After she left Peter took a long, languid shower. The shower loosened him, relaxed him deeply, and he padded slowly through the upstairs hallway with a towel around his waist and went into his room. He flopped out on his bed naked and took a nap.

He woke up an hour later and dressed slowly and smartly for the night. He was thinking he would go downtown, have a good supper somewhere, and then go to an early movie. He was supposed to meet Laurie at eleven, when she got out of work.

When he came down onto the Main Street of Hyannis it was about eight o'clock. He was walking slowly, mentally picking out the place where he would eat. Once in a while he caught a glimpse of the dropping, orange ball sun behind buildings and trees. It was a cloudless blue and orange sunset. The streets were almost deserted at this time on a weekday evening. The tourists were home, cleaning up from the beach, dressing slowly for dinner, deciding what to do with the young night. As the sun lost its hold the cool Cape ocean air was rustling in the trees.

Peter was coming up Main Street from the east end and he entered the business part of town walking by the old railway station. He was on the sidewalk across from it. There was a bend to the road as he walked by the stoop of the Grayson Hotel. When he came around it he saw Jimmy.

Jimmy was sitting on the concrete step path that led into the doorway of a closed jewelry store. His back was against the store front, leaning on the black facade below the show window, and he was tying his shoes.

"Jimmy," Peter said bending over him, "what are you doing here?"

"Hi, kid. I'm tyin' my shoe."

"Your supposed to be at work, aren't you?"

"Not for a couple of hours yet I ain't," he answered back slowly, finishing with his second shoe.

Peter stepped back and thought that one over. Not for a couple of hours yet? What the hell, had Spiro fired him for something and was he sitting there lying, just being a bum. Or maybe he's making up his own work hours now. Not for a couple of hours yet.

Then he began to realize, or almost realize, what had happened. He didn't want to push the realization too quickly. He wanted to believe it, but believe it slowly; let it come on him slowly.

Peter stood there with a crazy, half funny, half sad smile on his face. Jimmy looked up at him dumbly, aware that something was wrong because of Peter's attitude, waiting for an answer from him, whose behavior was suddenly so strange.

Peter began turning, with his palms up to the sky. He shuffled around in a slow circle looking up at the faint light of the setting sun in the sky, looking down the quiet, early summer evening, deserted Main Street. It could have been morning; it could have been. Jimmy had awakened in the dusk and thought it was dawn.

"You know what time it is, Jimmy?"

"About six-thirty, seven o'clock," he said, looking at Peter strangely.

"No, Jimmy. It's night time. That's the sun set over there." He pointed, slowly, stiffly.

"No it ain't," Jimmy said with a tremble. He shook twice more where he was sitting and tried to get hold of himself. "I was just goin' to have breakfast."

"No fooling, Jimmy. Really. It's night time."

"You mean that, huh?" he hushed weakly.

"Yes," Peter said softly, knowing now what pain it was for him to know. "How did you do that, Jimmy? What happened?"

"Oh," he said touching his eyes tenderly with his thumbs, "I had . . . a few drinks last night."

"You want me to walk you down to work, Jimmy? Spiro must be wondering where you are."

"No, kid."

"That's all right, Jimmy, really. I'll walk you down if you aren't feeling too good. Christ, Spiro must be wondering where you are. He must think you've quit."

"No, kid," Jimmy said more loudly.

"Aren't you going? You could go late and tell Spiro what happened."

Jimmy didn't answer.

"Aren't you going?"

"No," Jimmy said sharply. "Go away, kid, will ya. Go away."

Peter stared down at him for a long minute, but Jimmy just looked down at his shoes. Peter took one step away and stopped, looking back. He took another step, and stopped again. He took a few more steps and found himself walking slowing away from Jimmy.

When he was two blocks away from where he had left him, he stopped and leaned on a store front. The cold, heavy chain of Jimmy's life was suddenly bound about his stomach again. What's to become of him he thought, and what's to become of me came in the same voice.

He waited there for the chain to unbind itself. He waited for that unconscious strength to come to him again, as it had done two days ago in the restaurant, and break this binding, clammy thing away from his life. But the whole irony of Jimmy's lost day was with him too strongly, and he was feeling it as if it were his own. In mockery of the promise and fitness of the things to come to him, the chain would not fall away.

He wished to run away with it somewhere then, to go to someone and ask their help with it. He thought of his mother, sitting in her kitchen. "Ma, look what I've got. What is this thing? Help me take it off." But his mother would slam the door in his face; slam it on a leper.

It was his chain, his problem, his leprosy. How will I carry it with me he thought, putting his hand on his stomach as a pedestrian passed by in his blurred vision and a car rolled past in his muffled hearing.

He worried for himself then, worried for the life he hadn't

even begun to live yet, and wanted for a way to save himself. He knew suddenly what would become of him for that night of that day at least. He would start to walk through the normal motions of his life with a quiet, hidden terror that would come and go, come and go the rest of the days of his life. He wondered if the terror, the chain, the leprosy would ever become so agonizing that they would drive him to some action to free himself.

He looked for an answer in Jimmy, whose leprosy was now upon him.

What would become of Jimmy? He reached for a cigarette in his shirt pocket and lighted it, for all his troubles, like a well dressed kid lounging on the sidewalk of a summer town. He smoked staring at nothing, cold, reflecting to find the end of his life in Jimmy's.

His mind talked to him now and made him live a thousand years. A thousand years he passed, standing on that sidewalk, leaning on that store front. The cities that Jimmy had been to barked and rolled out echoing in his mind from a ghostly stationmaster's address system: Bal . . . timore, Phil . . a . . delphia, Cleve . . . land, Pitts . . . burgh, Al . . . bany. Their walls fell and crumbled to dust with the erosion of a thousand years' time. All signs of life passed away. The only ruin that remained was the sidewalk he stood on and the store front he leaned on. He was the only living man in all the world.

Nothing existed anymore, and there was nothing anymore to be. There remained of those cities what had gone through them: the wind.